TEACHING
THE HISTORY OF CHEMISTRY
A SYMPOSIUM
SAN FRANCISCO, CALIFORNIA, U.S.A., APRIL 1968

TEACHING
THE HISTORY OF CHEMISTRY
A SYMPOSIUM

SAN FRANCISCO, CALIFORNIA, U.S.A., APRIL 1968

EDITED BY

GEORGE B. KAUFFMAN , ed.

Professor of Chemistry, California State College at Fresno
Fresno, California, U.S.A.

AKADÉMIAI KIADÓ
PUBLISHING HOUSE OF THE HUNGARIAN ACADEMY OF SCIENCES
BUDAPEST 1971

QD
40
.K3x

CONTENTS

6 CONTENTS

PREFACE

The present volume contains the eighteen lectures delivered at the Symposium on Teaching the History of Chemistry held on April 4–5, 1968 at the 155th National Meeting of the American Chemical Society, San Francisco, California, U.S.A. as well as six additional papers written especially for this volume (Larder, Paper 14; Patterson, Paper 16; Crosland, Paper 21; Kalugai, Paper 22; Szabadváry, Paper 23; and Solovyev, Paper 24). The symposium was sponsored jointly by the Division of the History of Chemistry and the Division of Chemical Education of the American Chemical Society with the undersigned as Symposium Chairman. To the best of my knowledge, this volume is the first to be devoted exclusively to a much neglected topic.

The papers, written by distinguished authorities from a variety of backgrounds and countries, underscore the current diversity of viewpoints characteristic of the field, and they range in content from general to specific. While some are concerned mainly with the advantages and importance of the history of chemistry (*e.g.*, Swanson, Paper 5; Debus, Paper 13; Larder, Paper 14; and Bent, Paper 15), others deal with specific pedagogical problems of, and approaches to, teaching the subject (*e.g.*, Garrett, Paper 3; McConnell, Paper 7; Schufle, Paper 9; Farber, Paper 10; Kauffman, Paper 11; Cassidy, Paper 12; and Patterson, Paper 16). In some cases (*e.g.*, Baker, Paper 6; Danehy, Paper 8; and Ihde, Paper 18), descriptions of actual courses are given, while other authors (*e.g.*, Hildebrand, Paper 1; Bulloff, Paper 2; and Hein, Paper 4) deal with general philosophies which should form the basis of such courses. Although a number of papers present the state of the teaching of the history of chemistry in various universities and countries (Hannaway, Paper 17; Ihde, Paper 18; Trengove, Paper 19; Tamamushi, Paper 20; Crosland, Paper 21; Kalugai, Paper 22; Szabadváry, Paper 23; and Solovyev, Paper 24), they also deal with general aspects of the subject. Furthermore, related topics, such as creativity (Garrett, Paper 3; McConnell, Paper 7; Kauffman, Paper 11; Cassidy, Paper 12; and Bent, Paper 15), are touched upon in some of the papers.

Even a cursory reading of the papers will reveal that all the authors are not in agreement with each other on various points. Indeed, controversy could be said to be the keynote of the symposium. Two authors (Hildebrand, Paper 1, and Hein, Paper 4) are even opposed to separate courses in the history of chemistry. On other questions, too, some participants are at odds with one another, *e.g.*, phlogiston theory as a case history (pro: Baker, Paper 6, and Schufle, Paper 9; con: Bulloff, Paper 2;

Cassidy, Paper 12; and Trengove, Paper 19), the existence of "crucial experiments" (pro: Schufle, Paper 9; con: Bent, Paper 15), the biographical approach (pro: McConnell, Paper 7; Kauffman, Paper 11; Bent, Paper 15; and Trengove, Paper 19; con: Baker, Paper 6), and coverage of modern chemistry in preference to earlier chemistry (pro: Bulloff, Paper 2; con: Debus, Paper 13). In short, the symposium raises more questions than it answers. On one point, however, all participants are in agreement: If the history of chemistry is to be more than a course of mere antiquarian interest, it must not be taught as an isolated subject but must be taught with an interdisciplinary, integrated approach as a natural part of human activity. While it is possible to *train* a *chemical technologist* without giving him a knowledge of the history of chemistry, it is difficult to *educate* a *creative chemist* without such knowledge.

In editing the papers that comprise this volume, I have kept changes to an absolute minimum. I have not Americanized the spelling of British authors. On several papers by authors whose native languages are not English, I have taken the liberty of rendering the texts into correct English. In some cases, I provided abstracts. I have made no attempt to eliminate duplication or to reconcile opposing views. Thus, the volume should reflect by its emphases and contradictions the present state of the field.

The appearance of this volume only after a delay of almost three years has been due to my difficulties in finding a publisher, and I wish to thank my fellow symposium participants for their patience, cooperation, and understanding. I was able, through the good offices of one of our participants, Prof. Ferenc Szabadváry, to secure the services of *Akadémiai Kiadó*, the Publishing House of the Hungarian Academy of Sciences, which offered to publish the manuscript. It is, then, no mere formality when I gratefully acknowledge the services of this organization without which the publication of this volume would have truly been impossible. I also wish to acknowledge the assistance of the History and Philosophy of Science Program, Social Sciences Division of the National Science Foundation (Grant GS-1580), the donors of the Petroleum Research Fund administered by the American Chemical Society (Grant 1152-B), the American Philosophical Society (Johnson Grant 876), and the California State College at Fresno Research Committee. Last but not least, to my wife Laurie and to my daughters Ruth and Judith, a word of apology for the occasions on which I was forced to neglect them while organizing the symposium and editing the book.

GEORGE B. KAUFFMAN

Cabin 76, Camp Fresno
Dinkey Creek, California, U.S.A.
July, 1970

Chairman, Division of
the History of Chemistry
American Chemical Society

ALPHABETICAL LIST OF CONTRIBUTORS

1. A. Albert Baker, Jr., History of Science Department, Grand Valley State College, Allendale, Michigan, U.S.A.
2. Henry A. Bent, Department of Chemistry, North Carolina State University at Raleigh, Raleigh, North Carolina, U.S.A.
3. Jack J. Bulloff, Department of the History and Systematics of Science, State University of New York at Albany, Albany, New York, U.S.A.
4. Harold G. Cassidy, Department of Chemistry, Yale University, New Haven, Connecticut, U.S.A.
5. Maurice P. Crosland, Department of Philosophy, The University of Leeds, Leeds, England
6. James P. Danehy, Department of Chemistry, University of Notre Dame, Notre Dame, Indiana, U.S.A.
7. Allen G. Debus, Department of History, University of Chicago, Chicago, Illinois, U.S.A.
8. Eduard Farber, The American University, Washington, D. C., U.S.A.
9. Alfred B. Garrett, The Ohio State University, Columbus, Ohio, U.S.A.
10. Owen Hannaway, Department of the History of Science, The Johns Hopkins University, Baltimore, Maryland, U.S.A.
11. George E. Hein, Educational Development Center, Open Education Follow Through, 55 Chapel Street, Newton, Massachusetts, U.S.A.
12. Joel H. Hildebrand, Department of Chemistry, University of California, Berkeley, California, U.S.A.
13. Aaron J. Ihde, Department of the History of Science, University of Wisconsin, Madison, Wisconsin, U.S.A.
14. I. Kalugai, 41 Rav Harlap Street, Jerusalem, Israel
15. George B. Kauffman, Department of Chemistry, California State College at Fresno, Fresno, California, U.S.A.
16. David F. Larder, Notre Dame University of Nelson, Nelson, British Columbia, Canada
17. Virginia F. McConnell, Department of Chemistry, Newcomb College, Tulane University, New Orleans, Louisiana, U.S.A.
18. Elizabeth C. Patterson, Albertus Magnus College, New Haven, Connecticut, U.S.A.
19. J. A. Schufle, Department of Chemistry, New Mexico Highlands University, Las Vegas, New Mexico, U.S.A.
20. Yuriĭ Ivanovich Solovyev, Institute of the History of Science and Technology, Moscow, U.S.S.R.

21. James M. Swanson, Department of History, University of South Florida, Tampa, Florida, U.S.A.
22. Ferenc Szabadváry, Institute of General Chemistry, Technical University of Budapest, Budapest, Hungary
23. Bun-ichi Tamamushi, Nezu Chemical Institute, Musashi University, Nerimaku, Tokyo, Japan
24. Leonard Trengove, Department of History and Philosophy of Science, University of Melbourne, Melbourne, Victoria, Australia

1. HOW DOES ONE "LEARN" HISTORY?

JOEL H. HILDEBRAND

Department of Chemistry, University of California, Berkeley, California, U.S.A.

History of chemistry differs from subjects such as thermodynamics in that it does not have a well defined content that can be mastered and applied to the solution of problems. Its role in education is liberal, not professional. This difference should be reflected in the way in which it is presented to students. This is done most naturally and effectively by the common practice adopted by skillful writers and teachers of presenting topics as onflowing streams instead of static reservoirs. Another way of developing a sense of history is to assist a student to discover that he could find it fascinating to read history and biography that has superior literary and scholarly quality. Books of this sort should be made available in inviting surroundings, and curricula should not be jammed so full of required courses as to leave no leisure to read for profit and pleasure. Give a course in the history of chemistry only if the department has an instructor who can make the subject so interesting as to inspire students to read further "on their own".

In the early years of the Great Depression of the nineteen thirties, I was chairman of a faculty committee on educational policy. Part of our task was to discover fatty tissue among the courses being offered in my university that might be excised or at least starved with least harm to the essential functions of the organism. I attacked the problem by asking what is essential. I asked several respected members of the committee to draw up model curricula for liberal education. The plans that they submitted were well conceived and logical, but no two of them were essentially alike. That experience convinced me that there is no combination of courses that can be guaranteed to produce a liberally educated person. Consequently, when I later did a brief tour of duty as Dean of the College of Letters and Science, I tried to improve education by more rational means than by building a utopian curriculum. I decided that a liberal education can at best be only *begun* in a university and that the evidence is to be sought not at graduation but years later in the quality of the former student's reading and conversation.

Clifton Fadiman wrote, in his introduction to "The Case for Basic Education" (James D. Koerner, ed., Atlantic-Little, Brown),

The root of our trouble...lies in the circumstance that somehow the average high school graduate does not know who he is, where he is, or how he got there. It lies in the fact that naturally enough he "will settle for shallow and trivial meanings". If nothing in his early education has convinced him that Newton, Shakespeare and Lincoln are both more interesting and more admirable than Frank Sinatra, Jerry Lewis and Pat Boone, he will find answers to his questions in Sinatra, Lewis and

Boone, and not in Newton, Shakespeare and Lincoln. If he has learned little or no history, geography, science, mathematics, foreign languages, or English he will, naturally enough, learn (for even if all men do not desire to know, in Aristotle's sense, surely they desire to know *something*) golf, quail-shooting, barbecuing, and some specialized technique of buying and selling.

In accordance with his luck and his temperament, he may become happily lost or unhappily lost. But lost he will become. Lost he will remain. Lost he will die.

And if we allow these lost ones to multiply indefinitely, they will see to it that our country is lost also.

Now what has this to do with teaching the history of chemistry? Let me say, first, that I discovered very early in life that history can be fascinating. I read the historical novels for boys by G. A. Henty: "With Hannibal in Italy", "With Lee in Virginia", "With Cortes in Mexico", *etc.* The last of these inspired me to read Prescott's "Conquest of Mexico and of Peru". Sarah K. Bolton's "Poor Boys Who Became Famous" and "Famous Men of Science" contributed direction to my life. In a grandfather's library I discovered and devoured Plutarch's "Lives" and Creasy's "Fifteen Decisive Battles of the World". As a senior in college, I won the prize for the varsity athlete with the highest academic standing; it was a set of the works of Washington Irving that included the "Knickerbocker History of New York". All these I read.

My early discovery that history, if well written, can be very interesting, especially if you can read it just for fun, without having to prepare to regurgitate it later in an examination, was followed in later years by frequent reading of history and biography. I have even become a historian of sorts myself; I wrote "A History of Skiing in California", "London at War", and "Fifty Years of Chemistry at Berkeley". I was happy to write for the Biographical Memoirs of the National Academy of Sciences accounts of the scientific careers of Gilbert Newton Lewis, William Crowell Bray, and Wendell Mitchell Latimer.

An historical sense is a nearly essential ingredient of a liberal education, but I question whether courses in history are the best or the necessary means for gaining it. History is not a discipline with a logical progression of subject matter as is calculus; it contains no particular facts that every serious student must learn. Courses in differential equations by different teachers would necessarily have similar content, but two good courses in the history of chemistry by different teachers would almost certainly be very different. It would be virtually impossible to devise a fair general examination to determine whether students in different institutions have "learned" history of chemistry. The historical sense is not something that can be "learned" and measured. The only kind of course in the history of chemistry that I would favor would be one given by a teacher who is able to make his material so interesting as to inspire students to read further on their own. I would have no examinations and give unit credit for attendance only.

A wise department of chemistry would provide students with a list of "Great Books" in the history of science, books that can stand up as literature as well as science. I am thinking of such books as:

(a) "The Romance of Leonardo da Vinci" (Merezhkovski, Modern Library). A highly dramatic picture of the contrast between a scientific mind and authoritarian minds.

(b) "The Common Sense of Science" (J. Bronowski, Harvard University Press).

(c) "The Crime of Galileo" (G. de Santillana, University of Chicago Press). Contains a thrilling account of how "Galileo went to work on learned nonsense and academic prejudice and brought forth what has remained in history as a breviary of the scientific method."

(d) "Foundations of Modern Physical Science" (Holton and Roller, Addison-Wesley Publishing Co.).

(e) "1066 And All That" (Sellar, Methuen and Co.).

Many of our bachelors and doctors of chemistry would be more humanely educated if curricular requirements were not designed to use so much of their time as to leave no leisure for reading for profit and pleasure. They have to spend much of their time learning stuff that will be obsolete in twenty years. Much of the chemistry forced upon me as a student turned out later to be either untrue or unimportant.

I was pleased to find that my son, Roger, while a sophomore majoring in chemistry, had arrived at the second volume of Gibbon's "Decline and Fall of the Roman Empire". He was reading it entirely on his own and with a dictionary at hand. How much better to read Gibbon than to take a course with a professor of lesser stature than Gibbon. Also, why read dull biography when you might read Winston Churchill's "Great Contemporaries"?

An historical sense is most effectively and naturally developed by the practice adopted by the best courses, books, and teachers of placing topics in their historical settings. The first chapter in my little paperback, "An Introduction to Molecular Kinetic Theory", deals with "The Development of the Concepts". Most texts in general chemistry contain many historical items. However, the historical sequence of ideas is not necessarily the clearest path for the student to travel. We have today ways of explaining to high school students that the formula of water is H_2O, not HO, simpler than the evidence available to Avogadro.

Let me say in conclusion that I do not think that the members of the Division on the History of Chemistry should feel that the measure of their success should be the number of students enrolled in formal courses in the history of chemistry. History is a subject to read, to hear, and to enjoy; it is not a discipline to be imposed. I once led a movement to abolish courses in physical education as a requirement in all "Lower Division" curricula in the University of California at Berkeley, a requirement that made it necessary for some students to take swimming lessons twice weekly at 8 : 30 a.m., out of doors, even in a San Francisco Bay fog. A few overweight professors who opposed me assumed that students would take no exercise unless they were compelled, but I won my case, and the immediate result was a large increase in the demand for gymnasium lockers. If you wish your students to take an interest in history of science (I do not write *the* history of science), I suggest that your department make easily available a few books that are good reading and direct your students not to read them. A little girl told her mother that in her school pupils were not expected to know anything that their teachers had not taught them. Such a policy is not appropriate in a college.

2. TEACHING THE HISTORY OF CHEMISTRY AS PART OF THE HISTORY OF SCIENCE AND OF HISTORY AS A WHOLE

JACK J. BULLOFF*

Department of the History and Systematics of Science, State University of New York at Albany
Albany, New York, U.S.A.

Pupils and teachers will benefit, and teaching and research will improve as the emphasis in the teaching of the history of chemistry passes from that of technical chronicle to that of explanation of basic historical forces affecting and affected by chemists. As the teaching of the history of chemistry evolves to serve history as well as chemistry students, curricular cooperation beetween departments of history and chemistry will grow and improve. The immediate problem is that of teaching the history of chemistry as part of the history of science and technology and as part of social, economic, political, and military history, and of political science. It is shown how such teaching can be effected.

Introduction

For a first course in the history of chemistry, the more the history of chemistry is related to the history of science and to history as a whole, the better the course will:

1. Serve students of the history of science, of technology, and of the interactions of science and technology (cultural, social, economic, political, and military), as well as the students of chemistry and of the history of chemistry.

2. Attract teachers who can perform, guide, and inspire meritorious research in chemistry, the history of chemistry or of its border sciences, the history of technology, the philosophy, logic or methodology of science, and the philosophical, cultural, social, economic, political, or military aspects of chemical research, development, manufacture, education, or legislation.

3. Justify upgrading to a full-credit first-rate course deemed academically desirable for majors in logic and scientific method, philosophy of science, science education, science writing, chemistry, chemical engineering, chemical education, history of chemistry, history of science, history of technology, industrial or technological revolution or development, economic history or history of economics, and modern history.

This paper is a study of how far this relating can be carried with present knowledge.

The pertinent knowledge has been gathered in part in continuing studies on:

* Work done at Columbus Laboratories, Battelle Memorial Institute, Columbus, Ohio, U.S.A.

1. Mathematical, scientific, and technical revolution in the graphic arts industries, conducted since 1956 (*1–4*).

2. Industrial and research and development revolution since the birth of modern chemical industry in the Ruhr about 1860, conducted since 1953 (*5–7*).

3. Electronic-nuclear change of atomic-molecular ideas, conducted since 1945 (*6–7*).

In part, pertinent knowledge has been derived from added recent search of the literature. This knowledge is too extensive for complete documentation here, *e.g.*, the last of the above three studies involved 217,453 references for the period of history 1924–1962. Thus only salient references are given, except where added bibliography can be provided for the reader by inclusion of a less important reference. Nor is there room in one brief paper for mention, much less discussion, of more than a few of the myriad interweavings of educational, cultural, philosophical, historical, social, political, economic, financial, commercial, business, agricultural, industrial, technological, scientific, and chemical information that bears on describing the historical forces that affect and are affected by chemists.

Historical Analysis

The problem of determining how far the relations significant for teaching a course on the history of chemistry as a part of the history of science and of history as a whole can be determined from current knowledge is neither small nor simple. A compromise has to be made between what is desirable to teach to serve both society and the potential of individual students and teachers, and what can be taught from the small amount of already teachable material and the vast mass of relevant but as yet incompletely analyzed information and knowledge.

Even when the facts of history are known and the forces they affect or which affect them are known, historical analysis can be imprecise, even if objective, because historical data cannot always be quantified or qualified unambiguously. Thus Phyllis Deane points out that the dates of origin of the Industrial Revolution are variously set at from 1550 to 1760 by believers in gradual advances in a continuum of history and from 1750 to 1850 by believers in revolutionary advances in a history of changing backgrounds (*8*). The condition of history is reminiscent of that in geology before the catastrophists and the uniformitarians found their debate closed.

There are both subjective and objective elements in such divergences up to the time that discovery of new evidence eliminates the divergence. Thus the well known debate on indeterminacy and probabilism conducted between Einstein and Bohr had both of these elements and exhibited both kinds of historic beliefs. Historians try to eliminate the subjective elements by cultivating personal detachment (*9, 10*) and exercising the methodology of their craft impersonally (*11–19*). This is difficult.

Some methodologies for explaining history assume the validity of the concept of laws of history and of assumed laws (*13, 14, 16, 19–21*). Hempel contrasts explanation in history with explanation in science (22). Burck-hardt and Dilthey advocate that self be surrendered and no objectives be assumed in the synthesis of history (23–24). As Charles Beard and others have noted, and as Henry Guerlac has most recently reminded us, there is actual history and written history (25–27). Much methodology and much attitude bog down right at this ambiguity in the word history, for actuality and record interact—and even the medium may be the message (28–31).

Theories of history and its methods (11–22, 32–41) do not treat even this first problem of history adequately, and, as observers of natural phenom-ena did before science took hold, historians of difficult history turn to philosophy for explanations. But epistemology has its antinomies, as Kant demonstrated, and there are possible alternative views as to how historical data may be quantified or qualified, or as to how data that is not in question may be interpreted (42–44). Different relations can be held valid or true at different stages of historical consciousness or different levels of abstraction (42, 45). Thus philosophies of history can be as varied as philosophy itself (10, 19–24, 33, 36–44, 46–65), and choice between them, and then between methods, can seem to be objective and yet be ultimately subjective. Just as there is uncertainty in dating the origins of the Industrial Revolution, so it has been difficult to date historical movements and scientific revolutions that involve chemical ideas or knowledge, especially when several move-ments and several revolutions, each complex, are in complicated interac-tion (1–8).

Unlike the laws of the physical sciences and an increasing proportion of the laws of space, earth, or life sciences, that can be expressed in mathe-matical language and then be used for predictions of quantities that can be measured from observation or experiment, the laws or phenomena of most other disciplines cannot be so formulated, manipulated, or observed. Thus they are derived and expressed with considerable uncertainty and ambiguity, especially where logical or semantic confusion tends to be creat-ed (20, 66–71). The difficulty of quantifying history has bred some scientism. The jurist Cuneo has equated historical force and physical momentum (72). Zucker, an amateur historian, based the historical field theory on the electromagnetic field that he thought was derived from Einstein's relativ-istic electrodynamics (65). The phase rule of Josiah Willard Gibbs influ-enced Henry Adams, noted historian and scion of a family of historians and makers of history (73–74).

History, like many other disciplines, has been associated in varying degree and with variable success with scientific method or with the notion or notions of science, from Vico (63) to the present (36, 70, 71). Generali-zations in history (75), whether scientific or scientistic, fail if they are simple or unsophisticated, as can be seen in the large works of the great meta-historians (62, 75–80). The literature of history, the history of history, and the history of historical writing (9–11, 27, 44, 48, 62, 75, 77, 81–93) give few quantitative guides for determining when an attempt to relate the history of chemistry to the history of science and to the whole of history outruns available knowledge and information, when it reaches a point of usefulness for student and teacher, and whether there is a gap between these two points that is small enough to warrant teaching a course so related in the near future.

The Point of Usefulness

The use of history is variously considered by historians (*18, 25–32, 48, 49, 56, 59, 62, 87, 94, 95*), and little in their education (*96*) suggests that their address to history as a craft (*9–75, 81–92*) can ever consider use as aptly as their address to history as actuality (*6–8, 76–80*). The latter is found in thousands of books, and those of concern here deal with chemistry, science, and technology most variously. They include works about the:

1. History of the chemical (*97–115*), formal (*116–128*), physical (*98–100, 111, 115, 117, 124, 128–136*), life (*99, 112, 137–139*), earth (*100, 140*), and space (*141, 142*) sciences.

2. Historical (*98, 99, 115, 117, 128, 143–162*), cultural (*125–141, 163–171*), social (*172–180*), and military (*178, 181–185*) aspects of science.

3. Historical (*150, 174, 186–190*), cultural (*28–31, 93, 191–193*), economic (*8, 194, 195*), political (*196–198*), and military (*181, 184, 185, 194, 198–201*) aspects of technology.

These show the uses to which the history of science and technology is put. The uses of science and technology for historical ends and the historical forces involved can also be discerned in literature about the problems of chemistry (*202*), education (*203–206*), information and communication (*207–215*), science and research (*216–219*), scientific methods (*220–226*), cybernetics and control (*227–232*), automation (*116, 198, 201, 229–247*), technology (*248–258*), defense (*259–261*), politics (*262–267*), and society (*269–283*). From all of these sources, it can be seen that the gap between available knowledge and information and between the amount of knowledge needed to teach a useful course in the history of chemistry as part of the history of science and of history as a whole is indeed small and is diminishing. The diminution would be accelerated by teaching courses so related.

From recent history of chemistry, science, and technology, and from recent literature on the problems of chemistry, science, and technology, the point of usefulness in a related course would seem best and most easily reached, with more of the benefits outlined, if the course:

1. Aimed at chemists as citizens (*7, 281*) rather than as professionals (*204*).

2. Aimed at a reconciliation of educative backgrounds in chemistry (*202*) and history (*96*), and the unification of scientific and humanistic cultures (*163–171*).

3. Emphasized scientific method and the philosophy of science, the problems and limitations of science, mathematics, logic, and scientific method, and the other interdisciplinary factors that bear on chemistry as a discipline.

4. Emphasized current history that bears on chemistry as a profession.

5. Examined the past more selectively and in perspective with regard to present ideas and forces, with less attention to detailed chronicle and more attention to eternal principles and values.

This involves considerable difference from the course outlines that could be derived from the best of today's books on the history of chemistry (*101, 105, 108, 109*), even Ihde's outstanding synthesis with its modern emphasis.

Modern Emphasis

Today the chemist is concerned with the future of chemistry as a discipline and as a profession (*202*). As a discipline, chemistry tends to increasingly formalized expression as more and more of its phenomena can be explained atomically. A reflection of this is found in the use of chemistry to effect the formalization of the life sciences as molecular biology and of the materials sciences as molecular engineering. On the other hand, as a profession, chemistry tends increasingly to diversify in commercial, civic, and military application, entering more frequently into interdisciplinary research and development, and serving more often as the focus of educational, social, economic, political, or cultural attention.

Thus the classical division of chemistry into inorganic, organic, physical, analytical, and biological chemistry is blurred by the growth of new border sciences such as chemical physics, cosmochemistry, geochemistry, radiochemistry, nuclear chemistry, solid-state chemistry, structural chemistry, crystal chemistry, and medical chemistry. Each division tends to break up into independent subdivisions and specializations, *e.g.*, ultrapressure chemistry, plasma chemistry, chemical genetics, and photochemistry. Chemical engineering and industrial chemistry have fragmented so diversely that a major work is needed to list the gamut from reactor fuel reprocessing to fermentation biosynthesis.

This diversification has accompanied an overall growth generally estimated as a doubling every decade (*202*). This kind of growth is occurring in science as a whole (*147, 148*). Ninety percent of the chemists—and scientists— who ever lived are alive today (*216*). Of course there is a presumption that the democratization of chemistry merely means that a few geniuses are diluted by an ever larger mob of blockheads (*156*), but even if revolutionary papers are no greater in number than the availability of genius, there is a knowledge explosion today (*155, 212, 214–216*). The so-called knowledge industry was already a third of the gross national product before this decade opened (*205*). In expanding since, it has run into greater complications (*28–31, 155, 201*).

The chemist working within his discipline and as a specialist is confronted with a network of papers (*208*) that defies search and understanding (*209, 225, 226*) and is published in a way that emphasizes the obsolescence of its content (*210, 218*). High school teachers do better than college and university teachers and research workers in coping with the disunity and anachronism of publication today in deriving teaching materials from the

knowledge explosion (*212*). Further, when a student's time can no longer
be stretched to accomodate newer and more necessary information, and
the course cannot be further enlarged, the least important material has
to be discarded.

Thus it is more important that the beginning history of chemistry course
states that Kurt Goedel's revolutionary paper on metamathematics affects
the computer revolution, information theory, quantum indeterminacy,
probabilism, and genetic coding (*2, 136, 207, 211, 217, 220–223, 229–232*)
than that it includes alchemy (*101, 106, 108, 110, 113, 159, 162*). It is more
important that electronic-nuclear change of atomic-molecular ideas be
understood today (*1–7, 110–112, 129–132, 136*) than that the state of
chemistry before the atomic-molecular era be explained in polemical detail.
The emphasis required today demands texts that devote most of their pages
to modern chemistry; it cannot be served by the history of chemistry courses
taught in the past.

The modern emphasis also requires a more realistic approach to the purpose of teaching the history of chemistry. James Conant—a maker of
history (*178, 200*), widely regarded as an educator, and a leader of the
case history teaching method (*99*)—does not believe that the work of the
scientist is benefited by education in history (*204*). Conant means proper
education in history and not chronology or chronicle developed in a sectarian
or specialized way. There is a case for teaching history to the scientist to
make him a citizen of his time (*149, 206*). Even the teaching of history by
historians tends to fall into a chronology of too much detail for early history and neglect of later history. Historians may be excused for fleeing the
time they know best, the present (*65*), in order to gain detachment (*9, 10*)
from contemporary passions. However, they can never be excused for trying
to anchor the builders of tomorrow to anything but live tradition, an
understood present, and a carefully considered future.

Thus the first course in the history of chemistry should be one related
to the history of science and to history as a whole with adequate concentration on the origins and development of historical forces significant today.
To do this and gain the benefits listed in the introduction, a first-rate full-
grade course is needed. The usefulness of this paper as a tutorial bibliography (*2–4*) becomes apparent once a description of the course model
used to derive it is examined.

Course Description

The course model used to advance the thesis of this paper was derived
by using Ihde's book (*108*) as a guide and a number of current history of
chemistry courses as a skeleton (italicized in the course description that
follows). The description of the course so constructed, in course catalog
style, is:

HISTORY OF CHEMISTRY. 3 lectures, 1 round table, 1 workshop
(technical and/or humanistic literature options, one required, both recommended). Prerequisite: Permission of and prior agreement with the instructor on workshop project and course report.

OUTLINE OF THE COURSE. Two cultures? Historical and scientific method since 1500. Philosophy of science and of history. Cosmological revolution. Industrial revolution after 1550. *Chemical revolution since 1775.* The Constitution of the United States, science, technology, and production, and high consumption. *Atomic–molecular ideas after Dalton. Organic chemistry and mechanistic biology.* The Ruhr, *industrial chemistry*, chemical engineering, and today's research, development, and systems revolution. *Periodicity since Mendeleev. Tetrahedral carbon* and modern structural chemistry. *The rise of physical chemistry.* Gibbs' phase rule and the materials, products, and processes sciences and technologies. *Sub-atomic chemistry since Arrhenius' ionic theory. The rise of electronic theory. Radiochemistry and the rise of modern chemistry.* The quantum-relativity, indeterminacy-stochastic, operations-games revolutions. *Electronic-nuclear change of atomic-molecular ideas* (Author's note: part new). The world amuck, 1914–1945, the *rise of American chemical industry* and the defense and detente technologies since 1945. Current societal problems; the chemist as citizen and scientist and chemistry as a discipline and as a profession.

The two options would apply with various weights to the student's workshop activities and oral discussion and written term reporting. Perhaps students would select report topics like:

1. The chemical industry in Germany's desires for world power.
2. Chemistry in the planning of Soviet and Chinese economies.
3. Chemical trade in the European Common Market.
4. The lag in acceptance of the ionic theory in American teaching.
5. The persistence of the concept of the static electronic atom in the minds of American chemists.
6. The spread of the mathematical revolution into physics, chemistry, and biology.
7. The utilization of ideas of chemical reaction in studying nuclear reactions and constructing nuclear reactors.
8. The extension of the phase rule of Josiah Willard Gibbs to highest and lowest temperatures and pressures.
9. The chemistry of the stars since the discovery of spectroscopy.
10. The history of metal prosthetic atoms in respiratory pigments of sessile invertebrates.
11. Chemical programs of the United States Government between and during the two World Wars.
12. Chemical traditions in Latin America.
13. Chemical training in the foreign aid programs of the United States.
14. Construction of an information center for professional attitudes of chemists.
15. Problems in tracing the history of chemistry in recent publications.

How these topics and the course outline can be documented from the references given should be obvious; then this documentation could be expanded as desired by use of common bibliotechnic, bibliographic, and reference, abstract, and review indices and publications.

Perhaps the principal service of this paper other than showing how a broader, deeper, and more interdisciplinary course can be taught using the existing courses and books on the history of chemistry as a skeleton is in showing the interdisciplinary possibilities that exist for the future. These can be more quickly realized by a bold movement to adopt the kind of course in the history of chemistry that has been advocated here.

Literature Cited

(1) Bulloff, J. J., *Proceedings of the Technical Association of the Graphic Arts*, **13**, 63 (1961); cf. *Mod. Lithography*, **29** (10), 60 (Oct., 1961), *ibid.*, (11), 73 (Nov.), and *Graphic Technol.*, 55–62 (May–June, 1962), *ibid.*, 5059 (July–Aug.).

(2) Bulloff, J. J., *Proceedings of the Technical Association of the Graphic Arts*, **17** 349 (1965).

(3) *Ibid.*, **18**, 126 (1966).

(4) *Ibid.*, **19**, 66 (1967).

(5) Bulloff, J. J., and Hiler, M. H., *Chem. & Eng. News*, **32** (25), 2475 (1954).

(6) Bulloff, J. J., *J. Chem. Educ.*, **34**, 452 (1957).

(7) *Ibid.*, **36**, 465 (1959); cf. Blecher, M. D., and Paase, M. E., "Readings for Technical Writers", pp. 358–367, The Ronald Press Co., New York, 1963.

(8) Deane, P., "The First Industrial Revolution", Cambridge University Press, New York, 1965.

(9) Snyder, P. L., "Detachment and the Writing of History: Essays and Letters of Carl L. Becker", Cornell Univ. Press, Ithaca, New York.

(10) Becker, C. L., "Everyman His Own Historian", Appleton–Century–Crofts, Inc., New York, 1935; cf. *Am. Hist. Rev.*, **37**, 221 (1932).

(11) Bloch, M., "The Historian's Craft", Alfred A. Knopf, Inc., New York, 1953.

(12) Garraghan, G. J., "A Guide to Historical Method", Fordham University Press, New York, 1956.

(13) Hackett, H. C., "Critical Method in Historical Research and Writing", 3rd ed., Macmillan & Co., New York, 1955.

(14) Johnson, A., "The Historian and Historical Evidence", Kennikat Press, Inc., Port Washington, New York, 1965.

(15) Langlois, C. V., and Seignobos, C., "Introduction to the Study of History", Duckworth & Co., London, 1898, repr. Barnes & Noble, Inc., New York, 1966.

(16) Lucey, W. L., "History: Methods and Interpretation", Loyola Univ. Press, Chicago, Ill., 1966.

(17) McIlwain, C. W., *Am. Hist. Rev.*, **42**, 207 (1937).

(18) Quigley, C., "The Evolution of Civilizations", Harper & Row, New York, 1965.

(19) Renier, G. J., "History, Its Purpose and Method", Harper & Row, New York, 1965.

(20) Dray, W., "Laws and Explanation in History", Oxford University Press, New York, 1957.

(21) Gardiner, P., "The Nature of Historical Explanation", Oxford University Press, New York, 1955.

(22) Hempel, C. G., pp. 7–33 in Colodny, R. G., ed., "Frontiers of Science and Philosophy", University of Pittsburgh Press, Pittsburgh, Pa., 1962.

(23) Burckhardt, J., "Force and Freedom: Reflections on History", Pantheon Books. New York, 1943.

(24) Hodges, H. A., "William Dilthey: an Introduction", Routledge and Kegan Paul, London, 1944.

(25) Guerlac, H., pp. 797–812 in Crombie, A. C., ed., "Scientific Change", Basic Books, Inc., New York, 1963.

(26) Beard, C. A., *Am. Hist. Rev.*, **39**, 219 (1934).

(27) Weiss, P., "History: Written and Lived", Southern Illinois Univ. Press, Carbondale, Ill., 1962.

(28) McLuhan, H. M., and Fiore, Q., "The Medium is the Message", Random House, New York, 1967.
(29) McLuhan, H. M., "The Gutenberg Galaxy: The Making of Typographic Man", University of Toronto Press, Ontario, Canada, 1964.
(30) McLuhan, H. M., "Understanding Media: The Extensions of Man", McGraw-Hill Book Co., New York, 1964.
(31) McLuhan, H. M., "Understanding Marshall McLuhan", Holt, Rinehart, and Winston, Inc., New York (in press).
(32) Commager, H. S., "The Nature and Study of History", Charles E. Merrill, Inc., Columbus, Ohio, 1965.
(33) Croce, B., "Theory and Practice of Historiography", Russell & Russell, New York, 1917; cf. "History: Theory and Practice", idem., 1917, 1960.
(34) Fitzsimmons, M. A., et al., eds., "The Development of Historiography", Kennikat Press, Inc., Port Washington, New York, 1967.
(35) Gardiner, P., ed., "Theories of History", The Free Press, Glencoe, Ill., 1962.
(36) Hughes, H. S., "History as Art and as Science", Harper & Row, New York, 1964.
(37) Mandelbaum, M., "The Problem of Historical Knowledge", Liveright Publ., Corp., New York, 1938.
(38) Popper, K. R., "The Poverty of Historicism", Routledge & Kegan Paul, London, 1957.
(39) Stover, R., "The Nature of Historical Thinking", Univ. of North Carolina Press, Chapel Hill, N. C., 1967.
(40) Teggart, F. J., "Theory and Processes of History", 2 vols. in one, 3rd printing, Univ. of California Press, Berkeley, Calif., 1963.
(41) White, M., "Foundations of Historical Knowledge", Harper & Row, New York, 1965.
(42) Berdyaev, N., "Meaning of History", Geoffrey Bles, London, 1936.
(43) Dilthey, W., "Pattern and Meaning in History", Harper and Row, New York, 1962.
(44) Ferguson, W. K., "The Renaissance in Historical Thought: Five Centuries of Interpretation", Houghton Mifflin Co., Boston, Mass., 1948.
(45) Korzybski, A., "Science and Sanity", 3rd ed., International Non-Aristotelian Library Publ. Co., Lakesville, Connecticut, 1948.
(46) Aron, R., "Introduction to the Philosophy of History", Beacon Press, Boston, Mass., 1961.
(47) Becker, C. L., "Progress and Power", Alfred A. Knopf, Inc., New York, 1949.
(48) Butterfield, H., "Man on His Past", Cambridge University Press, New York, 1955.
(49) Carr, E. H., "What Is History?", Alfred A. Knopf, Inc., New York, 1962.
(50) Collingwood, R. C., "The Idea of History", Oxford University Press, New York, 1946.
(51) Croce, B., "History", Russell & Russell, Inc., New York, 1960.
(52) Croce, B., "History and the Story of Liberty", Meridian Books, New York, 1955.
(53) Croce, B., "Philosophy, Poetry, History", Oxford University Press, New York, 1966.
(54) Croce, B., "The Philosophy of Giambattista Vico", Russell, New York, 1913.
(55) Danto, A. C., "Analytical Philosophy of History", Cambridge Univ. Press, New York, 1965.
(56) Jaspers, K., "The Origin and Goal of History", Yale Univ. Press, New Haven, Conn., 1953.
(57) Koht, H., "Driving Forces in History", Harvard Univ. Press, Cambridge, Mass., 1964.
(58) Lee, D., and Beck, R. N., Am. Hist. Rev., 59, 566 (1954).
(59) Mannheim, M., "Essays on the Sociology of Knowledge", 2nd ed., Oxford Univ. Press, New York, 1952.
(60) Maritain, J., "On the Philosophy of History", Charles Scribner's Sons, New York, 1957.
(61) Ortega y Gassett, José, "Toward a Philosophy of History", W. W. Norton, Inc., New York, 1947.

(62) Sorokin, P. A., "Modern Historical and Social Philosophies", Dover Publ., New York, 1964.
(63) Vico, G., "Principles of New Science Concerning the Common Nature of Nations", Cornell Univ. Press., Ithaca, New York, 1948, repr. of 1744 posthumous rev. of 1725 orig. ed.
(64) Walsh, W. H., "Philosophy of History", Harper and Row, New York, 1960.
(65) Zucker, M., "The Philosophy of American History", 2 vols., Arnold Howard Publ., New York, 1945.
(66) Adams, B., "The Laws of Civilization and Decay", Alfred A. Knopf, Inc., New York, 1943.
(67) Adams, G. B., *Am. Hist. Rev.*, **14,** 221 (1909).
(68) Adams, H., *Ann. Rept. Am. Hist. Assn.*, **1894,** 17 (1895).
(69) Berlin, I., "Historical Inevitability", Oxford University Press, New York, 1954.
(70) Berlin, I., pp. 60–113, of Riasnovsky, A., and Riznik, B., eds., "Generalizations in Historical Writing", Univ. of Penna. Press, Philadelphia, 1963.
(71) Hempel, C. G., pp. 459–471 of Feigl, H., and Sellars, W., eds., "Readings in Philosophical Analysis", Appleton–Century–Crofts, New York, 1949.
(72) Cuneo, E., "Science and History", Duell, Sloan, and Pearce, New York, 1963.
(73) Adams, H., "The Degradation of the Democratic Dogma", Macmillan & Co., New York, 1919.
(74) Adams, H., "The Education of Henry Adams", Houghton–Mifflin Co., Boston, 1918.
(75) Riasnovsky, S., and Riznik, B., eds., "Generalizations in Historical Writing", Univ. of Penna. Press, Philadelphia, 1963.
(76) Pareto, V., "Mind and Society", 4 vols., Harcourt, Brace & Co., New York, 1935.
(77) Parrington, V. L., "Main Currents in American Thought", 3 vols. in one, Harcourt, Brace & Co., New York, 1938.
(78) Spengler, O., "The Decline of the West", 2 vols., Alfred A. Knopf, Inc., New York, 1932.
(79) Toynbee, A., "A Study of History", 12 vols., Oxford University Press, New York, 1934–1961, 2nd ed., 1940–1961, abridgment, 1961.
(80) Voegelin, E., "Order and History", 6 vols., Louisiana State Univ. Press, Baton Rouge, La., 1946–1964.
(81) Ausubel, H., "Historians and Their Craft", Columbia Univ. Press, New York, 1951.
(82) Barnes, H. E., "A History of Historical Writing", Dover Publ., New York, 1962.
(83) Powicke, F., "Modern Historians and the Study of History", Odhams Press, London, 1955.
(84) Shotwell, J., "The History of History", Columbia Univ. Press, New York, 1939.
(85) Smith, P., "The Historian and History", Alfred A. Knopf, Inc., New York, 1964.
(86) Thompson, J. W., "A History of Historical Writing", 2 vols., Macmillan & Co., New York, 1942.
(87) Howe, G. F., et al., eds., "The American Historical Association's Guide to Historical Literature", Macmillan & Co., New York, 1961.
(88) Barraclough, J., "History in a Changing World", Oxford University Press, New York, 1955.
(89) Bury, J. B., "The Idea of Progress", Dover Publ., New York, 1955.
(90) Fussner, F. S., "Historical Revolution", Columbia Univ. Press, New York, 1962.
(91) Gottschalk, L., "Understanding History", Alfred A. Knopf, Inc., New York, 1951.
(92) Gottschalk, L., *Univ. Kansas City Rev.*, **8,** 75 (1941).
(93) Ware, C. F., "The Cultural Approach to History", Kennikat Press, Inc., Port Washington, New York, 1965.
(94) Commager, H. S., "The Search for a Usable Past", Alfred A. Knopf, Inc., New York, 1967.
(95) Nietzsche, F., "The Use and Abuse of History", Liberal Arts Press, New York, 1949.
(96) Perkins, D., Snell, J. L., and Committee on Graduate Education of the American

Historical Association, "The Education of Historians in the United States", McGraw-Hill Book Co., New York, 1961.

(97) Bolton, H. C., "Select Bibliography of Chemistry, 1492–1902", 4 vols., Gale Research Co., Detroit, Mich., 1893–1904.

(98) Boorse, H. A., and Motz, L., "The World of the Atom", 2 vols., Basic Books, Inc., New York, 1966.

(99) Conant, J. B., "Harvard Case Histories in Experimental Science", 2 vols., Harvard Univ. Press, Cambridge, Mass., 1957.

(100) Ewald, P. P., "Fifty Years of X-ray Diffraction", N. V. A. Oosthoek's Uitegersmaatschappij, Utrecht, Netherlands, 1962.

(101) Farber, E., "The Evolution of Chemistry", Ronald Press Co., New York, 1952.

(102) Farber, E., "Great Chemists", Interscience Publishers, New York, 1961.

(103) Farber, E., "Nobel Prize Winners in Chemistry, 1901–1961", Abelard Schuman, New York, 1963.

(104) Ferguson, J., "Bibliotheca, Chemica", 2 vols., Banner Press Publ., Birmingham, Alabama, 1906; cf. the various catalogs of H. Sotheran.

(105) Findlay, A., "A Hundred Years of Chemistry", 3rd ed., Gerald Duckworth and Co., Ltd., London, 1965.

(106) French, S. J., "The Drama of Chemistry", The University Soc., Inc., New York, 1937.

(107) Hildebrand, J. H., "Science in the Making", Columbia Univ. Press, New York, 1957.

(108) Ihde, A. J., "The Development of Modern Chemistry", Harper & Row, New York, 1964.

(109) Leicester, H. M., "The Historical Background of Chemistry", John Wiley & Sons, Inc., New York, 1956.

(110) Nobel Foundation, "Nobel Lectures in Chemistry", 3 vols., American Elsevier Publ. Co., Inc., New York, 1964–1965.

(111) Nobel Foundation, "Nobel Lectures in Physics", 3 vols., American Elsevier Publ. Co., Inc., New York, 1964–1966.

(112) Nobel Foundation, "Nobel Lectures in Physiology-Medicine", American Elsevier Publ. Co., Inc., New York, 1964–1965.

(113) Partington, J. R., "A History of Chemistry", vols. 2–4, St. Martin's Press, New York, 1962–1964.

(114) Platt, J. R., "Excitement of Science", Houghton-Mifflin Co., Boston, 1962.

(115) Schwartz, G. I., and Bishop, P. W., "Moments of Discovery", 2 vols., Basic Books, Inc., New York, 1966.

(116) Berkeley, E. C., "The Computer Revolution", Doubleday & Co., Inc., New York, 1962.

(117) Bochner, S., "The Role of Mathematics in the Rise of Science", Princeton University Press, New Jersey, 1966.

(118) Carruccio, E., "Mathematics and Logic in History and Contemporary Thought".

(119) Eves, H., "Introduction to the History of Mathematics", Holt, Rinehart, and Winston, New York, 1964.

(120) Freebury, H. A., "History of Mathematics", Macmillan & Co., New York, 1961.

(121) Guerlac, H., "Introduction to Scientific Methods", Cornell University Press, Ithaca, New York, 1954.

(122) Hadamard, J., "Psychology of Invention in the Mathematical Field", Princeton University Press, Princeton, New Jersey, 1945.

(123) Kac, M., "Mathematics, Its Trends, and Its Tensions", offprint, Rockefeller Institute Press, New York, 1961.

(124) Kline, M., "Mathematics and the Physical World", Doubleday and Co., Garden City, New York, 1954.

(125) Kline, M., "Mathematics in Western Culture", Oxford University Press, New York, 1963.

(126) Meschkowski, H.. "The Ways of Thought of Great Mathematicians", Holden-Day, Inc., San Francisco, Calif., 1964.

(127) Passmore, J., "A Hundred Years of Philosophy", Macmillan & Co., New York, 1957.

(128) Sarton, G., "Study of the History of Mathematics and the Study of the History of Science", Dover Publ. Co., New York, 1936.
(129) Birks, J. B., "Rutherford at Manchester", Benjamin Publ. Co., New York, 1963.
(130) Born, M., "Physics in My Generation", Pergamon Press, New York, 1962.
(131) Born, M., "Physics and Politics", Basic Books, Inc., New York, 1962.
(132) D'Abro, A., "The Rise of the New Physics", 2 vols., Dover Publications, Inc., 1951.
(133) Hanson, N. R., "Patterns of Discovery", Cambridge Univ. Press, New York, 1959.
(134) Holton, G. J., and Roller, D. H. D., "Foundations of Modern Physical Science", Addison–Wesley Publ. Co., Reading, Mass., 1958.
(135) Von Laue, M., "History of Physics", Academic Press, New York, 1950.
(136) Whittaker, E., "A History of Theories of the Aether and Electricity", 2 vols., Thomas Nelson and Sons, Ltd., New York, 1951–1953; Whittaker carries the story to 1926, the birth of the new quantum theory. The story has been carried from 1924 forward by J. J. Bulloff in a series of progress reports on the history of electronic-nuclear change of atomic-molecular ideas; up to 1962 over 217,000 literature citations are involved. A backward cast from 1924 to 1905 has to be made to correct critical omissions in Whittaker's work, involving the role of A. Einstein in the quantum-relativity revolution.
(137) Brooks, C., and Cranfield, P. F., "Historical Development of Physiological Thought", Hafner Publ. Co., New York, 1959.
(138) Keilin, D., and Keilin, J., "The History of Cell Respiration and Cytochrome", Cambridge Univ. Press, New York, 1966.
(139) Singer, C., "History of Biology", rev. ed., Abelard–Schuman Co., New York, 1959.
(140) Adams, D., "Birth and Development of the Geological Sciences", Dover Publ., New York, 1938.
(141) Berenda, C. W., "World Visions and the Image of Man", Vantage Press, Inc., New York, 1965.
(142) Singh, J., "Great Ideas and Theories of Modern Cosmology", Dover Publ., New York, 1965.
(143) Bernal, J. D., "Science in History", Watts, London, 1954.
(144) Butterfield, H., "Origins of Modern Science", G. Bell & Sons, London, 1949.
(145) Claggett, M., ed., "Critical Problems in the History of Science", Univ. of Wisconsin Press, Madison, Wisconsin, 1959.
(146) Crombie, A. C., "Scientific Change", Basic Books, Inc., New York, 1961.
(147) de Solla Price, D. J., "Little Science, Big Science", Columbia Univ. Press, New York, 1963.
(148) de Solla Price, D. J., "Science since Babylon", Yale Univ. Press, New Haven, Conn., 1961.
(149) Dingle, H., "The Scientific Adventure", Isaac Pitman & Sons, Ltd., London, 1952.
(150) Forbes, R. J., and Dijksterhuis, E. J., "History of Science and Technology", 2 vols., Penguin Books, Ltd., London, 1962.
(151) Garrett, A. B., "The Flash of Genius", D. Van Nostrand, Inc., Princeton, N. J., 1963.
(152) Gillispie, C. C. "The Edge of Objectivity", Princeton Univ. Press, Princeton, N. J., 1960.
(153) Guerlac, H., "Science in Western Civilization, a Syllabus", Ronald Press Co., New York, 1952.
(154) Jordan, P., "Science and the Course of History", Yale Univ. Press, New Haven, Conn., 1955.
(155) Kochen, M., ed., "The Growth of Knowledge", John Wiley & Sons, Inc., New York, 1967.
(156) Kuhn, T. S., "The Structure of Scientific Revolutions", University of Chicago Press, Chicago, Ill., 1962.
(157) Merz, J. T., "History of European Thought in the 19th Century", 4 vols., Smith, Peter, Publ., Gloucester, Mass., 1965.
(158) Rickert, A., "Science and History: A Critique of Positivist Epistemology", D. Van Nostrand & Co., Inc., Princeton, N. J., 1962.

(159) Sarton, G., "Introduction to the History of Science", 3 vols., Williams & Williams Co., Baltimore, Md., 1927-1947.

(160) Taton, R., ed., "History of Science", 3 vols., Basic Books, Inc., New York, 1963-1965.

(161) Taton, R., "Reason and Chance in Scientific Discovery", Hutchinsons Sci. and Tech. Publ., London, 1957. Taton's and Garrett's, ref. 151, findings should be compared with those of other students of accidental discoveries and prepared minds.

(162) Thorndike, L., "History of Magic and Experimental Science", 8 vols., Columbia Univ. Press, New York, 1923-1958.

(163) Brooks, H., pp. 70-87, in Holton, G., ed., "Science and Culture", Houghton Mifflin Co., Boston, 1965.

(164) Green, M. B., "Science and the Shabby Curate of Poetry", W. W. Norton & Co., Inc., New York, 1965.

(165) Holton, G., ed., "Science and Culture", Houghton Mifflin Co., Boston, 1965.

(166) Leavis, F. R., "Two Cultures? The Significance of C. P. Snow", Chatto & Windus, London, 1962, cf. *The Spectator*, Mar. 9, 1962, and Yudkin, M., "Sir Charles Snow's Ride Lecture", bound with Leavis in the Pantheon Books ed., New York, 1963.

(168) Seaborg, G. T., *Sci.*, **144**, 1199-1203 (1964).

(169) Snow, C. P., "The Two Cultures and a Second Look", Cambridge Univ. Press, New York, 1964.

(170) Snow, C. P., "The Two Cultures and Scientific Revolution", Cambridge Univ. Press, New York, 1959, cf. *The New Statesman*, Oct. 6, 1956.

(171) Trilling, L., *Commentary*, quoted as (Jan. or June, 1959); cf. *ibid.*, **31**, 501-506 (June, 1961).

(172) Bernal, J. D., "The Social Function of Science", George Routledge & Sons, London, 1939.

(173) Crowther, J. G., "The Social Relations of Science", Macmillan & Co., New York, 1941.

(174) Goldsmith, M., and MacKay, A., "The Science of Science, Society in the Technological Age", Souvenir Press, London, 1964.

(175) Kaplan, N., ed., "Science and Society", Rand, McNally & Co., Chicago, 1965.

(176) Lilley, S., ed., "Essays on the Social History of Science", E. Munksgaard, Copenhagen, Denmark, 1953.

(177) Lindsay, R. B., "The Role of Science in Civilization", Harper & Row, New York, 1963.

(178) Smith, A. K., "A Peril and a Hope: The Scientist's Movement in America, 1945-1947", University of Chicago Press, Chicago, Ill., 1965; a sharp contemporary reaction to this movement was voiced in a lecture, now out of print, Bulloff, J. J., "The History of Atomic Misinformation", Division of History of Chemistry, American Chemical Society National Meeting, Sept. 20, 1949, Abstract 4, pp. 2J-3J, and p. 2915, *Chem. & Eng. News*, 2915 (Oct. 10, 1949) and *New York Times*, p. 27, col. 2 (Sept. 21, 1949).

(179) Steinhardt, J., "Science and the Modern World", Plenum Press, New York, 1966.

(180) Thornton, J. E., ed., "Science and Social Change", The Brookings Institution, Washington, D. C., 1939.

(181) Crowther, J. G., and Whiddington, R., "Science at War", Philosophical Library, New York, 1948.

(182) Fieser, L. F., "Scientific Method", Reinhold Publ. Corp., New York, 1964.

(183) Jungk, R., "Brighter Than a Thousand Suns", Harcourt, Brace, & Co., New York, 1958.

(184) Smyth, H. D., "A General Account of the Development of Methods of Using Atomic Energy for Military Purposes under the Auspices of the United States Government", Princeton Univ. Press, Princeton, N. J., 1945.

(185) Wilhelm, Jr., D., "The West Can Win: A Study in Source and World Power", Frederick A. Prager, New York, 1966.

(186) Jewkes, J., Sawers, D., and Stillman, R., "The Sources of Invention", St. Martin's Press, New York, 1959.

(187) Singer, C., et al., "A History of Technology", 5 vols., Clarendon Press, Oxford, 1954–1958.
(188) Lilley, S., "Men, Machines, and History", International Publ., New York, 1966.
(189) Singer, C., et al., "A History of Technology", 5 vols., Clarendon Press, Oxford, 1954–1958.
(190) Spengler, O., "Man and Technics", Alfred A. Knopf, Inc., New York, 1932.
(191) Ashby, E., "Technology and the Academics", Macmillan & Co., New York, 1958.
(192) Dijksterhuis, E. J., "The Mechanization of the World Picture", Clarendon Press, Oxford, 1961.
(193) Nef, J. W., "Cultural Foundations of Industrial Civilization", Cambridge Univ. Press, New York, 1958.
(194) Nef, J. W., "War and Human Progress: An Essay on the Rise of Industrial Civilization", Harvard University Press, Cambridge, Mass., 1960.
(195) Rostow, W. W., "The Stages of Economic Growth", Cambridge University Press, New York, 1960.
(196) De Schweinitz, K., "Industrialization and Democracy", Free Press, New York, 1964.
(197) Ford, G. S., *American Historical Review*, **53**, 253 (1930).
(198) Erickson, J., Crowley, E. L., and Galay, N., eds., "The Military-Technical Revolution", Frederick A. Prager, New York, 1966.
(199) Friedrich, C. J., and Blitzer, C., "The Age of Power", Cornell Univ. Press, Ithaca, New York, 1957.
(200) Hewlett, R. G., and Anderson, Jr., G. E., "The New World, 1939/1946", Penna. State Univ. Press, Univ. Park, Pa., 1962.
(201) Steele, G., and Kircher, P., "The Crisis We Face—Automation and the Cold War", McGraw-Hill Book Co., Ltd., London, 1960.
(202) NAS-NRC Committees for the Survey of Chemistry and on Science and Public Policy, "Chemistry: Opportunities and Needs", Washington, D. C., 1965.
(203) Brickman, W. W., and Lehrer, S., "Automation, Education, and Human Values", School & Society Books, Inc., New York, 1965.
(204) Conant, J. B., *Am. Scientist*, **48**, 528 (1960).
(205) Machlup, F., "The Production and Distribution of Knowledge in the United States", Princeton Univ. Press, Princeton, N. J., 1962.
(206) Weinberg, A. M., *Science*, **149**, 601 (1965).
(207) Brillouin, L., "Science and Information Theory", Academic Press, New York, 1956.
(208) de Solla Price, D. J., *Science*, **149**, 510 (1965).
(209) Hubbert, M. K., *Science*, **139**, 884 (1963).
(210) Pasternack, S., *Physics Today*, **19**, 38 (May, 1966).
(211) Shannon, C., and Weaver, W., "The Mathematical Theory of Communication", Univ. of Illinois Press, Urbana, Ill., 1949.
(212) Sweeney, F., ed., "The Knowledge Explosion", Farrar, Strauss & Giraux, New York, 1966.
(213) Szilárd, L., *Z. für Physik*, **53**, 840 (1929).
(214) Weinberg, A. M., "Science, Government, and Information: The Responsibilities of the Technical Community and the Government in the Transfer of Information", U.S. Government Printing Office, Washington, D. C., 1963.
(215) Weinberg, A. M., *Intern. Sci. & Technol.*, 65–74 (April, 1963).
(216) Auger, P., "Current Trends in Scientific Research", United Nations, New York, 1961.
(217) Bohm, D., "Causality and Chance in Modern Physics", D. Van Nostrand Co., Inc., Princeton, N. J., 1957.
(218) Burton, R. E., and Kebler, R. W., *Am. Doc.*, **11**, 18 (1960).
(219) Lewisohn, R., "Science, Prophecy, and Prediction", Fawcett Publ., Inc., Greenwich, Conn., 1962.
(220) Bulloff, J. J., Hahn, W., and Holyoke, T., "Logic and Its Relation to Mathematics, Natural Science, and Philosophy", Springer–Verlag, Berlin (to be published).
(221) Goedel, K., *Monatsh. für Math. u. Phys.*, **38**, 173 (1931), cf. Meltzer, B., transl., "On Formally Undecidable Propositions of Principia Mathematica and Relat-

ed Systems", Basic Books Inc., New York, 1962, cf. Nagel, E., and Newman, J. R., pp. 1668–1695 of Newman, J. R., ed., "The World of Mathematics", 4 vols., Simon & Schuster, Inc., New York, 1956.
(222) McMullin, E., pp. 35–84 of Steinhardt, J., "Science and the Modern World", Plenum Press, New York, 1966.
(223) Nagel, E., "The Structure of Science", Harcourt, Brace, and World, New York, 1961.
(224) Popper, K. R., "The Logic of Scientific Discovery", Basic Books, Inc., New York, 1959.
(225) Wigner, E., pp. 757–765 of Feigl, H., and Broadbeck, M., "Readings in the Philosophy of Science", Appleton–Century–Crofts, Inc., New York, 1953.
(226) Wigner, E., *Proc. Am. Phil. Soc.*, 422–427 (1950).
(227) Broida, V., "International Bibliography of Automatic Control", 4 vols., Gordon and Breach Sci. Publ., Inc., New York, 1962–1965.
(228) Greenberger, M., "Computers and the World of the Future", The M. I. T. Press, Cambridge, Mass., 1962.
(229) Hilton, A. M., "Logic, Computing Machines, and Automation", Spartan Books, Inc., Washington, D. C., 1963.
(230) Taube, M., "Computers and Common Sense: The Myth of Thinking Machines", Columbia Univ. Press, New York, 1961.
(231) Turing, A. M., *Proc. Lond. Math. Soc.*, (2) **42**, 230 (1937).
(232) Turing, A. M., *Mind*, **59**, 433 (1950).
(233) Bagrit, L., "The Age of Automation", New Am. Library of World Literature, Inc., New York, 1965.
(234) Bowen, H. R., "Automation and Economic Progress", Prentice-Hall, Inc., Englewood Cliffs, N. J., 1966.
(235) Diebold, J., "Beyond Automation", McGraw-Hill Book Co., Inc., New York, 1964.
(236) Dunlop, J. T., "Automation and Technological Change", Prentice-Hall, Inc., Englewood Cliffs, N. J., 1962.
(237) Goodman, L. L., "Automation Today and Tomorrow", Iota Services, Ltd., London, 1958.
(238) Landers, R. R., "Man's Place in the Dybosphere", Prentice-Hall, Inc., Englewood Cliffs, N. J., 1967.
(239) Mayer, I., pp. 28–35 to 28–37 in Canaverace Council of Technical Societies, "The Challenge of the 1970's", Cocoa Beach, Florida, 1967.
(240) Philipson, M., ed., "Automation: Implications for the Future", Vintage Books, Inc., New York, 1962.
(241) Pyke, M., "Automation: Its Purpose and Future", Philosophical Library, Inc., New York, 1957.
(242) Schuh, J. F., "Principles of Automation: What a Robot Can and Cannot Do", D. Van Nostrand & Co., Princeton, N. J., 1965.
(243) Silberman, C. E., "The Myths of Automation", Harper & Row, New York, 1966.
(244) Terborgh, G., "The Automation Hysteria", Machinery and Allied Products Inst., Washington, D. C., 1965.
(245) von Neumann, J., pp. 2070–2098 of Newman, J. R., ed., "The World of Mathematics", 4 vols., Simon and Schuster, New York, 1956.
(246) Weeks, R., ed., "Machines and the Man: A Sourcebook on Automation", Appleton–Century–Crofts, Inc., New York, 1961.
(247) Zipf, K., "Human Behavior and the Principle of Least Effort", Addison–Wesley, Inc., Reading, Mass., 1949.
(248) Ackoff, R. L., Gupta, S. K., and Minas, J. S., "Scientific Method: Optimizing Applied Research Decisions", John Wiley & Sons, Inc., New York, 1962.
(249) Baade, F., "The Race to the Year 2000", Doubleday & Co., Garden City, New York, 1962.
(250) Barach, A. B., "1975 and the Change to Come", Harper & Row, New York, 1962.
(251) Boyko, H., ed., "Science and the Future of Mankind", Indiana Univ. Press, Bloomington, Ind., 1961.
(252) Bulloff, J. J., and Hiler, M. H., *Chem. & Eng. News.* **32**, (25) 2475 (1954).
(253) de Solla Price, D. J., *Technol. & Culture*, **6**, 555 (1965).

(254) Gilfillan, S. C., pp. 738–754 of Bright, J. R., "Research, Development, and Technological Innovation", Richard D. Irwin, Inc., Homewood, Ill., 1964.
(255) Goodman, N., "Fact, Fiction, and Forecast", Harvard Univ. Press, Cambridge, Mass., 1954.
(256) National Comm. on Technol., Automation, & Econ. Progr., "Technology and the American Economy", Vol. 1 and Appendix Vols. I–VI, U.S. Government Printing Office, Washington, D. C., 1966.
(257) Teller, E., pp. 148–166 in Bright, J. R., "Technological Planning on the Corporate Level", Harvard Univ. Press, Boston, 1962.
(258) von Neumann, J., *Fortune*, **51**, 106–108 (June, 1955).
(259) Blackett, P. M. S., "Fear, War, and the Bomb", McGraw-Hill Book Co., Inc., New York, 1949.
(260) Hsieh, A. L., "Communist China's Strategy in the Nuclear Era", Prentice-Hall, Inc., Englewood Cliffs, N. J., 1962.
(261) Lilienthal, D. E., "Change, Hope, and the Bomb", Princeton Univ. Press, Princeton, N. J., 1963.
(262) Barker, R. J., "The Politics of Research", Public Affairs Press, Washington, D. C., 1966.
(263) Gilpin, R., and Wright, G., "Scientists and National Policy-Making", Columbia Univ. Press, New York, 1964.
(264) Nieburg, H. L., "In the Name of Science", Quadrangle Books, Chicago, Ill., 1966.
(265) Penick, Jr., J. L., Pursell, Jr., C. W., Sherwood, M. B., and Swain, D. C., "The Politics of American Science", Rand, McNally & Co., Chicago, Ill., 1965.
(266) Price, D. K., "The Scientific Estate", Harvard Univ. Press, Cambridge, Mass., 1965.
(267) Snow, C. P., "Science and Government", Harvard Univ. Press, Cambridge, Mass., 1961.
(268) Armytage, W. H. G., "A Social History of Engineering", Pitman & Sons, New York, 1961.
(269) Ayres, C. B., "Toward a Reasonable Society: The Values of Industrial Civilization", Univ. of Michigan, Ann Arbor, Mich., 1961.
(270) Brady, R. A., "Organization, Automation, and Society, The Scientific Revolution in Industry", Univ. of California Press, Berkeley, Calif., 1963.
(271) Brown, H., Bonner, J., and Weir, J., "The Next Hundred Years", Viking Press, New York, 1967.
(272) Clarke, A. C., "Profiles of the Future", Harper & Row, New York, 1962.
(273) Commoner, B., "Science and Survival", Viking Press, New York, 1966.
(274) Ellul, J., "The Technological Society", Alfred A. Knopf, New York, 1964.
(275) Gabor, D., "Inventing the Future", Alfred A. Knopf, New York, 1964.
(276) Heilbroner, R. L., "The Future as History", Harper & Row, New York, 1960.
(277) Lakoff, S. A., "Knowledge and Power", The Free Press, New York, 1966.
(278) Pyke, M., "The Science Myth", Macmillan & Co., New York, 1962.
(279) Rossi, P. H., *Daedalus*, **93**, 1142 (1964).
(280) Weinberg, A. M., "Reflections on Big Science", M. I. T. Press, Cambridge, Mass., 1967.
(281) Weinberg, A. M., *Science*, **134**, 161 (1961).
(282) Weinberg, A. M., *Chem. & Eng. News*, **32**, 2188 (1955).
(283) Woolf, H., ed., "Science as a Cultural Force", Johns Hopkins Press, Baltimore, Md., 1964.

3. CASE STUDIES OF THE FLASH OF GENIUS: PROFITABLE SPIN-OFFS IN THE STUDY OF THE HISTORY OF CHEMISTRY

ALFRED B. GARRETT

The Ohio State University, Columbus, Ohio, U.S.A.

Case studies of discoveries from the history of chemistry are recommended for incorporation into chemistry courses. Such an approach encourages students and teachers to read the original literature, gives the teacher a "feel" for research and how it can enrich his teaching, is a functional and interesting way to study history, gives students opportunity to fit the parts of the pattern together to get the profile of history and to see the transition from paradigm to paradigm in the growth of knowledge, provides a search for the trigger-tripping process in discovery, is an approach to exploring man's creative potential, gives a profile of the creative mind, and suggests methods for stimulating creativity.

The many possible spin-offs from the case history approach can be the main argument for history of science courses.

One area for exploitation, which offers several opportunities for spin-offs, consists of several facets of the trigger-tripping process of discovery which may be resolved into a study of creativity. Man's capacity for creativity is probably his least tapped potential. Some authorities assert that a youngster shows considerable creativity until about the fourth school grade. By that time he has been so effectively bombarded by home, school, and community into conforming to "patterns of acceptable behavior" that most of his unorthodoxies are transformed into conformities, and he becomes one of us! Time is ripe to tackle this problem in science. One approach is to use the rich literature of the history of chemistry to do case studies on the flash of genius (1).

Let us list a variety of net profits to the consumer which the case study approach to teaching history can yield:

1. It encourages students and faculty to read the original literature.
2. It gives the teacher a "feel" for research and how it can enrich his teaching.
3. It is a functional and interesting way to study history.
4. It gives students opportunity to fit the parts of the pattern together in order to get the profile of history and to see the transition from paradigm to paradigm in the growth of knowledge.
5. It provides a search for the trigger-tripping process in discovery.
6. It is an approach to testing man's least tapped potential—his potential for creativity.
7. It gives a profile of the creative mind.
8. It suggests methods for stimulating creativity.

1. It encourages students and faculty to read the original literature

There is something genuine about a story told in the words of the discoverer. Part of the richness is lost in predigested form. Listen to the excitement in the story of:

Sir Ernest Rutherford, as he analyzed the data on the deflection of alpha particles by metal films and by gases (*1, 2*),

Then I remember two or three days later Geiger coming to me in great excitement and saying, 'We have been able to get some of the α-particles coming backwards....' It was quite the most incredible event that has ever happened to me in my life. It was almost as incredible as if you fired a 15-inch shell at a piece of tissue paper and it came back and hit you. On consideration I realized that this scattering backwards must be the result of a single collision, and when I made calculations I saw that it was impossible to get anything of that order of magnitude unless you took a system in which the greater part of the mass of the atom was concentrated in a minute nucleus. It was then that I had the idea of an atom with a minute massive centre carrying a charge.

Amedeo Avogadro, as he analyzed the problem of combining volumes (*1, 3*),

M. Gay-Lussac has shown in an interesting Memoir that gases always unite in a very simple proportion by volume, and that when the result of the union is a gas, its volume also is very simply related to those (volumes) of its components. But the proportions of weight of substances in compounds seem only to depend on the relative number of molecules which combine, and on the number of compound molecules which result. It must then be admitted that very simple relations also exist between the volumes of gaseous substances and the numbers of simple or compound molecules which form them. The first hypothesis to present itself in this connection, and apparently even the only admissible one, is the supposition that the number of integral molecules in any gas is always the same for equal volumes, or always proportional to the volumes.

Stanislao Cannizzaro, as he analyzed the problems of combining volumes (*1, 4*),

I believe that the progress of science made in these last years has confirmed the hypothesis of Avogadro, of Ampère, and of Dumas on the similar constitution of substances in the gaseous state; that is, that equal volumes of these substances, whether simple or compound, contain an equal number of molecules; not, however, an equal number of atoms, since the molecules of the different substances, or those of the same substance in its different states, may contain a different number of atoms, whether of the same or of diverse nature.

Cannizzaro then goes on to tell how he explains molecules to his students. He concludes, "The atom of hydrogen is contained twice in the molecule of free hydrogen".

F. August Kekulé, as he searched for the structure of benzene (*1, 5*),

During my stay in Ghent, Belgium, I lived in a fine room on the main street. I sat in this room and wrote on my textbook, but could make no progress—my mind was on other things. I turned my chair to the fire and sank into a doze. Again the atoms were before my eyes. Little groups kept modestly in the background. My mind's eye, trained by the observation of similar forms, could not distinguish more complex structures of various kinds. Long chains here and there more firmly joined; all winding and turning with snake-like motion. Suddenly one of the serpents caught its own tail and the ring thus formed whirled exasperatingly before my eyes. I woke as by lightning, and spent the rest of the night working out the logical consequences of the hypothesis.

Henri Becquerel, as he studied the fluorescence of pitchblende (*1, 6*),

I wrapped a Lumière photographic plate with bromized emulsion with two sheets of thick black paper, so thick that the plate did not become clouded by exposure to the sun for a whole day. I placed on the paper a plate of phosphorescent substance and exposed the whole thing to the sun for several hours. When I developed the photographic plate I saw the silhouette of the phosphorescent substance in black on the negative. If I placed between the phosphorescent substance and the paper a coin or a metallic screen pierced with an open work design the image of these objects appeared on the negative.

It is important that this phenomenon seems not attributable to luminous radiation emitted by phosphorescence, since at the end of one hundredth of a second these radiations become so feeble that they are scarcely perceptible.

Becquerel concluded that the radiations must be coming from a hitherto undiscovered element. The phenomenon was called radioactivity.

2. It gives the teacher a "feel" for research and how it can enrich his teaching

Much has been said *and* written about teaching and research with the unfortunate implied dichotomy which so often culminates in the unsavory topic of "publish or perish". Case studies of discovery can certainly bring to teachers and students alike a "feel" for the process, the planning, the thinking, and the perspiring involved in the steps leading to the discovery. For example:

the long tedious days and months spent by Goodyear in searching for the process of "curing" rubber —now known as the vulcanization process (*1*),

the ingenious several hours of labor in the library and the discovery of a critical error in the literature by Midgley and Henne as they designed the molecule of Freon—followed by the labor of synthesis that involved persistence coupled with a certain amount of luck (*1*), and

the careful planning of Becquerel as he followed an incorrect hypothesis but was willing to have an open mind when the unexpected was observed (*1*).

These stories enrich the teaching and the learning process. The research processes observed become an important element in the learning process. Any inferred dichotomy melts away and teacher and student both enter into this exciting venture of searching for an interpretation of the universe.

3. It is a functional and interesting way to study history

The facts of discovery—time, place, and person—are usually encyclopedic, but the processes leading to the trigger-tripping process are educational, enriching, full of human interest, and certainly capable of capturing the imagination of most of the least science-minded students. A strong supporting argument is that a student learns some of the basic or funda-

3 Teaching the History of Chemistry

mental aspects of science as he studies cases of discovery. Furthermore, while no set pattern of discovery can be recognized, nevertheless, a study of discoveries made by many men not unlike the student himself is bound to instill in that student a kind of optimism that he too might make discoveries; in science this confidence is reinforced by the realization that many of the discoveries have been made by young men.

4. It gives students opportunity to fit the parts of the pattern together in order to get the profile of history and to see the transition from paradigm to paradigm in the growth of knowledge (7)

A series of case studies and their relevancies gives a student an excellent opportunity for self-initiated learning as his interest is pricked and his concern is stimulated to search further for the cause and effect of each discovery. The discovery process, as related in the cases, then becomes an important stepping stone in learning the process of the growth of knowledge within a given paradigm. But of even more value is the evidence of the growth of knowledge from paradigm to paradigm, as represented by the quantum theory, the structure of the atom, or the theory of relativity; or with new possible quantum jumps to additional new paradigms such as a theory of matter derived from data on fleeting particles, the nature of nuclear forces, a possible fourth law of thermodynamics, or the nature of the life process.

5. It provides a search for the trigger-tripping process in discovery

The birth of an idea is mysteriously interesting. The *fact* of the birth is important and to some people may be interesting; the *birthing process* is mysterious to most of us and likewise intriguing and interesting. A search to understand better the process can lead us in many directions—the thought process, the atmosphere for creative thinking, the teaching process, the learning process, the characteristics of the creative mind—all important in education, in business, in the professions, and in life.

Furthermore, in life, for example, the fact that Columbus discovered America in 1492 is important to students, but of deeper interest might be the process of thought and action involved in the processes leading to this discovery. The fact that Becquerel discovered radioactivity in 1896 is interesting, but of more use and interest are the processes involved in this discovery. Students deserve to know these and can use them as they explore the discovery process.

A search for clues to understand or explain the trigger-tripping processes of discovery has really just begun. Arbitrarily we can identify the following methods of discovery—trial and error, planned research, and accident.

Discoveries by trial and error are usually explained by supposing that the researcher has done enough significant experiments. Discovery by planned research may result from the process of elimination (Madame

Curie's work) or the appearance of a pattern (Arrhenius' work, Mendeleev's work, or Mendel's work). To explain discovery by accident we need at least two factors: the ability to see in the commonplace the unusual, the interesting, the exciting—known as the element of serendipity—coupled with the prepared mind. In fact, the prepared mind is a common element in all of these discoveries. But the problem of discovery by accident is not yet completely solved. For example, why did Fermi not discover the theory of the process of fission? Certainly he had the prepared mind and could see the unusual in the commonplace?

6. It is an approach to testing man's least tapped potential—his potential for creativity

An important by-product in the use of case studies might be a clue or clues to how one can test for creative *potential* (We might assume, from the case being studied, that it is unnecessary to test for creative *performance*). As a first step in developing such a test, we may look for factors that may be tested. Some of the factors involved in testing for creative potential may be motivational, temperamental, and aptitudinal, according to Guilford, in the form of interests and attitudes, emotional dispositions, and abilities. Much work is now being done on studies of testing.

The type of question used in such a test may well be quite different than for our run-of-mine, everyday tests. An example of such a test that might be used to pick out highly creative chemistry majors is the following:

1. How would you teach a blind man what a shadow is?

2. How would you separate a mixture of sugar and salt without destroying either one?

3. Assume that the face of the planet Mercury is at a temperature of 450 degrees Centigrade and that its periods of rotation and revolution are identical. Predict some unique chemical substances that you might find on the face and back of the planet that are not found as such on the planet Earth.

4. Can a neutron gas be liquefied? Show arguments to support your answer.

5. Demonstrate or prove that the integral of the differential $- dc/dt = kc$ is $\ln c = -kt + C$.

7. It gives a profile of the creative mind

Ready identification of potentially creative persons is difficult in most instances. No one characteristic serves to identify such a person. The creative artist differs from the creative scientist; the creative writer differs from the creative designer. The best that we can do yet is to list a series of characteristics to give a profile; this list includes the following for scientists:

3*

1. They are intellectually curious.
2. They are flexible.
3. They recognize problems and define them clearly.
4. They can put information together in several ways.
5. They seek recognition and praise.
6. They are anti-authoritarian and unorthodox.
7. They are mentally restless, intense, strongly motivated, and persistent.
8. They are highly intelligent.
9. They are goal oriented—not method oriented.
10. They probably showed these characteristics early in life.

This profile is supported by conclusions drawn from a six-year study by D. W. MacKinnon (8) at the University of California, who states:

There are many paths along which persons travel toward the full development and expression of their creative potential, and... there is no single mold into which all who are creative will fit. The full and complete picturing of the creative person will require many images. But if, despite this caution, one still insists on asking what most generally characterizes the creative individual as he has revealed himself in the Berkeley studies, it is his high level of effective intelligence, his openness to experience, his freedom from crippling restraints and impoverishing inhibitions, his esthetic sensitivity, his cognitive flexibility, his independence in thought and action, his high level of creative energy, his unquestioning commitment to creative endeavor, and his unceasing striving for solutions to the ever more difficult problems that he constantly sets for himself.

8. It suggests methods for stimulating creativity

Many of us would like to know this secret. Some guidelines are now being clarified. The first approach seems to be a negative one, which peculiarly enough may have positive results. This is typified by the answer Diogenes is supposed to have given Alexander the Great, who asked Diogenes how he could help him—the answer, "just keep out of my light!" Another approach seems to be to discover and set the proper atmosphere for the free flow of ideas. This may differ for different scholars in the various disciplines and even for different scholars in the same discipline. A pattern of atmospheres is difficult to describe, so is a schedule of activities to stimulate creative ideas—the time for lab work and research can be scheduled, but this is not always so if we try to schedule our time to generate our best ideas. It may depend upon the time of day or night, the degree of fatigue, the beauty of the surroundings. A third approach is to search for some guidelines that can be useful; several of these are the following (9):

1. Provide as much opportunity as possible for self-initiated learning.
2. Set up non-authoritarian learning environment.
3. Encourage people to overlearn, to saturate themselves with the subject matter.
4. Try to set up an atmosphere to encourage creative thought processes; avoid imposition of conformity, ridicule, criticism, etc.

5. Wait until the creative process has run its course before the step of objectivity is imposed on the ideas generated.

6. Encourage intellectual flexibility.

7. Encourage self-evaluation rather than national norms!

8. Cultivate sensitivities to people, things, and situations.

9. Prepare to fail as well as to succeed.

10. Encourage craftsmanship.

11. Develop the Socratic procedure.

This facet of the problem, too, requires much more attention and study.

Some precautions to observe

A good procedure is seldom void of some pitfalls. Fortunately, here there are few. In this case study approach, a tendency exists in an effort to make the cases interesting, to make the discoveries appear too easy and almost magic. Furthermore, some scholars might develop a habit of looking back over their shoulder too often to look for consistency within a paradigm and miss the possibility of a quantum jump from paradigm to paradigm. But these are alerts only and no real danger to the scholar.

Recommendation

I recommend that you experiment with several case-studies of discovery in your teaching—these will enrich your scholarship and your teaching.

Literature Cited

(1) Garrett, Alfred B., "The Flash of Genius", pp. 63–64, 86, 114, 164, 167, D. Van Nostrand Co., Princeton, N. J., 1963.

(2) Rutherford, Sir E., *Phil. Mag.*, **21**, 669–688 (1911); "Background to Modern Science", ed. by Joseph Needham and Walter Pagel, pp. 67–69, Cambridge University Press, Cambridge, 1938.

(3) Avogadro, Amedeo, *Journal de physique de chimie d'histoire naturelle et des artes*, **73**, 58–76 (1811).

(4) Cannizzaro, Stanislao, "Sketch of a Course in Chemical Philosophy", Alembic Club Reprint No. 18, E. & S. Livingstone, Ltd., Edinburgh, 1961.

(5) Kekulé, August, *Ber.*, **23**, 1306 (1890). Japp, Francis R., *J. Chem. Soc.*, **73**, 97–138 (1898). A more complete translation of this speech by O. Theodor Benfey is found in *J. Chem. Ed.*, **35**, 21 (1958).

(6) Becquerel, Henri, *Compt. rend.*, **122**, 420 (1896). An English translation is found in "A Source Book in Physics", ed. by William Francis Magie, McGraw-Hill Book Co., Inc., New York, 1935.

(7) Kuhn, Thomas S., "The Structure of Scientific Revolutions", Chicago University Press, Chicago, 1962.

(8) MacKinnon, D. W., *Saturday Review*, February 10, 1962, pp. 15 ff.

(9) Guilford, Joy Paul, *Theory into Practice*, **5**, 186–189 (1966).

4. LET US NOT TEACH THE HISTORY OF CHEMISTRY

GEORGE E. HEIN

Educational Development Center, Open Education Follow Through, 55 Chapel Street,
Newton, Massachusetts, U.S.A.

Should the history of chemistry be taught at all in chemistry departments? A symposium on the teaching of history of chemistry must face this question. Many prominent and thoughtful chemists believe that the history of chemistry is a luxury that we cannot afford to include in an increasingly crowded curriculum. To consider the history of chemistry as a branch of chemistry, like analytical chemistry or biochemistry, is unfortunate. It sharpens the distinction between the chemistry of the past and that of the present, and it forces the history of chemistry to become an esoteric, antiquarian pursuit. We should recognize that the history of chemistry as a separate academic discipline is not viable in chemistry departments, especially not in those with a strong interest in research. We should strive to incorporate historical material into the entire chemistry curriculum. There is reason to hope that this will result in better trained scientists who can more thoroughly assess current science and can make more creative contributions to chemistry in the future.

We have assembled as chemists, historians of chemistry, and educators in order to discuss at an ACS meeting the teaching of the history of chemistry.

Although I am delighted to be participating in this symposium, I really wish it were not taking place. Or, at least, I wish that its topic were different.

One can ask, "Why discuss this question at all?" Do the organic chemists meet to discuss the teaching of organic chemistry? Do the biochemists or the inorganic chemists ask the same question? In one sense they do—there are constant symposia and discussions on the teaching of any subject. But when organic chemists approach the topic, they come together with some very important agreements. There is little question among them that organic chemistry should be taught and that it is worth learning. No chemist needs to apologize for studying organic chemistry, and no professor needs to look furtively over his shoulder while teaching it. What they discuss is the method of teaching or new topics or new insights into the field.

We are not so fortunate. When we meet to talk about teaching the history of chemistry, we are really asking whether it should be taught at all. Now, I do not intend to question the existence or justification of the history of chemistry as an intellectual discipline. For better or worse it exists, and one can point to a number of scholars, past and present, who are clearly historians of chemistry. But this is not the issue which concerns us. What we are asking in a symposium of this type is, "Is there any place for the history of chemistry in a chemistry department and in a chemistry curriculum?"

And now we are dealing with a sharp question, one that is pertinent to us. Let us look at the situation as it exists in chemistry departments. What is the role of the history of chemistry in them? It is obvious that across the country the history of chemistry is not a popular pursuit among academic chemists. Many departments do not offer any courses in the subject. I once taught at a university with a long tradition in teaching the history of chemistry—including an interesting library specializing in eighteenth- and nineteenth-century works. This department not only scorned the topic but allowed the library to decay by turning it into a general university classroom—with the books still on the shelves (each year a few less of them and in greater disorder).

Some participants here feel that the history of chemistry is on the rise—more papers are published than in the past, and more scholars are engaged in historical work than in the past. But can we say that the history of chemistry has taken a more central role in chemistry curricula? I do not think so. I believe that it is the overwhelming judgement of practicing academic research chemists that the history of chemistry has only a minor role (if any) in the training of chemistry students. Perhaps in the general chemistry course and in the course for secondary school teachers a few historical topics are desirable, but for chemistry majors? Yes, as a side line they may be interested, but otherwise they are too busy, there is too much "important" material to learn for them to spend their time on history.

Before we try to answer this critique we must note that this charge must be taken seriously.It is made by thoughtful and dedicated professionals— by the leading chemists in our departments. More than once I have had colleagues, including some of the brightest and most productive chemists that I have met, seriously ask me why I, a research worker, would be interested in historical topics.

I began my talk by stating that I was sorry to see this symposium take place. I am unhappy because by holding it we must face the question that I have raised and by meeting and rallying to the banner of the history of chemistry as a discipline we put ourselves in a very bad position relative to that question. As long as the history of chemistry is a subject, like organic chemistry or biochemistry or photochemistry, then I think that the hard-line chemists are right—it has no significant place in a chemistry curriculum, and it will not be a viable part of a chemistry curriculum. As long as we concede that there is a chemistry of yesterday and another chemistry of today—what scientists once believed and what they now believe, the rejected theories of the past and the accepted concepts of the present—then it seems clear to me that the task of a chemistry department is to discuss the chemistry of today—the current belief, the modern concept.

But this is all a trap. There is a very real sense in which the science of the past is part of the chemistry of the present. I shall discuss this below, but let me first introduce an instructive example.

There are disciplines in which the history and current thinking of the subject are inexorably intertwined. One field where this is the case, and which I at least know a little about, is philosophy.*

---

* There is a modern ahistorical trend in philosophy which parallels the ahistorical attitude of many practicing scientists. Although this school is important, I shall not discuss it here. If pressed, I would probably end up saying the same thing about these philosophers that I would about chemists who are only concerned with present knowledge: one does not really understand a thing unless one knows its history,

No philosopher, no teacher of philosophy, and no student of philosophy would consider himself knowledgeable in the field unless he were well acquainted with the history of philosophy. In many universities the history of philosophy is one of the first subjects taught; in most universities it is an integral part of the students' education. Philosophies, no matter what their origin or their contemporary relevance, are often described in terms of their historical antecedents. One can discuss today's world or today's thought in Neo-Platonic or Aristotelian terms. These words are used not only to describe someone, who, *e.g.*, holds the same views of causality that Aristotle held, but also someone who may hold somewhat different views if they are related in kind to Aristotle.

Philosophical discussions abound with historical references, no matter what the topic. A seminar on the aesthetics of art may be as full of references to Plato as one on traditional painting.

Why is there this difference? Why do philosophers continually and openly return to their historical tradition when chemists do not? There is a standard and obvious answer to this question. Philosophy, in common with many other subjects in the humanities, is not cumulative. A good idea is a good idea no matter when it evolved. In contrast, science *is* cumulative; it builds on the work of the past; when we understand the present science we not only know all that is necessary, we also really know all that there is because modern science incorporates all that is worthwhile from the past.

There is some truth to this answer, but it is not the whole story. To say that chemistry is cumulative and philosophy is not is to point to some attributes of each but not to describe each completely. A philosopher who holds an historical position, on any subject—Aristotle's or Descartes' or Kant's—without considering the criticisms which have been raised against that position, would be considered naïve and not taken seriously. Philosophy, or at least the western philosophical tradition, is cumulative to some extent. Positions, views, and arguments develop, expand, and become clarified during a period of study and debate. Certain arguments have been shown to be invalid, certain positions demonstrated to entail others, certain theses noted to be contradictory. All this has been a progressive movement. The writings and criticisms of one generation have forced the next generation to take certain positions. One tradition is not just a reaction to another; it is a consequence of the rethinking required when the previous position was studied in detail. And similar positions at different times are not interchangeable. They show an historical trend as objections are met and overcome.

One point of my example is that there are similarities between a so-called non-cumulative field, philosophy, and a so-called cumulative one, chemistry. Philosophical positions develop and change with time. But

---

and knowing the history makes any practitioner more effective. But as soon as one sets up the history of a subject as an entity separate from the subject itself, then it has only antiquarian value. It is not surprising that this particular school of philosophy should share this position with many scientists, inasmuch as these philosophers look to science for their models and methods.

philosophers still go back to their original sources and trace the ideas because they feel that this is valuable today.

But one may still ask, "What is the relevance of this example to chemistry?" Granted that historical antecedents enrich philosophical ideas, how do these antecedents affect chemical principles? Does a knowledge of alchemy help in preparing rocket fuels? Does Goethe's theory of color explain atomic spectra? The answer is clearly "no".

There are indeed vast areas of modern science (or I should say current science because the statement is true at all times) which are relatively independent of their historical antecedents. There are regions of chemical usage where the example that I have just developed has no relevance. The day-to-day practice of science is controlled to a large extent by a combination of current knowledge and personal experience. Take, for example, synthetic organic chemistry. The vast majority of practitioners require just this combination of information and little else. A particular structural theory, one which can be represented by physical models, which assigns fixed valences to atoms, and which concerns itself especially with stereochemical properties, has proven to be incredibly fruitful. This theory, along with a wide fund of empirical information about techniques, apparatus, and particular cases, has permitted chemists to synthesize almost any compound conceivable within the theory as long as the molecule is not too large. The amount of information required to become successful in this field was, and is, enormous. It is so great, in fact, that there are few individuals who could become proficient at it and still have the time and energy to learn much else. The rewards of this endeavor have also been great. On the one hand, our society is now supplied with an incredible number of synthetic products, the result of this effort, and on the other hand, our understanding of biology owes a great deal to the ability to synthesize many of the molecules found in nature.

One measure of the enormous influence and significance of synthetic and analytic organic chemistry can be noted in the widespread employment and training of organic chemists in universities. There are still universities where perhaps half of the graduates are preparing for a career in organic chemistry.

But despite this vast and influential effort, synthetic organic chemistry is just a small corner of the field of science. From a practical point it has contributed a great deal, but it has provided very little new insight into chemistry or science in general. A majority of practicing organic chemists are highly trained and skilled, but their vision is limited. They can work effectively within their system but not beyond it. If we want some understanding of the state of chemistry or its relation to science in general, we would not go to these practitioners.

My point is that one can develop a flourishing technology and practical science with little regard for historical background. Our universities turn out, to a large extent, highly competent technologists—people who can work efficiently within a given framework of laws and theories. Within this system, historical perspective plays a relatively minor role, and when pressed for training time it is dropped for a number of good reasons.

(I want to make it clear that when I describe our chemistry departments as places which turn out many high-level technicians, I do not say this critically. Our society and our science need them. It is an honorable pursuit. A man who can synthesize a complex organic molecule has accomplished as much as one who develops a new twist to a theory.)

But the training of research workers who will spend their professional lives working within the confines of theory developed by others is not the only duty of chemistry departments. These institutions also train the future theoreticians and innovators, and they expose the general educated community to science. It is here that I think the example of philosophy can serve a purpose.

To what should a scientist be exposed during his training? He should know the current state of science and know it critically, i.e., he should be able to step back and note the state of his own field. But how is this to be achieved? I believe the best way to do this is to infuse into the training at all levels a large historical component. This is different from teaching the history of chemistry as a separate subject.

At what sort of goals should the historical material aim? First, I firmly believe that no concept can be thoroughly understood unless one knows the history of that concept. Like philosophical ideas, scientific ideas do not emerge, de novo, to answer some questions. Instead, they are developed through a series of trials and formulations until they assume a particular form at a particular time. They arise within a climate of opinion. Structural organic theory was developed to meet particular needs: to explain certain types of isomerism, to rationalize certain different compounds with the same empirical formulas. We must know that it was developed in the late nineteenth century and that it pre-dates electronic theories. A good deal of misapplication of structural organic chemistry can result when people forget this. On the other hand, once we know its origin and its status, the theory can be amended to incorporate or reflect current electronic concepts. The merging of resonance concepts with structural organic theory was a fruitful example of the incorporation of modern material into an older theory, although the two might have been totally independent of each other. In fact, resonance and the use of Kekulé formulas to describe it are disappearing from the literature, although the structural theory remains.

All this historical perspective is part of what allows us to understand structural organic theory today. We do not need the information or insight if we address ourselves only to the relatively simple problem of "writing all the isomers of hexane", but we do need it if we want to answer questions about organic compounds which cannot be satisfactorily pictured by the structural theory: benzene, sydnones, salts, etc. And we need it if we want to modify or amend the theory.

Another way in which the history of chemistry plays an important part in understanding current chemistry is in shedding light on methodology. A number of activities in a science or key experiments which help shape our ideas are influenced by their particular historical setting. Again, to use the example of organic chemistry, there are a number of reactions which are discussed in most texts that appear to have no reasonable place in the scheme of things. One example is the Wurtz reaction, a terribly messy reaction which no chemist would dream of using if he could possibly help it. It is in our texts because it was historically important. Unfortunately, only its less interesting history is usually remembered. The reaction is presented for its synthetic value. More interesting is the problem of empirical and molecular formulas illustrated by the reaction. Historically, this led to a good deal of confusion. My point in this case is that, in fact, historical material is taught—but ahistorical teachers do not know why and so do not do it well. Only by acquiring some historical perspective can we and our students understand and evaluate what we are doing.

To conclude, I believe that there are important lessons to be learned from history. But these lessons should not be considered apart from our current work on a subject. When we treat the history of chemistry as an entity independent of modern chemistry, then we must struggle in an effort to justify its place in a chemistry curriculum. Let us instead strive to incorporate it into the mainstream of chemical education. We can work toward this goal by urging that texts and lectures include some perspective on the material that they are presenting. When we recognize that there is not one chemistry of the past and another of the present, but rather a continuing, everchanging stream of interrelated ideas, we will have introduced a living history firmly into the curriculum.

5. THE REVOLUTION IN THE HISTORIOGRAPHY OF SCIENCE AND ITS IMPLICATIONS FOR THE HISTORY OF CHEMISTRY

JAMES M. SWANSON

Department of History, University of South Florida, Tampa, Florida, U.S.A.

The history of science as an academic discipline has experienced qualitative and quantitative changes in recent years that have been described as products of an historiographic revolution. At the most, they are products of a limited *coup d'état* which is leading to the progressive isolation of the discipline. Chemists should be aware of the methodological improvements resulting from these changes, but they should avoid exclusively embracing the internal history of science approach utilized by professional historians of science. Instead, chemists should participate in the real revolution in science teaching today—a revolution committed to viewing science in a broad humanistic-historical perspective.

As a student of revolutions, aware of the semantic and philosophical problems attendant in the use of the noun "revolution" to describe the development of an academic discipline, I feel uneasy when I hear historians of science use the word to account for the dramatic changes that have taken place in their once sterile, ill-defined academic pursuit. Consequently, I sense an obligation to discover precisely what historians of science mean when they speak of revolution.

There are two levels on which the "historiographic revolution" is said to be under way—one qualitative, the other quantitative. Qualitatively, the revolution implies a striking change in the methodological-philosophical foundations of the history of science. It is clear that at this level the revolt is still being fought behind the barricades of academe.

As late as 1962, Kuhn and Agassi admitted that an historiography of science was still in its formative stages. Kuhn noted that historians were beginning to ask new questions about the development of science: "Rather than seeking the permanent contributions of an older science to our present vantage", he writes, historians of science "attempt to display the historical integrity of that science in its own time" (1). In a more revolutionary spirit, Agassi delivered a scathing attack on the two prevailing philosophies of the history of science (which he called the inductive and conventional schools), proposing instead a new philosophy based on the ideas of Karl Popper. Agassi was particularly critical of the inductivist who contends that the primary responsibility of the historian is to record the facts and let these facts speak for themselves. In history as a whole, this approach was discarded at least thirty years ago, yet its widespread use in the history of science, by professionals and amateurs alike, absolves Agassi from the charge of beating a dead horse. What incensed Agassi (aside from the process of simply discovering the facts—a process he accused only of being boring) was that the inductivist approach led to other serious philosophical problems. The inductivist, he asserted, tends to "paint ideas and even thinkers as black or white", and his "criterion for whiteness is the up-to-date science textbook" (2). He therefore saw the function of the inductivist as a kind of high priest who carries out a form of ritualistic ancestor worship and whose only problem is deciding "whom to worship".

The difficulty of determining priorities in scientific discovery was a major theme in Kuhn's book as well, indicating that the problem has become a rallying point for the so-called historiographic revolution. As an issue it is likely to generate considerable opposition. Eduard Farber, the late distinguished historian of chemistry and participant in this symposium, said, in response to the problem of priorities: "As an historian, a chemist remains true to one of his scientific aims, to make discoveries. How happy he is to discover a chemist who has been unduly neglected, or factual evidence of work which antedates that considered original" (3). Establishing priorities, to Farber, was thus both the aim of the historian and a source of happiness. In answer to Agassi's criticism, Farber cautioned against making "loose indefinite statements like 'most historians have neglected my hero' or 'the date usually given must be corrected'." Yet he answered Agassi's most serious charge of viewing scientists and their contributions in history as black or white by asserting: "It is less presumptuous and more convincing to state exactly and specifically who has been wrong."

I submit that what is being described here as a revolution is merely the birth pangs of a new school of historiography, more relevant to the 1960's perhaps, but hardly revolutionary except that it employs a revolutionary tactic—the polemic, a kind of verbal violence. It also seems to be revolutionary because it has yet to advance beyond its initial stages. There is little ferment at this methodological-philosophical level outside the history of science discipline. Chemists *qua* historians still follow the inductivist pattern and shy away from giving explanations or from admitting that history is a creative enterprise. A perhaps unwitting symbol of the state of historical awareness in the chemical profession is the *Journal of Chemical Education*, a major publishing outlet for historical articles. Looking at its index, one is reminded of Descartes' "trash heap of the mind". Anything that would not fit into his mathematico-deductive system of the world, Descartes relegated to the category of the mind. Anything not strictly related to teaching techniques in chemistry the *Journal of Chemical Education* relegates to its category of "history". Here we find everything from memorabilia to, of all things, textbook errors.

Several factors are responsible for the refinements in the methodological-philosophical growth of the history of science. All are interrelated. One factor has been the development of independent history of science departments which, in turn, have developed rigorous graduate programs in order to train specialists in the discipline. A second factor is the close relationship that historians of science have established with philosophers of science. In many universities, the history and philosophy of science are united in a single departmental structure. Indeed, most professional historians of science, I suspect, would make few real distinctions between philosophical and historical problems in the development of science. It is perhaps only natural, then, that the wedding of historian and philosopher would give rise to a more systematic philosophy of history.

Another factor in the professionalization of the history of science has been the requirement of a strong scientific background and training for potential candidates in the discipline. Historians of science are understandably sensitive to the criticism, at one time frequently advanced by scientists, that their judgements on the history of a particular scientific discipline were valueless because historians were not practicing scientists in that discipline. Today's product of a graduate program in the history of science has completed, in most cases, an undergraduate degree in one of the sciences. Many hold master's degrees and even doctorates.

This emphasis on scientific training, as valuable as it has been, is in many respects an overreaction to criticism and reflects a high degree of disciplinary insecurity. Furthermore, it has not been without some potentially bad effects. At many graduate schools a candidate for a history of science degree could graduate without taking any courses in political or social history. While one might justify this in the case of the student who has a strong background in history, justification seems rather tenuous in the case of the student entering the program directly from a science department. In other words, insistence on a high degree of scientific sophistication has resulted in a pendulum swing which opens the discipline to criticism from the historian.

To escape from criticisms of this nature, historians of science, it seems, have retreated to a position of sharply defining the area of their interests and competence. They have, in essence, carved out a highly specialized branch of historical inquiry centered upon the internal development of science, the evolution of scientific concepts and methodology. This has meant abandoning problems in the cultural integration of science—the interplay of science and society through history. It is true, of course, that *Isis*, the journal of the History of Science Society, is described in a subtitle as a journal devoted to the "History of Science and its Cultural Influences". At the same time, however, a glance at the articles published in the journal reveals an almost exclusive emphasis on the internal history of science. It is in this realm that the "historiographic revolution" (or should we use the term "historiographic *coup d'état*"?) has produced its most brilliant studies in the history of science. Yet its very success has tended to restrict any horizontal growth in the discipline.

As I have indicated earlier, there is a quantitative aspect to this *coup* in the history of science discipline. New programs are being created every year. Every issue of *Isis* brings news of four or five new courses. Under the pressure of crowded curriculums, busy professors, and acute economic problems in most chemistry departments, one alternative to staffing courses in the history of chemistry is to transfer this responsibility to the growing history of science departments. Needless to say, such an alternative is at present open only to a relatively few universities, despite the tremendous growth of the discipline. More important, it is unlikely that there will ever be enough professional historians of chemistry to supply every university in the country.

I am certain that this symposium will offer many solutions to the problem suggested above. I would only wish to add the following remarks. The example of what is being done at our major universities is of little value at an institution, like my own, where the prospects of even having a full time historian of science, let alone an historian of chemistry is depressingly dim. For some time to come, the history of science discipline will be absorbed with its research functions and with the training of graduate students. Until there is more "spin-off" from the practice of the major history of science departments trading graduates to staff their own expanding graduate programs, the history of chemistry will have to be taught using the resources of the chemistry departments.

It is clear, under these circumstances, that chemists need to develop a new image of history. History cannot be seen merely as a custodian of the past—a process of collecting outmoded ideas and practices thrown on the trash heap of the past. Without such a change it is likely that the pressure of new knowledge, of keeping the student up-to-date in an expanding chemical world, will continue to take its toll not only in the number of separate history of chemistry courses but in the historical approach in general chemistry courses. For the moment this may be a blessing in disguise. Creative chemistry is effectively destroying uncreative history— history used only as color, as interior decorating to illustrate by contrast the brilliant hues of new discoveries.

By the same token, the factors which have led to the decrease in the use of history in general chemistry will give a revitalized, relevant concept of history an opportunity to assume an important role. It is becoming increasingly evident that as chemical knowledge expands it will soon be physically impossible to do more than acquaint the student with each advance. General chemistry will be forced to revert to its original purpose— training the student to think critically about problems in chemistry, about what chemistry is, and how it is done. This is being carried out now in most of the progressive chemistry departments though perhaps not as boldly and imaginatively as in physics. Studies by the American Physics Institute and various specialized societies in physics have been undertaken in recent years aimed at totally revamping the lower level physics courses. The Harvard Project Physics has already attracted international attention. Significantly, most of the programs, including Harvard Physics, are deeply committed to the utilization of history in their approaches. It should be noted, however, that the word "history" is used here in the widest or broadest sense. It is not synonymous with "history" as practiced by professional historians of science.

If there is a "revolution" brewing, I. I. Rabi has captured its spirit. In an address before the Educational Policies Commission of the American Association for the Advancement of Science during the 1966 meeting in Washington, Rabi said:

I believe, basically, we have not been creative enough of one meaning of science in our generation, to teach it in a way which would be understood and appreciated and felt by the students. We have little of the positive values of science outside of the applications which are obvious to anybody living in this age. In other words, my claim is, and this is something we should discuss, that we have not been teaching our science in a humanistic way...

So what I propose as a suggestion for you is that science be taught at whatever level, from the lowest to the highest, in a humanistic way. By which I mean, it should be taught with a certain historical understanding, with a certain philosophical understanding, with a social understanding and a human understanding in the sense of the biography, the nature of the people who made this construction, the triumphs, the trials, the tribulations (4).

Such an approach would indeed be a revolution in the classical sense of the term. Its effect would be felt throughout the entire scientific community.

No doubt, to many chemists and professional historians of science, what Dr. Rabi is calling for would be accepted in principle, but ignored or rejected in application. Typically, chemistry courses for non-majors have been established which do utilize this principle. Yet its penetration into the curriculum for students majoring in chemistry is viewed as a threat to professionalism. The historian of science seems even more reluctant to step beyond his narrowly defined discipline to embrace this concept and make it workable.

The question which should be discussed at this symposium, then, is to what extent this conservatism on the part of the chemist and historian is justified. Clearly, the successes of chemistry and history can be directly attributed to their high degree of specialization. The new movement, on the surface, smacks of watered-down interdisciplinarianism, the specialist's perpetual boogeyman, who still haunts the classrooms of universities today. The real revolution, however, is not interdisciplinary. It rests upon a more tenable philosophy of education, the basic tenet of which is that through vertical specialization one must develop horizontally as well. It asserts that to be a good chemist one must explore everything that is related to chemistry, everything that influences chemical development or that chemistry itself influences. The humanistic-historical approach thus becomes an invaluable tool in such an endeavor.

The revolution in the historiography of science thus calls for us to go beyond merely trying to understand better the structure of chemical theories and the logical patterns of explanation by studying the philosophy of science; or to understand better the evolution of chemical thought and refinement of methodology by studying the history of science (products, in other words, of the *coup d'état* in the history of science). It means using one's experience and sophisticated specialization in order to reach out beyond the narrow limits of what goes on in the research laboratory and try to understand and make meaningful for our students the manifold relationships of chemistry to our world, to humanity. This, as I see it, is our obligation to our society and to ourselves.

4 Teaching the History of Chemistry

Literature Cited

(1) Kuhn, Thomas, "The Structure of Scientific Revolutions", University of Chicago Press, Chicago, 1962.
(2) Agassi, Joseph, "Towards an Historiography of Science", *History and Theory*, Beiheft 2, vii, Mouton and Co., S'Gravenhage, 1963.
(3) Farber, Eduard, "Towards an Historiography of Chemistry", *J. Chem. Ed.*, **42**, 124 (1965).
(4) Rabi, I. I., Address before the AAAS Educational Policies Commission, 27 December 1966, Washington, D. C. as quoted in *The Physics Teacher*, **5**, No. 5, (1967).

6. HISTORY OF CHEMISTRY IN A LIBERAL ARTS COLLEGE

A. Albert Baker, Jr.

[History of Science Department, Grand Valley State College, Allendale, Michigan, U.S.A.

There is an increasing tendency to eliminate from chemistry courses, descriptive chemistry and the historical development of chemistry. In a small liberal arts college with a restricted number of course offerings, it is particularly difficult to include such material in the conventional chemistry curriculum. Currently being explored at Grand Valley State College are two possibilities for giving students a broad view of chemistry as a discipline, how it has developed, and how it works as a science: (1) a beginning course which includes descriptive chemistry and historical content, consisting, in part, of reading original sources; and (2) a history of chemistry course directed at students who have some knowledge of the present state of chemistry.

In an address delivered before the joint meeting of the Division of Chemical Education and the Section of the History of Chemistry of the American Chemical Society at Los Angeles, August 6, 1925, Professor William Albert Noyes of the University of Illinois said that students of the history of chemistry "should learn how men have built on previous knowledge, and have slowly found their way to a better understanding of the principles of chemistry" (1).

Forty-three years later Professor Noyes' goal for studying the history of chemistry has lost none of its validity, and though we may not argue with this goal, we may take issue with his recipe for achieving it. Professor Noyes stated unequivocally that it is essential that students entering such a class should know the fundamental outlines of chemistry. At this point, the professor of history of chemistry in a small, state supported, liberal arts college, such as Grand Valley State College in Michigan, runs into difficulty with Professor Noyes' suggestions. Though he agrees that it would be highly desirable, if not essential, that his students have an understanding of chemistry, the professor in such a situation must face the economic facts of minimum class enrollments, faculty-student ratios, and other sometimes unpleasant factors which determine if a history of chemistry course can be a part of the curriculum.

The planners of Grand Valley State College thought that courses in the history of science might help to keep at a minimum the walls that seem to thrive on most campuses, dividing the sciences from the humanities and from the social studies. In line with this idea, it was thought that such courses should be open to as many students as possible; therefore the prerequisites should be held at a minimum. The course offerings in the history of science department were to be: (1) history of ancient science; (2) history of modern science; (3) history of chemistry; (4) history of physics; (5) history of mathematics; (6) history of biology; and (7) a special topics seminar for senior students minoring in the history of science.

4*

Part of the value of the projected interdisciplinary character of the history of science courses was lost when it was decided that the history of science department would be a part of the division of sciences and mathematics rather than letting it stand independent of, but linking, the divisions of humanities, social studies, and sciences and mathematics.

Grand Valley State College first opened its doors to students in the fall of 1963, admitting freshmen only. All students were required to complete nine foundation courses, constituting a full academic load for the freshman year: three five-credit-hour courses each quarter. These courses were physical science, biological science, mathematics, Greek and Roman history, philosophy, political science, English, and two terms of a foreign language (a third term to be taken in the sophomore year). Each of these courses was taught through lectures, discussion sessions, and individual and group tutorials. The two science courses also had regularly scheduled laboratories.

The physical science course was essentially an historical approach to the study of astronomy, physics, and chemistry. Approximately one-third of the course was devoted to the study of chemistry within the framework of atomic theory. Knowing that all students would have at least this introduction to chemistry in their background, it was decided that no other prerequisites for a history of chemistry course would be named, but that a student should have at least junior standing before he could enroll in the course.

Keeping in mind the minimum preparation that a student might have for the course, I began the actual planning of the course itself, taking a number of other factors into consideration as well. One of the first questions that I dealt with was: how will a course in the history of chemistry fit into the curriculum of the chemistry department? I took a hard look at the chemistry curriculum, which I had helped devise, and noted that it reflected the general trend in eliminating much descriptive chemistry and the historical development of chemistry. In a small liberal arts college with a restricted number of course offerings, it is particularly difficult to include such material in the conventional chemistry curriculum, and even more difficult at Grand Valley State College where the foundations program had forced us into a one-quarter term introductory chemistry course to be taken at the beginning of the sophomore year followed by two quarters of organic chemistry. A history of chemistry course, stressing the important role played by descriptive chemistry in the development of the science, was welcomed by the other chemistry faculty and was approved as a chemistry elective for chemistry majors.

Also taken into consideration were the kinds of students who would likely be taking the course in addition to the few chemistry majors who might elect it. The history of chemistry course was to be strongly recommended to those chemistry majors and minors preparing themselves to be high school teachers and to group-science majors planning to be elementary and junior high school teachers. Other students would be those majoring in humanities or social studies, who are taking the course in order to satisfy partially the college requirements that each student must take at least two science courses beyond the foundations program. The latter would be those students having a minimum knowledge of the "fundamental outlines of chemistry" (1).

Since no student would be entering the course totally innocent of what chemistry is about, I decided to spend as little time as possible teaching chemistry and as much as possible teaching the history of chemistry. I selected as a text "The Development of Modern Chemistry" by Aaron J. Ihde of the University of Wisconsin. Anticipating an enrollment of less than fifteen students, I scheduled four one-hour lecture-discussion meetings per week rather than separating the discussion sections from the lectures as is usually done at Grand Valley State College. I decided to require each student to schedule three one-hour tutorial sessions with me during the term, primarily to discuss the progress of their term paper and to defend the finished product.

A unique feature of the course, as originally designed, made use of the students' study of foreign languages. Before enrolling in the course each student had completed three or more terms of study in German, French, Russian, or Spanish, and I asked each student to read a short article in the language that he had studied and to make an oral or written report on the article. Most of the selections were made from current scientific journals, international history of science journals, and, as suggested by a student having difficulty finding anything appropriate in Spanish, encyclopedia articles (this unique feature of the course was reluctantly removed the following year after the faculty voted to remove the study of foreign languages from the list of degree requirements).

I decided that the main purpose of a term paper in the course would be to give the student an opportunity to learn a great deal about a narrow topic. With this view in mind I did not have to apologize quite so much for the dearth of original sources in our library. Those few students capable of handling a twentieth-century topic could find enough material, and the others could use such sources as the Alembic Club Reprints, and that great gift to the underprivileged library: "Source Book in Chemistry" by Henry M. Leicester and Herbert S. Klickstein. Also useful are two new paperback series from the Houghton Mifflin Company: "Classic Researches in General Chemistry" and "Classic Researches in Organic Chemistry". I encouraged students to choose topics dealing with the contributions made by an outstanding chemist or topics tracing the historical development of a chemical concept, and I discouraged biographical papers.

Since only juniors and seniors were permitted to enroll in the course, I dispensed with quizzes and gave only a final examination. I tried to make this one examination as comprehensive as possible, and perhaps the examination itself will indicate the content of the course, as I taught it, better than some other method would. Given below is the actual examination given to students in the course the second time that it was offered.

Final Examination

I.   Write on one topic from group A, one from B, and one from C.

A
1. Alchemy was rooted in Greek concepts of matter. Emerging in Alexandria, it reached its zenith as a theoretical science during the period when the Arabs were the intellectual leaders of the Western World. Discuss.
2. As alchemy declined in Europe, increasingly valuable contributions to the future science of chemistry were made by medicine and metal technology. From these the unifying theory of phlogiston arose. With little regard to its origination, discuss the phlogiston theory, particularly in its final form.
3. Discuss the flaws in the phlogiston theory and how the oxygen theory replaced it as a new unifying chemical theory.

B
1. Discuss Dalton's atomic theory, briefly touching on earlier ideas of atoms and the important aspects in which Dalton's theory differed from them.
2. Discuss the "atomic weight problem" and how it was ultimately solved. (Include: Dalton, Gay-Lussac's combining volumes, Avogadro, Berzelius' objections, Dulong and Petit's Law, Mitscherlich's law of isomorphism, and Cannizzaro.)
3. Discuss the classification of the elements with regard to Dösereiner, Newlands, Mendeleev, and how Moseley ultimately demonstrated what atomic number is.

C
1. The ancients knew seven metals and two non-metals, alchemy discovered some three more elements, and the rest were discovered through the interplay of science and technology. Discuss briefly how each of the following developments led to the discovery of elements (it is not necessary to name individual elements).
   1. Advances in mining techniques
   2. The pneumatic trough
   3. Electrolysis
   4. The spectroscope
   5. The periodic chart
   6. Discovery of radioactivity
   7. X-ray spectrum analysis
   8. The cyclotron

2. Discuss the development of organic chemistry during the 19th century, using the following as a possible outline:
   1. Significance of the term "organic"
   2. Wöhler's synthesis of urea
   3. The type theory and the radical theory
   4. Frankland and valence
   5. Tetravalence of carbon (Couper and Kekulé)
   6. Chemical structure (Hofmann's models, Crum Brown, Erlenmeyer, and Butlerov)
   7. Tetrahedral carbon (van't Hoff and le Bel)
   8. Synthetic dye industry

3. Discuss the development of ideas about atomic structure in the 20th century, emphasizing the following:
   1. Rutherford's nuclear atom
   2. Rutherford's planetary atom
   3. Bohr's orbit atom
   4. The orbital atom

II.   Briefly indicate the contributions of 10 of the following to the development of chemistry.

1. Becher	3. Berzelius
2. Becquerel	4. Black

5. Boyle
6. Cavendish
7. Curie
8. Davy
9. Dumas
10. Faraday
11. Gerhardt
12. Hales

13. Hope
14. Jabir
15. Klaproth
16. Liebig
17. Pasteur
18. Perkin
19. Priestley
20. Prout

21. Scheele

This history of chemistry course is now, in the spring term of 1968, being offered for the third time at Grand Valley State College. Enrollment has grown from twelve students in the spring of 1966 to twenty-five this spring. It is certainly encouraging to find more and more chemistry majors electing to take the course. I am convinced that in studying the development of chemistry, students will acquire a much better understanding of what the science of chemistry is, of how it works, and of its interactions with the other sciences and with man's other pursuits.

Literature Cited

(1) Noyes, William Albert, "The Teaching of the History of Chemistry", *J. Chem. Educ.*, **3**, 561 (1926).

7. PROBLEMS IN THE TEACHING OF THE HISTORY OF CHEMISTRY

VIRGINIA F. McCONNELL

Department of Chemistry, Newcomb College, Tulane University, New Orleans, Louisiana, U.S.A.

Since the organization of a course in the history of chemistry is, for the most part, in the hands of individual professors, the course may be taught from many different points of view. Three of these are considered in the present paper: the biographical, the ideational, and the historical approaches. The distinguishing features of each approach are analyzed and discussed together with the reasons which may underlie the choice of treatment. In conclusion, this question is considered: Is the difference between biographical history, the history of scientific ideas, and a strictly chronological history of chemistry important? In the final analysis, the purpose in offering a course in the history of chemistry is to impart to one's students an understanding of ways in which the development of chemistry has proceeded.

Every spring, when the question of the choice of a textbook in a course in general chemistry must be made, professors are faced with a large number of texts, each with its particular merits. However, upon comparison, most of the texts cover substantially the same material and in pretty much the same order. The very opposite is true of a course in the history of the physical sciences. There are few texts as such, but a bewildering number of books, journal articles, commentaries on and translations of original works confront a professor. The quantity of published material, the complexity of an interdisciplinary subject, and the necessity for weaving diverse strands into a comprehensible pattern demand the exercise of care and discrimination on the part of the professor of the history of any science. What determines his choice? This must be based on his own predilections, derived from his individual turn of mind, his background, his traditions, and the disciplines in which he has received training, as well as his reaction to all of the above. Furthermore, each instructor in the history of a science must provide the organization for his course, with the result that there are almost as many different approaches as there are professors. In view of the very heterogeneity of material and the diversity of interest on the part of those who teach the history of science, an examination of some of the ways in which such a course can be structured should be worthwhile. As it is impossible to treat all phases of the history of science here, we will limit our comments to the history of chemistry.

Before the organization of a course in the history of chemistry can be attempted, certain aspects must be considered in order to clarify the aims of the course. These can be grouped into at least three categories, namely:

(A) The biographical approach
(B) The ideational approach
(C) The chronological approach

(A) The Biographical Approach

Should the course be primarily biographical? As George Sarton has pointed out (1), the biographical method, irrespective of its merits or failings, will always be very popular. Being human beings, we are essentially interested in human beings, and their very differences (which make fair comparisons impossible) make the study of human beings fascinating, particularly to those whose foremost interest is other people. A study of the factors which have contributed to the development of genius and of the talents of hand and mind which make a great chemist has been among the senior interests of the history of chemistry.

But precisely here lies one of the most insidious stumbling blocks for a professor. No matter how objective he tries to be, he cannot help making judgments based on his own appraisal of a given individual. For example, an ardent reformer will regard Lavoisier from a different point of view than that of a convinced conservative. However, biases which are recognized are not incompatible with historical or scientific research. An honest admission of prejudice is necessary if one is not to become a propagandist rather than an historian. One must also examine the biases of the men who built the science of chemistry, an easier and pleasanter occupation than self-criticism. Berzelius is a favorite example here because he is known for his predilection for his own concepts as shown by his declaration in 1830 that Faraday's work was inaccurate when, as a matter of fact, he himself was unclear as to the difference between current quantity and current intensity (2). However, by 1837, Berzelius modified his opinion of Faraday (3). Although it was not easy for Berzelius to alter his ideas, his preconceptions did not prevent his becoming a great chemist. Hence, one important reason for studying the history of chemistry from the biographical viewpoint is the examination of preconceptions and their effect upon a man's science.

Furthermore, the biographical aspect of chemistry can be made to demonstrate that the work of an earlier investigator is the basis for conclusions drawn by later probers, who held a different set of ideas, as demonstrated by Ostwald's remarks on reading Arrhenius' dissertation on electrolytic dissociation.*

The mirror image of this analysis of preconceptions is seen in the resonance that existed between Adolf Baeyer and Emil Fischer. Even though Fischer soon departed from the work on phthalein dyes assigned to him for a doctoral dissertation by Baeyer, his interest in structural chemistry was doubtlessly sparked by Baeyer. Although each man independently

* Ostwald, who had been working for some time on affinity constants, wrote: "At first I was inclined to consider [the work] entirely nonsensical. However, I discovered some calculations of this obviously still young man which had led to his conclusions regarding the magnitude of affinity [constants] of acids that agreed well with the values which I had obtained by entirely different methods. And finally I was satisfied, after thorough study, that this young man had solved the great problem of the relationship between acids and bases, to which I had intended to devote my life..." (Ostwald, Wilhelm, "Lebenslinien: eine Selbstbiographie," Vol. 1, p. 217, Klasing and Co., Berlin, 1933).

accomplished much in quite different areas, there existed a reciprocal relationship between them, as shown by the fact that both worked on derivatives of phenylhydrazine and uric acid.* This close relationship was at once their strength and their weakness, for, although their achievements were elegant, such mutual admiration may have acted as a deterrent to a tendency to break with tradition.

"Chemical genealogy" and the consequent degree of indebtedness which one man owes to another pays dividends of interest in biographical studies. Baeyer's student, Fischer, trained Otto Diels, whose student was Kurt Alder. Together Diels and Alder worked out the diene synthesis. All of these investigators made distinctive contributions to structural chemistry (all four were Nobelists). Of course, the extent to which scientists are creative is a point which cannot be solved but which provides the basis for lively class discussions.

This thought brings up the question of priority, which becomes more elusive the closer that we try to pinpoint the time of discovery. The various difficulties of establishing priority have been competently discussed by Thomas Kuhn, who notes, in regard to historians of science. "As chroniclers of an incremental process, they discover that additional research makes it harder, not easier, to answer questions like: When was oxygen discovered?" (4) or: Was the real discoverer of benzene Faraday, who obtained it from condensed coal gas and analyzed it, or was benzene discovered some forty years earlier when an almost tasteless water was found in the distillate from coal tar? (5, 6). Furthermore, is the examination of property rights profitable? Undeniably, the science of chemistry has been built up by the exertions of individuals, but too much emphasis on "credit" makes the development of chemistry look like a series of accretions interlaced with a series of controversies.

If the biographical approach is selected, one other point must be settled. Are the main events of the history of chemistry determined by relatively few men or by great numbers of investigators, i.e., should we confine our attention to the pioneers? To do this may lead to the error of overemphasis on the achievements of the stars of the drama of chemistry and a neglect of contributions made by the supporting cast. Yet concentration on the minor actors may leave one's students with the impression of a play without a plot. A careful balance must be maintained here.

(B) The Ideational Approach

An alternative view of the development of chemistry emphasizes the point that the primary factor in bringing about scientific discovery is not individual genius but the relentless pressure of new knowledge. Should we, then, treat the history of chemistry as a history of ideas?

* Baeyer prepared oxindole (Ber., 11, 584 (1878)) and skatole (Ber., 13, 2339 (1880)) because of his interest in isatin and indigo; Fischer prepared indole from phenylhydrazine derivatives, beginning in 1883 (Ber., 16, 2241 (1883)). Fischer made phenylhydrazine in 1875 (Ber., 8, 589 (1875)), and Baeyer worked with phenylhydrazine derivatives in 1891 (Ber., 24, 2690, 2692 (1891)).

A study of the concepts which have emerged from the efforts of chemists avoids the incremental aspect of scientific achievements and is intrinsically interesting, especially if we trace the evolution of ideas. The ideational approach has the appeal that it searches for a consistent pattern applicable to the nature of chemical development (whether or not such a pattern exists is another question). The ideational and biographical approaches can be used simultaneously if studies are made into the ways in which the minds of scientists operate; and these are various. Scientists may think inductively, they may proceed by a hypothetico-deductive process, they may advance slowly from insight to insight until they find a physical explanation, or they may hit upon a tentative conclusion, which they believe to be correct, without consciously going through any particular train of thought. A man's own account of the route by which he has arrived at his ideas may be inaccurate. Dalton is known to have given several contradictory accounts of the origin of his atomic theory. Often the way in which a man gains real perceptions is not recorded. All of us know Kekulé's description of his flash of insight which resulted in his concept of the benzene ring. What is not so well known is his concept of the nature of the benzene molecule, which is not static nor in equilibrium but is a time-average distribution of collisions of neighboring atoms, a prevision of resonance (7).

Many a flash of genius may have led to wrong conclusions, but we do not hear of these. Creative people are often wrong, either because they are willing to gamble on their nonconformity or because they may have what appears to others as blind spots of conformity. The elements both of skepticism and credulity are present in Newton, who, in spite of his prudence in regard to hypotheses, devoted much time to copying alchemical manuscripts. Newton, of course, was not totally cautious. If he had been so, the chances are that he would have suppressed his own creativity because creative people necessarily modify or upset at least part of the *status quo*. An interesting phase of this question, especially to us, who live in a time when traditional ideas are in question, is the reaction of the body of scientists of the past to novel ideas, which were often suppressed or rejected because they did not fit with accepted dogma. Berzelius thought Laurent's substitution of chlorine for hydrogen impossible; Dumas concurred (8). Yet the nature of research is such that valid ideas survive. Shortly afterwards, Dumas made chloracetic acid by substitution (9). Do similar situations exist now?

An examination of creativity may show that new scientific concepts are simply alternative ways of viewing the same set of phenomena. Priestley and Lavoisier looked at the phenomenon of combustion from different angles. The calcination of mercury and the decomposition of mercuric oxide were given an antiphlogistic interpretation by Lavoisier and a phlogistic one by Joseph Priestley, who was, by his own statement, aware of the implications of this work. Priestley felt that his view was supported by the results of the heating of lead oxide with hydrogen. This work convinced Priestley "that under suitable circumstances one could 'see' phlogiston in the form of hydrogen being imbibed by a calx to form a metal even more vividly than Lavoisier's work had convinced him of the opposite" (10).

Another and more general illustration of alternative points of view will be found in the contrast between the aversion against speculation that characterized a good deal of the thought of the seventeenth and eighteenth centuries and the passion for vortices which marked the atomic debates of the nineteenth century.*

The study of the history of a science as a history of ideas becomes intriguing if "we take seriously the view that science is inquiry, for here questions are clearly primary. For 'science' will then not be a body of ordered statements or conclusions, of settled answers, but a way of asking questions" (11), the new questions that give rise to new theories. It seems that scientific questions and hence discoveries are of at least two kinds, those which were anticipated and those which could not be predicted from accepted theory in advance. Kuhn suggests that the latter are discoveries which are not only additions to scientific knowledge but are something more, for "they react back upon what has previously been known and cause those in whose area of special competence the new phenomenon falls, to see both the world and their work differently as they emerge from the extended struggle with anomaly which constitutes that phenomenon's discovery" (12). He goes on to say that the "discovery" of the role of oxygen in combustion demanded the profound readjustment in chemical theory and practice which has come to be known as the chemical revolution.

However, this passage overemphasizes the revolutionary aspect of the upheaval caused by a new approach, which is apparent at long range. The so-called revolutions in science develop so slowly that each one has more of evolutionary than revolutionary characteristics. Lavoisier's explanation of combustion was preceded by a series of experiments by Mayow, Wren, and Boyle, all of whom where aware of an "odd substance" in air a hundred years previously. The phlogiston theory was abandoned gradually. Conversely, revolutionary ideas are often not recognized as such either by their author or by the majority of investigators. According to Louis de Broglie (13), contemporary physicists did not comprehend the importance of Max Planck's fundamental papers, and Planck himself recoiled from the formidable consequence of his own ideas.**

Discussion of the degree to which each discovery is evolutionary or revolutionary is an exciting phase of the analysis of discovery.

---

* The search for mechanical models led to Helmholtz's vortex rings, Maxwell's vortices, Kelvin's vortex atoms, and Fitzgerald's wheels. J. J. Thomson explained the dissociation of gases in terms of rings whose radii were subject to disturbing influences.

** Stephen Toulmin, in "The Evolutionary Development of Natural Science", American Scientist, 55, 469 (1967), notes: "We tend to think of Planck as one of the conscious revolutionaries of science... Yet Planck put forward his hypothesis that the emission of electromagnetic radiation by material bodies is 'quantized' as a regrettable but necessary refinement of Maxwell's classical theories, not as their abandonment... Indeed the appearance of Einstein's theory of the 'photon' in 1905 filled him initially with indignation: he found himself quite unable to accept it, since it struck him as involving a needless abandonment of Maxwell's electromagnetism."

Closely associated with the study of the genesis and development of ideas is a consideration of the philosophy of science, for logical analysis of significant arguments belongs to both history and philosophy. It is the tracing of the geneses of ideas (whether predictable or not) and the read-justments consequent upon new theories which makes the ideational approach to history important in its own right. However, a study of ideas alone can fail to bring out the importance of the laboratory. There is no question that Berzelius' preeminence is largely due to his intensive labo-ratory work. Both biographical and ideational studies may also fail to show the relation of chemistry to the culture in which it is developed.

(C) The Chronological Approach

Should we, then, adopt a chronological approach in our presentation of the history of chemistry? For various reasons, outlined below, this approach has benefits to students which the other methods lack.

One advantage of this approach is that it makes twentieth-century chemistry appear as a consequence of what has gone before, for:

Our present day is not for us a system of forces improvised out of the void the day before yesterday and destined to melt away under the influence of other forces which will unexpectedly crop up the day after tomorrow. Our present day is the product of a social, moral, and intellectual evolution, whose origins are lost in the mists of time, and will in its turn be the necessary condition of future developments. From this conviction arises the fact that knowledge of the present disassociated from the knowledge of the past could never satisfy our curiosity (14).

If we apply the cited quotation from Salvemini to the study of chemistry, it follows that an understanding of the development of chemistry as a whole is essential to all understanding of the science. Hence, the story of the creation of chemistry may well be taught on the basis of its chronology. The historical approach can be made to show the influences which social and political history have on the creative efforts of investigators. In fact, any look at chemistry in historical perspective necessitates a look at the relations between political history and scientific history. Lehmann's remarks on philosophy apply also to chemistry: "It bears the general marks of the period to which it belongs; and the more powerful the ideas which it pro-claims, the more strongly it will be permeated by the currents of thought which fluctuate in the life of the period" (15). Because of this relation of chemistry to the *Zeitgeist* of a period, a study of its evolution and revolu-tions can well be made against a historiographic background, although a conscious encouragement of science by government (with the exception of certain Academies of Science) is largely a product of the nineteenth and twentieth centuries.

When the development of a science is compared with political history or history of the arts, it seems to be characterized by an important differ-ence in kind. Science is cumulative in character, although its rate of prog-ress fluctuates. Thus chemistry is not a "body of information which has accumulated in a linear series of discrete discoveries" (16), but it is a science which has progressed rapidly in one century, slowly in another. If a graph were drawn of the number of discoveries plotted against time, it might seem to be a smooth curve, but if the details of the graph were studied, the overall progression would be seen to have many irregularities. It is only too easy to describe the historical development of science as a steady uninterrupted progress, but the proponents of chemistry followed many false trails and erroneous interpretations.

The historical method also allows a study of the relationship of technology to theoretical science. The more closely we examine the reciprocal influences of these two spheres, the more we agree that the history of technology is an essential part of the history of science, and neither can be well understood without the other, for the development of applied science is now so extensive that a comprehensive view of it is necessary. In fact, the twentieth century has been termed an era of creative technology in which the engineer and scientist work so closely as to become one in many instances. One phase of this equilibrium is the influence of the invention of scientific instruments on discovery. In this century, the working alliance between the scientist and engineer has found one of its finest and most fruitful expressions in the development of scientific tools. The reciprocal influence, that of scientific instruments on the development of science, has become of equal importance as investigators depend upon instruments to an ever increasing degree.

An entirely different reason for the use of the chronological approach in teaching the history of chemistry is that most students like it. This is probably because they acquire the feeling that they have thus come into possession of a solid foundation of facts, "something to tie to". Yet those students who are more interested in ideas and people than in the interrelations of discovery and history will also find material of interest in this context. Therefore, whatever approach one takes to the history of science, it should be realistic. Careful evaluation of data and sources by student and instructor is paramount.

One more question: Is the difference between biographical history, the history of scientific ideas, and a chronological history of science important? The real purpose of the study of the history of chemistry is to explain how the structure of chemistry was developed, for we need:

...to see scientific thought and practice as a developing body of ideas and techniques. These ideas and methods, and even the controlling aims of science itself, are continually evolving, in a changing intellectual and social environment. ...We must take this evolutionary process seriously. Otherwise, we shall be in danger, as historians, of concerning ourselves too much with particular discoveries or doctrines or persons, with anticipations and anecdotes (17).

Literature Cited

(1) Sarton, George, "The History of Science and the New Humanism", 3rd ed., p. 3, George Braziller, Inc., New York, 1956.
(2) Ehl, Rosemary G., and Ihde, Aaron J., "Faraday's Electrochemical Laws and the Determination of Equivalent Weight", *Journal of Chemical Education*, **31**, 229, 230 (1954).

(3) Berzelius, J. J., "Kampf der Kontakt-Theorie mit der Chemischen, im Felde des Galvanismus", *Liebig's Ann.*, **24,** 159 (1837).
(4) Kuhn, Thomas S., "The Structure of Scientific Revolutions", p. 2, The University of Chicago Press, Chicago and London, 1962.
(5) Faraday, Michael, "Experimental Researches in Chemistry and Physics", pp. 159–161, R. Taylor and W. Francis, publishers to the University of London, 1859, reprinted from *Phil. Trans.*, **115,** 440 (1825).
(6) Schelenz, Hermann, "Benzin und Benzol", *Zeit. angew. Chem.*, **21,** 2577 (1908).
(7) Kekulé, August, "Ueber einige Kondensations-Produkte des Aldehyds", *Ann.*, **162, 77** (1877).
(8) Berzelius, J. J., "Lettre sur différents points de théorie chimique", *Compt. rend.*, **6,** 629 (1838); Dumas, J. B., "Réponse à la lettre de M. Berzelius concernant divers points de chimie théorique", *Compt. rend.*, **6,** 645, 646, 669 (1838).
(9) Dumas, J. B., "Note concernant un acide product par l'action du chlore sur l'acide acetique", *Compt. rend.*, **7,** 474 (1838); de Milt, Clara, "Auguste Laurent, Founder of Modern Organic Chemistry", *Chymia*, **4,** 98 (1953).
(10) Toulmin, Stephen, E., "Crucial Experiments, Priestley and Lavoisier", in "Roots of Scientific Thought", p. 484, ed. by Philip P. Wiener and Aaron Noland, Basic Books, New York, 1957.
(11) Randall, Jr., John Hermann, "The Art of Language and the Linguistic Situation: a Naturalistic Analysis", *Journal of Philosophy*, **60,** 42 (1963).
(12) Kuhn, Tomas S., "Historical Structure of Scientific Discovery", *Science*, **138,** 763 (1962).
(13) de Broglie, Louis, "The Revolution in Physics", pp. 108 and 111, trans. by Ralph W. Niemeyer, The Noonday Press, Inc., New York, 1953.
(14) Salvemini, Gaetano, "Historian and Scientist", p. 28, Harvard University Press, Cambridge, Mass., 1939.
(15) Lehmann, R., "Schopenhauer", p. 28, as trans. by Franz Boas in "The Mind of Primitive Man", p. 137, The Macmillan Company, New York, 1938.
(16) Gillispie, Charles C., "The Nature of Science", *Science*, **138,** 1481 (1962).
(17) Toulmin, Stephen, "Foresight and Understanding", p. 109, Indiana University Press, Bloomington, 1961.

8. TEACHING THE HISTORY OF CHEMISTRY TO CHEMISTS

JAMES P. DANEHY

Department of Chemistry, University of Notre Dame, Notre Dame, Indiana, U.S.A., 46 556

A study of the historical development of the most important concepts in chemistry beginning with their remotest antecedents can make a real contribution to the liberal education of a chemist. A course is outlined which has been developed and taught during the past ten years. It begins with the Ionian natural philosophers and ends with Cannizzaro. It includes a study of the scientific revolution of the sixteenth and seventeenth centuries because, while alchemy and nascent chemistry did not participate significantly in this revolution, chemistry was later to become a full beneficiary thereof.

About ten years ago, at my own request, I began to teach a one-semester course in the history of chemistry, and I have continued to develop and to offer it each year. My dubious credentials for this venture included the facts that I had long been a practicing organic chemist and that I had read widely in the history of chemistry and allied fields. Moreover, I had recently spent four years in developing and teaching a two-semester course in physical science for the students in Notre Dame's General Program of Liberal Education. This experience, more than anything else, impressed me with the importance and necessity of teaching the *rationale* of science as well as its content. But I was convinced then, as I still am, that chemical education in this country does not provide an intellectually satisfactory account of the relation between the facts of science and their interpretation.

Let me illustrate my concern by quoting the opening lines of the introduction to Linus Pauling's "General Chemistry", published in 1947:

Chemistry is a very large subject, which continues to grow, as new elements are discovered or made, new compounds are synthesized, and new principles are formulated. Nevertheless, despite its growth, the science can now be presented to the student more easily and effectively than ever before. In the past the course in general chemistry has necessarily tended to be a patch-work of descriptive chemistry and certain theoretical topics. The progress made in recent decades in the development of unifying theoretical concepts has been so great, however, that the presentation of general chemistry to the students of the present generation can be made in a more simple, straightforward, and logical way than formerly.

For example, every boy now knows about atoms, and accepts them as part of his world — they are split in the atomic bomb and in the comic papers, they stare at him from advertisements. In this book I begin the teaching of chemistry by discussing the properties of substances in terms of atoms and molecules. The subject is then developed in as orderly a manner as has seemed possible at the present stage of chemical knowledge.

Pauling, then, has given the pragmatic argument for adopting the conceptual framework for contemporary chemistry, and only a rash person

5 Teaching the History of Chemistry

would deny that it is a cogent one. But it does disavow any concern for our specific intellectual heritage. To paraphrase Stephen Toulmin, this approach gives the answers before the questions are asked. But Pauling's concern is for the orderly and efficient transmission of the empirical facts and the theoretical interpretations as associated within the framework of contemporary chemistry. Our concern here is for the introduction of the student to one important part of the history of the development of ideas, which we believe to be germane to his liberal education as a chemist.

My course has to be called "History of Chemistry" for departmental reasons. But I have interpreted the substantive words of the title as liberally as necessary in order to achieve the objective in view. Let me now give a running account, with commentary, of the content of the course. Finally, I will describe the structure of the course, including its component parts.

Chemistry is the latest of the major divisions of the natural sciences to arrive on the scene. While the word, *chemistry*, in the proper sense cannot be used much before 1750, its use in a looser, but nevertheless definable, sense can be extended to cover all those attempts to answer two great questions which we may formulate as follows:

(a) What is the ultimate nature of matter?
(b) How does a thing come to be that which it is not now?

The first question suggests a series of subsidiary or corollary questions. What, if anything, do all material things have in common? Is matter continuous (infinitely divisible) or is it particulate? Are there simple substances (elements) whose combinations account for the infinite variety of observable substances? If so, how many are there and what are they?

The second question deals with substantial change, or chemical reaction, as opposed to mere mixing or its converse. Stated more narrowly the question becomes: What can we know about what is happening at the subvisible level, which accounts for the sensible phenomena?

Since these are the questions with which the Greek natural philosophers concerned themselves, we must recognize that chemistry, in embryonic form, was being discussed almost six hundred years before Christ. Accordingly, we begin with the Ionians. In continuing, we recognize that the major alternatives developed in Greek natural philosophy—the Democritan, the Pythagorean-Platonic, and the Aristotelian positions—represent materialistic, idealistic, and compromise answers to the fundamental questions. Our acquaintance with the Democritan atom is made vivid by a reading of the first two books of Lucretius' "The Nature of Things". We note, despite the fantastic language of Plato's "Timaeus", the remarkable adumbration of the importance of mathematics in science suggested by this Pythagorean statement. We try to get some idea of the grandiose totality of Aristotle's closed and tightly packed world which was still important in Europe eighteen hundred years later.

We observe the rise of alchemy as one important product of a multicultural confluence in cosmopolitan Alexandria. Those features of alchemy which characterize all three of its well-defined periods are described: its conceptually retrospective character; its empirical achievements of a preparative nature; its obscure, occult, and allegorical language and symbolism; its failure to rise above the qualitative level. The transmission of Alexandrine alchemy to the Moslem world and from the latter to Western Europe is traced. The gradual merging of the activities of European alchemists and of somewhat more pragmatic craftsmen and technologists in the sixteenth and seventeenth centuries brings us to the beginning of chemistry proper.

Then, in an important and essential interlude, we consider the scientific revolution of the sixteenth and seventeenth centuries in which alchemy, much less chemistry, played no significant role. But when chemistry did mature, it was to participate fully in all that this revolution achieved.

Central to our study of the scientific revolution is a reading and discussion of much of Galileo's "Two New Sciences". This remarkable work is still well worth reading today, not because Galileo has included in it an account of his achievements in two quite unrelated fields (strength of materials and kinematics), but because in his old age he reflected clearly and consciously on the system of methods which must have emerged slowly from his subconscious during the many decades of his professional activity. He realized full well that what was needed was not the piecemeal correction of factual errors or theoretical interpretations but the replacement of an entire and self-consistent attitude toward the investigation of nature (the Aristotelian one) with a more effective one. Galileo did not invent any part of the scientific method, but no one before him had composed the parts in so harmonious and effective a fashion, nor has anyone since him presented the program of science in such a persuasive manner.

Written in an Italian* which de Santillana considers some of the finest prose of the seventeenth century, the work takes the form of a discussion between three Venetian gentlemen: Salviati (Galileo himself), Sagredo (an interested layman), and Simplicio (an Aristotelian). The First Day is a long introduction to the "new sciences", one of which is taken up in the Second Day, the other of which is divided between the Third and Fourth Days. The First Day appears to be an informal, spontaneous, conversational ramble, but this is the artfulness of the apparently artless. There are two distinct parts, each with its own subject matter and distinctly different kinds of conclusions, skillfully joined by a crucial point in Aristotelian physics. The first part is concerned with the nature of cohesion: not, mind you, with *how* things cohere, but *why* they cohere. Speculations are presented that could not possibly be checked by any imaginable experiments, and an attempt is made to support the theory by misuse of mathematical analogy. Galileo is really illustrating the futility of trying to answer the question *why* before we know enough about *how*. But this becomes clear only when we have read the Second Day, in which Galileo returns to the subject of cohesion, sticks exclusively to the question *how*, has the

---

* Formal, mathematical arguments are "quoted" from an imaginary treatise in Latin by the "Academician" (a literary disguise for Galileo).

imaginative perception of the applicability of the Archimedean lever principle, and is completely successful.

Salviati, in these misguided speculations in the first half of the First Day, has argued that solid bodies consist of an infinitely large number of infinitely small particles held together by an infinitely large number of infinitely small vacua. Simplicio objects by reviewing the arguments against the possibility of a vacuum taken from the fourth book of Aristotle's "Physics". On this pivotal point, selected by Galileo with great appropriateness, we are swung into the second half of the First Day. Here we are given a rapid and casual introduction to kinematics, but significant points in the new methodology are carefully introduced: the necessity for separating secondary from primary factors, and for extrapolating from real to idealized situations, in formulating physical laws; the convenience and utility of indirect observation (the planned experiment). The change in atmosphere is unmistakable.

We have already noted that the Second Day is an analysis of fracture in terms of the Archimedean lever principle to the relation between force and dimensions and an experimental justification (at least implied). In the third day Galileo presents kinematics more fully, perhaps much as he actually developed it: an initial postulation that naturally accelerated motion is uniformly accelerated, the development of what ought to be the physical consequences by purely mathematical means, and a final appeal to quantitative experiment for verification of the original postulate. But he takes full advantage of his literary form to introduce objections and difficulties which had actually plagued him and to bring back Sagredo and Simplicio with a twist of the wrist, when he finds them wandering off again in search of ultimate causes.

This is simply a wonderful book, and I hope that I have been able to give some reason for its being included in a course in the history of chemistry even though it is no part of the history of chemistry.

Every chemist has heard of Robert Boyle's "Sceptical Chymist", but which of them has read it? We read it for its iconoclasm: the four elements of the Aristotelians and the three principles of the Paracelsians are discredited, though there is nothing as yet with which to replace them. We read it also for its clearly comprehensible accounts of recognizable chemical phenomena, written in nonmolecular language.

In considering Boyle's pneumatics, we note the inverse of the sequence by which Galileo established kinematics. An accumulation of data is followed by an empirical generalization (an induction), not actually made by Boyle himself, and more than a century was to pass before a physical assumption was made and treated mathematically to yield the equivalent of the empirical generalization (the kinetic-molecular theory).

We consider the investigations of thermal phenomena that took place during the seventeenth and eighteenth centuries, the gradual clarification of concepts dealing with heat, and the ideas as to the nature of heat. Particular attention is paid to the work of Black and of Rumford.

Black's work on "Magnesia alba" is examined closely as the archetype of a quantitative study on the basis of which chemical conclusions can be drawn.

The problem of combustion is used as a thread (as it has been by others) with which to connect the works of many chemists.

The "Elementary Treatise" of Lavoisier provides us with a clear exposition of most chemical ideas and some chemical facts just before the ancient atomic idea finally becomes operational.

Dalton's presentation of his atomic theory is considered, with explicit recognition of the severe limitation imposed upon it by reason of its strictly gravimetric basis. The contributions of Gay-Lussac and Avogadro in providing an effective atomic-molecular theory are brought in. Some effort is made to see why this view was not accepted during the next five decades, and the course is concluded with an account of Cannizzaro's persuasive lecture of 1858.

This class uses textbooks for continuity, lectures for emphasis on topics reflecting the predilections of the writer, seminar discussion of classic texts, and term papers, so that the student can demonstrate his ability to strike out on his own. The students are provided with an extensive select reading list, all the titles of which are to be found in the University Library.

I enjoy teaching this course, and it is a pleasure to see a few students respond well. But the attitude of most chemists is one of indifference to anything so clearly expendable as this luxury item.

9. THE USE OF CASE HISTORIES IN THE TEACHING OF HISTORY OF SCIENCE*

J. A. Schufle

Department of Chemistry, New Mexico Highlands University, Las Vegas, New Mexico, U.S.A.

The methods that we use for teaching chemistry are sometimes out-of-date. We are obsessed with teaching facts. Students are discouraged by "fact" courses. Teaching the history of chemical ideas may be a viable alternative. We recommend the use of the case history method for teaching the history of science. Conant's "Case Histories in Experimental Science" make excellent reference materials. The use of the case of the overthrow of the phlogiston theory is described. In demonstrations before classes, we have shown how to discover phlogiston and how to invent the hot air balloon. Examples of Bergman's use of the phlogiston theory are described.

Introduction

The teaching of chemistry has for too long been a process in which facts are transmitted from the notebook of the professor into the notebook of the student without going through the heads of either. Students emerge from such courses firmly convinced that they have acquired a body of knowledge which will endure for all time. And we professors reinforce this belief by the kind of examinations that we give to students, if we are to judge by the lament of the late Professor Thomas S. Wheeler regarding the examination for the leaving certificate in the Irish school system. According to Wheeler, the examination is still the same as it was one hundred years ago, testing the student's knowledge of the "billiard ball atom and hard water".

But the problem is not simply one of replacing the older facts about chemistry with a lot of new facts. Students are not noticeably attracted to courses crammed with facts, no matter how current and dramatic the new information may be. Dr. W. T. Lippincott in the October, 1967 issue of the *Journal of Chemical Education* reports that a study of a sample of National Merit Scholars interested in science showed that over half of them changed from science to nonscience careers after entering college. I believe that students are not finding intellectual challenge in the science courses, including chemistry courses, that they are offered, no matter how many references to lasers or cyclotrons that we insert into our lectures.

And so some of us have tried side-trips into the history of chemistry hoping that students might gain an insight into the scientific method by learning something about how scientists think. I have used the term "the scientific method", and I will return to discuss this again later. And yet

* *The Texas Journal of Science*, **21**, 101–108 (1969). Reprinted with permission.

somehow even these courses in the history of chemistry fail, because they
are usually either a collection of anecdotes about people who discovered
the chemical elements or are a recitation of events and dates down through
the history of chemistry in chronological order.

Now there is also the problem of trying to understand science. Many of
us decide that to understand what modern science is all about we should
study the most modern textbooks of science. If we do this, we might
conclude that modern science is that collection of observations, laws, and
theories that we find described in these textbooks. Thus we might conclude
that scientific development is the process of assembling this collection of
facts. The job of the historian of science is therefore to determine when
and where various pieces of scientific data are collected and to explain
some of the erroneous early theories and how they slowed down the progress
of science, as some people think.

But it is not all that simple. The more that we study an event in the history
of science, for example, the discovery of oxygen or the discovery of the atomic
theory, the harder it is to answer the question: who made this discovery
and when did he make it? Some of us are beginning to suspect that perhaps
this is the wrong kind of question to ask. And the more that we study
the older, erroneous theories, like the phlogiston theory, the more difficult
it becomes to decide what was unscientific about them. The more that we
study the phlogiston theory or the caloric theory, the more clearly we see
how the older theorists could hold these "erroneous" views, and the more
difficult it becomes to prove that these theories were any less scientific
than some of the theories which we hold to be valid today. If the phlogiston
theory was a myth, then myths can be developed by the same process
by which we now develop what we call scientific knowledge.

We are, then, led to a new view of the study of the history of science.
It is not just a process of memorizing dates of important scientific discoveries or even of arranging these events in their proper order. Nor is it
just a way of making science interesting by supplying a lot of fascinating
stories about important scientists. Rather historians of science seem to
be discovering a new image of science different from the one that we have
held in the past.

For example, how do we decide what is a science and what is not a
science? Recently one of our college faculty members was nominated for
membership in the Society of the Sigma Xi, but the nomination was refused
by the chapter secretary because the man's field was sociology, not an
approved science in the opinion of the society. Yet sociologists are regularly
elected to membership in the American Association for the Advancement
of Science. These two groups of scientists must differ in their definitions
of science. But can a definition help a man decide whether he is a scientist
or not? I don't believe that chemists spend much time worrying about
whether or not chemistry is a science. If the social scientist seems to have
difficulty obtaining recognition as a scientist, is it perhaps because his
field does not move ahead as fast as does, for example, the field of chemistry
or physics? Progress seems to be the hallmark of science. Dr. Thomas
S. Kuhn, in his book "The Structure of Scientific Revolutions", says, "We

tend to see as a science any field in which progress is marked". Dr. Kuhn's idea was anticipated by Dr. James B. Conant in his book "Science and Common Sense", where he introduced "the concept of progress as a method of defining an area of intellectual activity" (*i.e.*, science).

How then does science make this rapid progress which is its identifying property? Again Dr. Kuhn gives us an answer when he says that science progresses by means of scientific revolutions, revolutions of thought in which one model or paradigm replaces an older conceptual scheme.

Development of the Method of Using Case Histories

About twenty years ago, Dr. James B. Conant and some of his colleagues at Harvard University began to take a hard look at what were then, and still are, some widely prevailing ideas about the value of learning the scientific method. Conant cites Karl Pearson's "The Grammar of Science" as evidence for the belief that such a thing as a scientific method can be identified. Pearson, professor of mathematics at University College, London, many years ago wrote: "The scientific method is marked by the following features: (a) careful and accurate classification of facts and observations of their correlation and sequence; (b) the discovery of scientific law by aid of creative imagination; (c) self criticism". It is with part (a) of Pearson's outline of the scientific method that Conant dissents entirely. And I think that you will gather from my foregoing remarks that I agree with Conant that science is somehow more than collecting and classifying facts; that in fact too much emphasis on classifying facts and arranging them in "logical" sequence has led to some of the more dogmatic ideas in science in the past. Dr. Conant summarizes nicely:

The stumbling way in which even the ablest of the scientists in every generation have had to fight through the thickets of erroneous observations, misleading generalizations, inadequate formulations, and unconscious prejudice is rarely appreciated by those who obtain their scientific knowledge from textbooks.

And how then do we work our way out of the state of mind that we are in? How do we get a new image of what science is, when the establishment of science has such a firm belief in the existence of scientific method? Perhaps the only way is to begin again, to go back to the original sources and study actual case histories of scientific discoveries.

The case history is a story about the development of a scientific idea. A few titles from the Harvard series, "Case Histories in Experimental Science", James B. Conant, editor, will give you some idea of the type of studies that we have in mind: "The Overthrow of the Phlogiston Theory"; "The Early Developments of Concepts of Temperature and Heat"; "The Rise and Decline of the Caloric Theory"; "The Atomic-Molecular Theory"; "Plants and the Atmosphere"; "Pasteur and Tyndall's Study of Spontaneous Generation"; "The Development of the Concept of Electric Charge". Another case history in the same vein is Everett Mendelsohn's "Heat and Life". Each one of these case histories is designed to "assist the student in recapturing the experience of those who once participated in the exciting events of scientific history. The study of a case may be to some degree the equivalent . . . of transporting the student to the scene of a revolutionary advance in science" (Foreword to "Harvard Case Histories in Experimental Science", edited by James B. Conant).

The case histories listed above are some of the more obvious cases of revolutions in scientific thought which have taken place in the past. We note something in common among all of them. A new model or paradigm replaces an older one. The new paradigm brings with it changes in the rules governing the practice of what had been a normal science. Adoption of the new theory makes it necessary to discredit much of the earlier work or at least requires that the prior work be reevaluated. The scientists who had been occupied in compiling the earlier facts would naturally resist having their work discredited or even looked at in a new way. The process of reevaluating took a long time and was seldom, if ever, accomplished by one man. No wonder historians of science have had difficulty in fixing exact dates on some of the scientific discoveries cited here. In the case history about plants and the atmosphere, Dr. Leonard Nash's table of chronology shows that this scientific revolution required about one hundred years for its completion.

Use of the Phlogiston Case History

The case of the overthrow of the phlogiston theory is one in which I have had a special interest since it deals particularly with chemistry. I have found that it is possible to build up in students a considerable interest in the phlogiston theory, even though most of them have never heard of phlogiston before we take it up in class. I have occasionally held a debate in class on the subject: "Resolved: That Phlogiston is a Chemical Element". I have usually assigned two students to each side. In order that the negative team not have too easy a time, I suggest to the class that we all limit ourselves to only those ideas which were known in about the year 1750. This means that we cannot discuss the element oxygen, which was not known at that time. The affirmative side has frequently resorted to a demonstration of the existence of phlogiston. A piece of paper is weighed on a triple beam balance in front of the class, the paper resting on an evaporating dish or watch glass. Then the paper is set on fire. In the process of burning, the demonstrator asks the class to note how something is obviously being given off. "Note the light being emitted. Hold your hand over here and feel the heat coming off", he may say. When the burning is complete, he weighs the residue, and the obvious conclusion is that something was lost. Even a moderately skilled debater can then convince his audience that this is evidence for the existence of a substance which is given off in combustion, which we could call phlogiston. If I ask the class to select the winning side in the debate, the affirmative usually wins.

In appearances before groups of high school students I have often done such a demonstration as that described above. I have asked the students to tell me what they observe as the burning process takes place. I list their observations on the blackboard, a list such as the following, perhaps:

1. Smoke is given off.
2. Light is emitted.
3. Odor is given off.
4. Heat is given off.
5. Weight is lost (after the weighing is completed).

Then I ask them to see if they can summarize their observations, and supposing that they were living in about the year 1750 and did not know anything about oxygen, to put their observations into a single statement. Almost always, with a little coaxing, they will agree that the statement, "Something is given off", will summarize their observations quite nicely. "Could we say that the substance, x, is given off?", I then ask, and again they agree. "And could we call x by the name of phlogiston?", whereby I demonstrate how phlogiston could have been discovered.

Sometimes I have then undertaken to confound the students by repeating the demonstration but the second time using a piece of magnesium ribbon as the material to be burned. This time, when the weighing is done after the combustion, we usually find very little weight lost, and sometimes we even find a gain in weight. And yet the observations about something being given off in the burning process are all the same. Still asking them to imagine themselves living in 1750, I ask them to see if they can explain the results with magnesium in terms of the phlogiston theory. The first time that I did this, a student, bless his heart, popped out with the idea, "Maybe phlogiston has a negative weight". I jumped on this idea and developed it with the help of the class. If phlogiston has a negative weight, could we use this unusual property? If we caught some phlogiston in a bag, what would happen? It was a fairly easy exercise in reasoning to show how hot air balloons might have been invented through the application of the phlogiston theory. And in the process I have also shown how we have applied the scientific method:

1. We made observations and collected these facts.
2. We summarized the observations in a concise statement.
3. We formulated a "law" (Phlogiston is given off).
4. We made deductions from this law.
5. We tested our deductions by further experiments.
6. We modified the law (Phlogiston has negative weight).
7. We developed a practical device (hot air balloon) from this idea.

All of these steps are outlined in many an introductory freshman chemistry textbook as "the scientific method". For example, Dr. Linus Pauling in "College Chemistry" says:

The first step in applying the scientific method is to obtain facts, by observation and experiment. The next step is to classify and correlate the facts by general statements. If a general statement is simple in form, it may be called a law of nature. If it is more complex it is called a theory. Both laws of nature and theories are called principles.

So we have followed these steps and come up with the phlogiston theory. The phlogiston theory is therefore a scientific theory. Furthermore, we have made practical use of this theory in inventing the hot air balloon.

But we took Dr. Pauling's outline of the scientific method out of context. Earlier he had qualified his statements:

> Part of the scientific method is the requirement that the investigator be willing to accept all the facts. He must not be prejudiced; prejudice might keep him from giving proper consideration to some of the facts, or to some logical arguments involved in applying the scientific method, and in this way keep him from getting the right answer. If you were to say, "I have made up my mind—don't confuse me with a lot of facts", you would not be applying the scientific method.

So today we would be unscientific not to admit that oxygen combines with an inflammable material during ordinary combustion. But in 1750 we did not know about oxygen. It had not yet been discovered. Were we prejudiced to trust our own eyes and to think that something was being given off in combustion? No, I do not think so. I think that even with Dr. Pauling's qualification, we were still applying his scientific method in 1750, and we came up with the phlogiston theory.

Torbern Bergman's Use of the Phlogiston Theory

Another identifying mark of science is the fact that it is fruitful of new ideas and further experiments. Here too, the phlogiston theory fits the picture. Professor Torbern Bergman, professor of chemistry at Uppsala, Sweden from 1767 to 1784, was one of the world's great theoretical chemists of his age and at the same time was a confirmed phlogistonist. In what was probably his greatest single contribution to theoretical chemistry, his "Dissertation on Elective Attraction", he presented a table of elective attractions in which fifty known chemical substances were placed and their relationship to each other described. The behavior of each substance toward the other substances in the table could be predicted from the table with considerable accuracy. This table in itself was a great scientific accomplishment, yet it was developed entirely within the framework of the phlogiston theory.

One of the most interesting columns in Bergman's table of elective attractions is the phlogiston column. Bergman was very interested in the affinity of phlogiston for the metals. Since he was one of the first to apply quantitative methods to chemical studies (he is sometimes called the "father of analytical chemistry"), it is quite likely that he might have discovered the principle of equivalent weights by these studies on phlogiston if he had not died at the relatively early age of forty-nine. But this is conjecture, and Bergman's phlogiston column contains another great contribution to chemistry, the electromotive series, which should demonstrate the fruitfulness of the phlogiston theory.

In Figure 1, I present the phlogiston column, column number 29 in Bergman's table of elective attractions. I have translated Bergman's chemical symbols into modern ones so that we can read his table more conveniently. His table of metals arranged in order of their affinity for phlogiston is actually a list of metals arranged in order of their ability to be reduced to the metallic state. That this is nothing other than an

Via Humida				Via Sicca		
1	⚛	phlogiston		31	♆ ☽☉	PtO
2	△n	air		32	+ ⊕	HNO_3
3	♆ ♉	MgO		33	♆ ☉	Au_2O_3
4	♆ ☿	HgO		34	+ ♋	H_2SO_4
5	⊕ ⚛	NH_3		35	⊶	H_3AsO_4
6	+ ⊕	HNO_3		36	♆ ☽	Ag_2O
7	+ ♋ ⚛	H_2SO_3		37	♆ ☿	HgO
8	+ ⊖ ⚛	$HClO$		38	△n	air
9	⊶	H_3AsO_4		39	♆ ♁	Sb_2O_3
10	+ ♎	H_3PO_4		40	♆ ♉	Bi_2O_3
				41	♆ ∘∘	As_2O_3
				42	♆ 8	NiO
				43	♆ ♀	CuO
				44	♆ ♋	CoO
				45	♆ ♃	SnO
				46	♆ ♄	PbO
				47	♆ ♂	FeO
				48	♆ ♉	MgO
				49	♆ ◠	ZnO
30	▽	water		50		

Fig. 1

electromotive series can be shown by listing the metals as Bergman has listed them (turning the list upside down) and beside each metal giving its oxidation potential on a modern scale (Table 1).

With two notable exceptions, copper and magnesium, we see that Bergman's list of metals is in approximately the same order as the metals would be listed in the modern electromotive series. I believe that Bergman was one of the first, if not the first, to present such a listing of the metallic chemical elements. Surely it must be granted that this constitutes a fruitful

TABLE 1

Order of Bergman's Affinities of Metals for Phlogiston

Metal	Modern Standard Oxidation Potential
Zn	0.76 volt
Mg	2.37
Fe	0.44
Pb	0.13
Sn	0.14
Co	0.28
Cu	—0.34
Ni	0.25
As	—0.25
Bi	—0.32
Sb	—0.15
Hg	—0.79
Ag	—0.80
Au	—1.3
Pt	—1.2

contribution to chemical science. And yet it was developed entirely within the framework of the phlogiston theory.

Bergman and the Crucial Experiment

It is an interesting aside to note here how Bergman explained the crucial experiment in which oxygen was first produced in the terms of the phlogiston theory. In studying the Harvard 'Case Histories'', we learn to look for a crucial experiment that supposedly cannot be explained in terms of the old paradigm and therefore requires that a new model be devised to explain this crucial experiment. The crucial experiment in the overthrow of the phlogiston theory was Scheele's first production of oxygen by heating mercuric oxide. In terms of the phlogiston theory, we must say that the calx of mercury (mercuric oxide) combines with phlogiston to yield the regulus of mercury (metallic mercury), and there does not seem to be any easy way to explain where the phlogiston which supposedly reacted with the calx came from and what the gas which is produced in the process is. Let us see how Bergman explains this, in the first published announcement of the production of oxygen, approximately one year earlier than Priestley's announcement was published:

Following [Mr. Scheele], I have conducted the following experiments, varying the method but little [from that of Scheele's].

Into a small retort, Figure 2, I have put a half ounce of *hydrargyrum nitratum* well calcinated to redness by fire; I have fitted on a long tube, and I have introduced its bent apex G into a receiving vessel IH, and when the base of the bulb was removed a little from ignition I have collected more than half a tank of gas which does not make *aqua calcis* turbid, but is most suitable for fire and respiration. The calx will be discovered to have been reduced to running mercury. From whence does this gas come? From the decomposition of *calor*, I reply, which penetrating through the porous vessel supplies its phlogiston to the metallic calx, and when this is done the liberated gas loses its faculty of passing through glass. This gas is not contained in the calx itself, for the calces of noble metals, on being reduced in the same manner

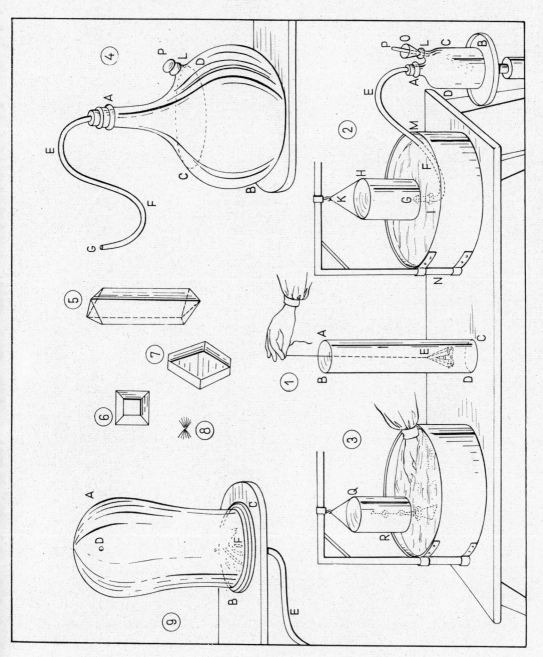

Fig. 2

as ignoble metals, require phlogiston, and nothing different happens here other than the greater strength with which the noble metals attract phlogiston to the extent that they can decompose *calor*, which the ignoble metals cannot do.

Bergman believed that *calor* was a compound of air and phlogiston, and since *calor* could obviously penetrate glass, that is how the air got inside the flask. This was the last gasp of the phlogiston theory. But even in the face of this crucial experiment, which now seems to have been the one experiment which was unexplainable in terms of the phlogiston theory, Bergman still came up with an explanation. As someone has said, new theories do not gain precedence by convincing the opposition, they gain precedence because the opponents eventually die.

In conclusion, I believe that we chemists have an exceptional opportunity to teach the history of science through the method of case histories by using the case of the phlogiston theory. I believe that its almost complete hold on the minds of the leading practitioners in the field of chemistry in its day may have been almost unique in the annals of science. The philosophical insights that we may gain by studying this phenomenon might be very great. I have even thought it might be worthwhile to establish a modern school of phlogiston chemistry, something like the flat-earth school, to see how many more observations could have possibly been explained in terms of the phlogiston theory if it had not been prematurely abandoned. I will wait with bated breath for the response to this suggestion.

10. THE USE OF COMPARISONS AND GENERALIZATIONS IN TEACHING THE HISTORY OF CHEMISTRY

EDUARD FARBER*

The American University, Washington, D. C., U.S.A.

From the viewpoint of the present topic, comparisons and generalizations can be divided into two classes: those that we find present in the historical documents and those that we are adding as our own contribution. With proper qualification, we can call the first internal, the second external. The latter can again be subdivided as we use them either to aid the memory or to increase the amount of details that become manageable by showing their significance. Advantages of using comparisons and generalizations extend over the entire historical course and content of chemistry and beyond to connections with the history of other sciences. Certain disadvantages can be foreseen and thus avoided. Specific suggestions are developed by citing examples.

Often enough, a plea for including history in the curriculum of chemists is rejected with the argument that the student should not be burdened with unnecessary material; though some historical incidents may be "interesting", what need is there for a whole course in history? In answer to such a question we endeavor to present the history of chemistry so that it becomes an essential part of chemical education, instead of a separate collection of facts to be learned as an extraneous and additional "burden". Among the means to reach this goal is the use of comparisons and generalizations. They are not proposed as a means for making "hard" facts "soft" by surrounding them with a haze or reducing them to undifferentiated lumps. By comparisons and generalizations we can provide aids to the memory and, beyond that, demonstrate the relevance of past events to our present efforts in science and its application. I hope the following ideas and examples will be of some help in achieving this aim.

First, a few words to provide some background and contrast. A novelist will describe the thunderstorm that caught his hero one particular afternoon on the mountains of the Sierra Leone: how the clouds gathered, gusts of wind shook the trees, then an ominous quiet for a few minutes before the winds rose again, a few large drops began to come down, and suddenly a violent burst with heavy sheets of water that knocked down big branches. Fortunately, the hero discovered a protective shelter in time and thus escaped injury. This individualizing narrative style would be appropriate for our report about historical events, but, except for a few instances, we lack the time and the detailed knowledge to present such narratives, and we avoid fictionalizing as carefully as romanticizing. Without the time, the

* Deceased July 15, 1969. An obituary notice can be found in *Chemical and Engineering News*, **47**, 54 (July 28, 1969), and biographies by Wyndham D. Miles and Robert P. Multhauf will appear in *Archives Internationales d'Histoire des Sciences* and *Isis*, respectively.

material, and perhaps also the skill of the novelist, how can we achieve
his result in bringing our story "to life" so that it becomes meaningful
for the lives of our students?

Through the passage of time, the individual event with which we are
dealing loses its "novelistic" reality, yet it gains a new effect from its dependence on the past and its radiation into the future. The active, or we may
say, creative, part of the teacher consists in bringing the old story into
that new life; he must describe not only that particular storm, as in the
novelist's story, but must connect it with origins, effects, and rules.

To do this by means of comparisons and generalizations is "natural",
because we find them in the material we want to present in our course.
Alchemy rests on comparisons, particularly those of metals with organisms,
and processes of raffination with healing the sickness of bodies. Paracelsus
declared that ripening of fruits was a natural alchemy. Going from comparison to the postulation of conformity, the alchemist saw the small world
in and around us corresponding to the macrocosm in signs and significances.
Those were the times when men were not satisfied with tentative suggestions or "heuristic" proposals; they wanted to grasp the real mysteries of
nature and thereby reveal the actual truths that had lain hidden. These
men took the possibility of comparing as a guarantee for finding the onto-
logical unity.

Perhaps even more abundant than historical comparisons are the historical generalizations. Louis Pasteur, who derived the asymmetry of tartaric
acid from the asymmetry of the universe (1), generalized his experiences
on fermentation with the rule: "La fermentation est la vie sans air" (2),
a statement which loses strength in translation: fermentation is life without
air. For Pasteur, this was a direct and compelling conclusion from the
evidence; for some of his contemporaries, it began to look like an exorbitant
extrapolation. Marcellin Berthelot summarized Claude Bernard's results
by stating: Not all fermentations are life without air, and life without
air is not always fermentation.

Generalizations were especially captivating when they were exorbitant,
but then the period of their uncontested acceptance was usually short.
Auguste Laurent and at some time also Friedrich August Kekulé thought
that atoms generally change their positions so much when "set in motion"
by a chemical reaction that it is impossible to represent the arrangement
of the atoms in the molecule by a formula. Edward Frankland and J. H.
van't Hoff must have thought that this generalization from a concept
of atomic free movement went too far; in their attempts to write molecular
formulas they relied more on the limiting bonds between the atoms.

The history of chemistry contains many comparisons and generalizations
of various kinds, and sometimes it may be doubted whether they belong
to one or the other category. Comparisons dissect the complexity of facts
to prepare their recurring similar parts without venturing into further
speculations. Generalizations are more ambitious; they connect the parts
again to a new entity. There is a form of comparisons that enumerates special
aspects of events so as to reduce their individual originality. In this respect,
generalizations can be so different as to be in contradictory opposition

to the former by throwing the light of a new revelation on the originality of the special event. The consequence can establish the apparent paradox that thereby the special event becomes highly important yet completely expendable, and every new factual discovery can extinguish the light of the revelation.

Usually, it is a question of modesty or its absence in a chemist whether he turns from comparison to generalization. Wilhelm Ostwald compared the historical course of theories to a process of crystallization, in which "impurities" were gradually thrown out to leave the "pure" product. This way of describing the history of a theory would be worthy of a poetical imagination, but Ostwald meant it as a scientific generalization (3). For the mind that seeks ultimate fulfillment in universalities, there is only a small step, or at any rate a compelling step, from the imaginative comparison to the generalization that the laws of crystallization also govern the historical progress of our thoughts.

In teaching the history of chemistry, we present comparisons and generalizations that have been elaborated; they have become real as historical products without thereby being true and valid today. The relationship between historical reality and present validity is complicated by the splendor of history, by the secret, mysterious persistence of a belief in a past golden age as the counterpart to the glamor of progress. The conviction that what is old must be, or must have been, good is particularly strong in moral and political affairs. In science, the complementary view is more prevalent. Often, the criterion for "goodness" is modernity. This view may well be used in judging textbooks; in historical comparisons, however, it should be limited and qualified as merely didactical. Otherwise, it may become ridiculous to state, for example, that Robert Boyle "did not have the modern view of the atom", as has actually been done (4).

As historical facts, comparisons and generalizations are not all on the surface and readily reported; most of them are interesting objects of our special searches. To these, which have been made by the discoverers themselves in expressing relationships and indebtedness to previous work, we as teachers are adding others in which we are the discoverers. The first have been influences on the course of chemistry, the second are our contributions to the understanding. The first depend upon the discoverer's awareness, the other upon ours. We would be getting into trouble if we tried to differentiate the ones as subjective, the others as objective, because there would be as much justification to attach one or the other of these adjectives to the historical comparisons and generalizations as to ours. For similar reasons, we should avoid calling comparisons analytic and generalizations synthetic, or we should at least use great care when we do so. Comparisons with the present state of science and research require courtesy and tact in addition to knowledge and recollection. Cannizzaro would have been justified in ridiculing the six or eight different formulas that had been proposed for acetic acid; we as historians would do better to explain the reasons by which these formulas were developed and seemed convincing.

The methodology of making comparisons comprises everything we know of logic and the subject matter, but it also requires the boldness of going beyond the obvious to new discoveries and their proof. Through such comparisons, special events in the history of chemistry can be connected with others that occurred in the same period or at a later time, revealing connections with the "spirit" of the time or with lines of development continuing through all times.

One of the most obvious comparisons is that based on the use and appreciation of certain numbers, e.g. 3, 4, and 7. Though obvious, the comparison has deep roots and wide implications. The story of trilogies in chemistry can be traced from ancient and alchemistic thoughts about elements to the correspondences which Jean Beguin constructed in 1619 (5) and the triads of analogous elements which were perceived, or conceived, just about two hundred years later. From there, the comparison can be extended to other triads that marked the further progress of chemistry, and beyond that to the establishment of the triadic CGS (centimeter-gram-second) system or to a wider view with philosophical and theological connections.

The history of hydrogen and water in the theories of combustion is well presented by the controversy between Heinrich Wieland and Otto Warburg with a comparative look at Moritz Traube's postulations. This look can be widened and expanded backward and forward in time. In 1846, Justus Liebig wrote: "The heat evolved in the respiration process is, therefore, not based on the oxidation of carbon, but rather on the transformation of the hydrogen of the substance into water and the entrance of one or more equivalents of oxygen in place of this hydrogen" (6). Our comparison can link this statement with the sequential forms of phlogiston theory and continue until it reaches the most recent explanation: "Work must be done to remove a hydrogen atom or an electron from an organic molecule, i.e., to oxidize it . . . The work of oxidation is performed by the reduction, and over and above that, the reduction yields enough energy to provide for all the manifestations of life" (7). Using comparisons like these, history becomes a "real" introduction into the results of present research, real because it follows the direction of the way to the new insights.

Similar values for the understanding of modern biochemistry are to be derived from comparing what Eduard Büchner did in dissociating alcoholic fermentation from the life of the yeast with our recent work on separating the photosynthetic apparatus from the living plant.

Comparisons are the basis for placing new discoveries in the context that shows their importance. Friedrich Wöhler's "synthesis" of urea in 1828 is to be compared with contrary opinions generally held and now disproved. When such comparisons are extended, they can lead to interesting questions and connections with later events. How long was it before Wöhler's isomerization was studied in some detail? What had happened to continue from the triumphant discovery to a problem that can be solved by experimentation? When did this develop into questions concerning the biological pathway to urea? Did somebody hit upon the idea of turning Wöhler's experiment around and trying to find a biological synthesis of urea from organic nitrogen? These questions would lead to topical arrangements of historical events, perhaps also to a string of examination problems. They can be pursued still further to include the curiously hesitant introduction of ammonia salts instead of proteinaceous substances in fermentations by yeast and to the development of industrial urea synthesis.

Comparisons have a wide field in the history of industrial developments. Many new inventions and discoveries did not look at all as glamorous in the beginning as they became after long persistence. In spite of Achard's enthusiastic support, Marggraf's discovery of sugar from beets grew to an industrial application only because of war conditions. A committee of the Institute of Paris rejected it in 1800; Napoléon Bonaparte furthered it by decree in 1809; after 1815, the beet sugar industry survived in France only by the heavy duties imposed on colonial sugar by the government. The industry began to thrive, but the cost to the consumer was so high that in 1829 the consumption was four pounds per capita in France, while it was twenty pounds in Great Britain (8). Compare this with the early history of synthetic indigo: In 1883, Adolf Baeyer concluded some ten years of research by saying that now the place of every atom in the molecule of this dyestuff had been established by experiment (9). Scientifically, this was a great achievement; economically, it continued for nearly twenty years to look like folly to manufacture indigo synthetically.

Biography is a very fruitful field for comparison (10). As before, the dualistic aims are in the main: to aid the memory by pointing to similarities and to deepen the insight by differentiations. The difference is that here the trend towards generalization is particularly strong and dangerous. We can see this in the work of Wilhelm Ostwald. He makes many fine biographical comparisons and then proceeds to the construction of scientific laws and absolute truths (11). Our critical analysis reveals them as arbitrary and time-bound, in fact quite metaphysical, contrary to the author's expressed intention and therefore the more objectionable. From here, we may be lured into our own generalizations and as teachers we provide the student with the fact that will guard him against an insidious trend that would result in considering Ostwald's excesses as "typically" German. Similarly, "Nature philosophy" would be made to appear as typical for the "metaphysical" nineteenth century.

These dual generalizations would be wrong on both counts. For documentation, it may be sufficient here to cite Gustav Fechner's "Elemente der Psychophysik" of 1860, in which the German author aims at "the exact science of the functional relations or dependences between body and soul." With this new effort, Fechner continued a considerable tradition, indicated, for example, by Johann Gottlieb Krüger's "Versuch einer Experimental-Seelenlehre" of 1756. Karl Friedrich Wilhelm Ludwig (1816–1895) and Hermann Helmholtz (1821–1894) are founders of an experimental physiology, which is still closer to chemistry. The teacher will have to decide how far to go into these matters; they lead away from strict history of chemistry but form a bridge to psychology and physiology. To make it more acceptable, the bridge can be introduced under the general name of "the experimental method".

In comparison with this topic, generalizations can be more limited or more extended. An example belonging to the first kind would be Multhauf's statement: "From the vantage point of modern chemistry we can say that Paracelsus was inhibited from discovering new substances by his disdain of residues" (12). Another example would be a collection of discoveries and inventions that usually go under the wrong name, such as "Boyle's law", which was discovered by Power and Towneley (13), "Coulomb's law", which was due to Daniel Bernoulli in 1760, or "Liebig's condenser", which was first constructed by Christian Wiegleb and attributed to Johann Friedrich August Göttling by Liebig himself (14). Such a list invites additions. Nevertheless, these limited generalizations carry a built-in guard against becoming excessive, for example, in a claim that discoveries and inventions always go under the wrong name. In the second group, there is a lurking danger of going from some to all, and from these times to every time, or from "not at this time" to never.

The history of chemistry contains many arguments that would have been perfectly justified when kept within limits but that were spoilt by adding the claim to universal validity. Thus, Hermann Kolbe argued against Alexander Mikhailovich Butlerov: "About the kind and manner, in which elementary atoms bind each other in a molecule, I have no way of arriving at an idea, and chemists will certainly never be able to gain one" (15).

A lecture can be enlivened by ridiculing statements like these, but afterwards they can be used to broaden the view on historical events. It has frequently happened that generalizations received especial attention because they aimed at universality and claimed to have reached it in subject and time. "Only excess brings success"—which is an intrinsically excessive judgment of the scope to be criticized. For some of the historical generalizations of the excessive kind, the three steps of creation, elation, and rejection followed each other in time, although with an irregular spacing.

By introducing his own generalizations, the teacher will often construct the background or the outlook that will permit him to anchor many fine details by their connections. Whether to dwell on this apparent paradox will depend on the opportunity or inclination to expand from history of chemistry to the ancient contest between nominalists and realists, or to the meaning that complementarity has more recently acquired through physics.

A particularly intriguing generalization is to "the spirit of the time". Under this heading, the idea about the atoms in the molecule, for which Hermann Kolbe was just cited, makes William Henry Perkin's reasoning on how to synthesize quinine much less silly than it would otherwise look. The "spirit" of synthesis, which began to rise around 1850, then, becomes part of the force in the ensuing avalanche of techniques for making dyestuffs synthetically.

Continuing in this way, one could easily arrive at the question of whether the spirit of materialism in the later nineteenth century was at the origins or among the results of the renewed intensity in biochemical efforts. This questions might be welcome as an alternate or an addition to the rather familiar concern with the theories of corpuscularity. The way to an answer would lead through many special topics for research papers.

The delight in making comparisons and discovering generalizations is easily marked by the criticism that they are uncertain and imperfect. The history teacher who suffers too deeply under such criticism may find reassurance in a remark by Michael Faraday: "If in such strivings, we . . . see but imperfectly, still we should endeavour to see, for even an obscure and distorted vision is better than none" (*16*). And he can derive further support from comparing Faraday's words with a statement made by Hermann Weyl almost seventy years later: "A picture of reality drawn in a few sharp lines cannot be expected to be adequate to the variety of all its shades. Yet even so the draftsman must have the courage to draw the lines firm" (*17*). The task of using comparisons and generalizations in teaching the history of chemistry is as definite, and as unfinished, as chemistry itself.

Literature Cited

(1) Pasteur, Louis, "Observations sur les forces dissymétriques", *Compt. rend.*, **78**, 1545–8 (1874).
(2) Pasteur, Louis, "Faits nouveaux pour servir à la connaissance de la théorie des fermentations proprement dites", *Compt. rend.*, **75**, 784–90 (1872); see also Velluz, Léon, "Vie de Berthelot", p. 226, Plon, Paris, 1964.
(3) Ostwald, Wilhelm, "Leitlinien der Chemie", p. IV, Akademische Verlagsgesellschaft, Leipzig, 1906.
(4) Boas, Marie, "Robert Boyle and 17th Century Chemistry", Cambridge University Press, Cambridge, 1958.
(5) Beguin, Jean, "Tyrocinium Chymicum, or Chymicall Essayes", p. 22, T. Passenger, London, 1669 (English translation from the first edition of 1612).
(6) Liebig, Justus, *Ann.*, **58**, 344 (1846) ("Aus der dritten Auflage von Liebig's Thierchemie").
(7) Wald, George, in "Current Aspects of Biochemical Energetics, Fritz Lipmann Dedicatory Volume", p. 32, Academic Press, New York, 1966; Farber, Eduard, "Oxygen and Oxidation Theories and Techniques in the 19th Century and the Beginning of the 20th", pp. 8 ff., 35 ff., Washington, D. C., 1967.
(8) Lankester, Erwin, "Vegetable Substances Used for the Food of Man", pp. 269 ff., Harper & Brothers, New York, 1855 ("Publisher's Advertisement" dated Sept. 1839).
(9) Baeyer, Adolf, "Über die Verbindungen der Indigoreihe", *Ber.*, **16**, 2188 (1883).
(10) Farber, Eduard, "Great Chemists", p. viii, Interscience–Wiley, New York, 1961.
(11) Ostwald, Wilhelm, "Grosse Männer", esp. p. 317, Akademische Verlagsgesellschaft, Leipzig, 1909.
(12) Multhauf, Robert P., "The Origins of Chemistry", p. 223, Oldbourne, London, 1967.
(13) Cohen, I. Bernard, "Newton, Hooke, and 'Boyle's Law', (Discovered by Power and Towneley)", *Nature*, **204**, 618 (1964).
(14) Kahlbaum, Georg W. A., "Der sogenannte Liebig'sche Kühlapparat", *Ber.*, **29**, 69 (1896).
(15) Kolbe, Hermann, "Moden der modernen Chemie", *J. prakt. Chem.*, **3**, 127 (1871).
(16) Faraday, Michael, "On the conservation of force", *Phil. Mag.*, (4) **13**, 225–39, esp. 238 (1857).
(17) Weyl, Hermann, "Philosophy of Mathematics and Natural Science", p. 274, Princeton University Press, Princeton, N. J., 1949 (from the article of 1927 in the "Handbuch der Philosophie").

11. THE BIOGRAPHICAL APPROACH TO TEACHING THE HISTORY OF CHEMISTRY

GEORGE B. KAUFFMAN

Department of Chemistry, California State College at Fresno, Fresno, California, U.S.A.

Inasmuch as both the biographical approach to history and the requirement of some sort of term paper are established practices in many history of chemistry courses, it is proposed that these two practices be combined. The advantages and limitations of such an approach are discussed, and practical suggestions for incorporating biographical term papers into the history of chemistry course are given.

"History is the essence of innumerable biographies." Lest this be regarded as a mere partisan statement by that eloquent proponent of the "great man" view of history, Thomas Carlyle, perhaps we should take pains to make it clear that others too have expressed similar ideas. "There is properly no History; only Biography."—Ralph Waldo Emerson. "The great object, in trying to understand history, political, religious, literary, or scientific, is to get behind the men and to grasp their ideas."—Lord Acton. "It is biography that binds together all the varied branches of thought and life".—Gamaliel Bradford.

There has never been a dearth of authorities to sing the praises, perhaps too extravagantly at times, of biography. And what is true in general is also true in the field of science. To quote George Sarton,

No one should be recognized a master in any subject who does not know at least the outline of history. Of course it would be foolish to except him to have any deep historical knowledge, but he should know the main landmarks and the leading personalities—he should be acquainted with his scientific ancestors. This is almost a moral obligation. We might compare it to the obligation for any educated citizen to know the history of his country. ...For a physicist not to be sufficiently familiar with Galileo and Newton is just as shocking as for an American not to know Washington and Lincoln" (1).

Or to quote Bernard Jaffe, "An effective way to teach the methods of science is to show how our great scientists reached their goals and how their minds worked in the process" (2). Or to quote one of our symposium participants, the late Eduard Farber, "The evolution of chemistry is a drama written and enacted by the great chemists" (3).

The benefits of a biographical approach in teaching chemistry have thus been widely recognized (2, 4–6). Indeed, several members of this symposium, Dr. Virginia F. McConnell in particular (Paper 7), have discussed its advantages and limitations in teaching the history of chemistry. Assuming the biographical approach in the history of chemistry course, then, as firmly established, let us leave this point and consider another well established practice in such courses, viz., the term paper. We will then consider the advantages of combining the two practices.

In opposition to the usual antiseptic definition of chemistry given in most texts, Prof. Joel Hildebrand, who opened our symposium, has suggested the operational definition "Chemistry is what chemists do and how they do it" (7). For our purposes, we can paraphrase this to read "History is what historians do and how they do it." We exemplify Prof. Hildebrand's definition whenever we include laboratory as part of a chemistry course, a practice that is virtually universal. In the same way, in order to give the student a first-hand acquaintance with historiography, *i.e.*, with what an historian does, most of us require some sort of term paper in our history of chemistry courses.

My purpose in this paper is a simple and not very profound one. I merely wish to suggest that a study of a chemist's life and work is an ideal topic for such a term paper. Admittedly, it is only one of a variety of subjects that might be chosen, so let me cite a few reasons why I believe a biographical approach to a term paper to be particularly fruitful. The categories of reasons given here, of course, are purely arbitrary, and they frequently overlap.

1. A Realistic Task for the Student

As realistic and pragmatic educators, let us begin with an assessment of the abilities and failings of the most important person involved in the term paper—the student. The topic of student shortcomings is a favorite complaint of educators and might well even be scheduled for a future symposium. Lyman C. Newell, one of the founders of the Division of the History of Chemistry, has cited what he considers the two most serious and prevalent of student limitations—lack of historical background and only a fragmentary knowledge of chemistry (5). With these limitations in mind, I feel that a biography constitutes an ideal topic for a term paper since it makes realistic rather than unrealistic demands upon the student.

2. The Human Element as a Means for Developing Motivation and Interest

Too often the human side of chemistry is neglected in the traditional chemistry course, and the student fails to realize that the imposing structure which he views as a finished product is in reality a growing body of knowledge which is the result of a long series of efforts, some more successful than others, by individuals similar to himself. The great American historian of chemistry, Edgar Fahs Smith, considered the personal element essential to interest in any chemistry course (6). In a history of chemistry course, the student can easily become preoccupied with dates, events, and theories. What better way is there to remind him, as Alexander Pope has said, that "the proper study of mankind is man" than to have him make a detailed study of a chemist's life and work? Regardless of how restricted such a study may at first appear, it will branch off into related areas, and the student will come to view an entire chronological period of chemistry

through the life of one chemist—to view the macrocosm through the microcosm, so to speak.

A student to whom the purely impersonal, factual, and scientific approach
does not appeal may be motivated by such a biographical or humanistic
approach, which may even exert an effect on teacher education in ever-
widening circles. If the student goes on to become an instructor, such an
approach may enable him to awaken an interest in chemistry in students
to whom, like himself, the impersonal approach holds little appeal. Exposure to the humanistic, biographical approach should also help him com-
municate better with his counterparts in the humanities, a desideratum
encouraged by C. P. Snow in his book "The Two Cultures and the Scientific
Revolution" (8).

3. Personality as Inspiration and Example

In the process of writing his biography, the student may come to identify himself with his subject and with his subject's trials and triumphs.
Hero worship, if maintained within reasonable limits, can be valuable for
a young person. Thus he should not succumb to the first resistance that
he encounters in his work, but inspired by his hero, he should persevere
and overcome even the greatest of adversities. He may even directly apply
the successes and failures of the past to his own present problems. Santayana's maxim that those who do not remember the past are condemned
to repeat it is definitely valid in chemistry.

4. A Need to Evaluate Data and Sources

One of the hallmarks common to the scientist and to the historian alike
is the ability to evaluate and interpret source material and data. With
as complex and multifaceted a phenomenon as man, data are often discor-
dant and sometimes even contradictory. A student writing a biography
will gain experience in carefully considering his sources and sifting his
data for evidence of bias, partisanship, jealousy, or inaccuracies. Keeping
all these influences in mind, he must strive to make his interpretation as
objective as possible. He must be aware of the tendency of scientists to
venerate their colleagues. As Richard Willstätter has pointed out in his
autobiography "Aus meinem Leben" (9):

I have noticed that my fellow scientists, who determine melting points conscien-
tiously to half a degree, apply a much less stringent standard to their historical
writing. In memorial essays individualities become blurred and inflated. Is it proper
for a biographer to obliterate characteristics and peculiarities? Should the equalizing
guideline 'De mortuis nil nisi bonum' be applied to literature?

On the other hand, the student biographer must be aware of the opposite
tendency in himself and in others, a predilection to minimize the achievements of the subject, i.e., to indulge in "Stracheyism," a practice named
after the "debunking" post-Victorian English biographer Lytton Strachey
(10).

5. The Need to Distinguish What is Important

One of the commonest failings in students is the inability to separate the wheat from the chaff. "What is important?" is a question that many students find extremely difficult to answer. We are all familiar, perhaps overly so, with the student who is an expert at memorizing details yet who is completely unable to grasp their significance or insignificance. I can think of no better practice for such a person than the preparation of a biographical paper. From a seemingly endless array of details, anecdotes, and quotations, he must weed out the superfluous items and from the remaining data fashion a portrait of his subject that depicts him as a man and as a scientist. A good biographer, like a good historian, must be selective.

6. Variety within a Restricted Topic

The personality and characteristics of an individual scientist can be extremely varied. To use Wilhelm Ostwald's dichotomy (11), he may be a classic figure or a romantic figure; he may be extroverted or introverted; he may be a teamworker or a lone wolf; he may have a multitude of outside interests or may confine himself exclusively to chemistry; he may have had the benefit of the best education that money can buy or he may be largely self-taught; in work habits, he may be systematic or careless; he may be a theoretician or an experimentalist; he may have an academic outlook or be extremely practical; he may have one all-consuming research goal or many different goals; his work may be primarily quantitative or primarily qualitative; he may be an early achiever or a "late bloomer"; he may favor complicated apparatus or he may prefer the simplest methods; he may have a rich and satisfying family life or he may be a recluse; he may be devoutly religious or he may be an atheist; his life may be a carefree one or he may be tormented by tragedies; he may be active or sedentary; he may be intuitive or coldly rational.

These are merely the extreme positions of a few of the ways in which scientists can and do differ, and of course all sorts of gradations and combinations are possible between these extremes. Creativity is today a much abused and overused word. Yet in investigating the work habits of his subject, the student biographer will approach the elusive wellsprings of creativity.

Science, like most human activities, does not move in a steadily ascending straight line. The superior student biographer will take note of his subject's failures as well as his successes. He will notice his contradictions and will watch a mind at work, "bad" as well as "good" as Willstätter has said. He will be aware of the relationships between the subject and his environment. In short, he should go beyond the confines of the subject's life and immerse himself in the political, social, cultural, and scientific *milieu* of the time.

7. A Short-Term Project

One of the commonest errors of the beginning student in his choice of a subject for a term paper is to "bite off more than he can chew." The project usually remains incomplete and a source of frustration and discouragement. Despite the variety and branching out characteristic of a biography, the project nevertheless remains circumscribed in scope and capable of completion within a reasonable length of time. If science, as Pasteur has suggested, can be likened to a temple, then the student biographer at least should have the satisfaction of adding another brick to the edifice. In a single semester, he should be able to proceed from the initial literature search, through the collecting of data, to the writing of the final paper. In fact, the fifteen topics suggested earlier in this symposium by my colleague Dr. Jack J. Bulloff (Paper 2), although excellent and challenging for advanced students, would probably prove too ambitious for most beginning students.

8. An Opportunity for Making a Definitive Contribution

June Z. Fullmer has claimed that a final, definitive biography of a scientist can never be written (12). Whereas this may be true for some of the major figures of chemistry such as Lavoisier, Davy, Priestley, or Berzelius, to whom a great amount of attention has been paid, it need not necessarily be true of chemists of lesser prominence, those whom Lyman C. Newell has called "overshadowed chemists" (6). According to Edgar Fahs Smith, these are scientists who "have not been mentioned in the customary texts of the history of chemistry, or if mention was made it was in such meagre form that no impression was left on the mind of the reader excepting, possibly, that these persons were unimportant" (6). A short study of such a scientist may be the only one in the literature and may very possibly become a definitive contribution. Surprisingly enough, many lesser American and British chemists have been neglected, and for students with only limited backgrounds in foreign languages such a biography is a natural choice. If a student has a particular foreign language skill, especially in one of the less common languages, so much the better, for his choice is then not as limited.

Some examples from my special field of interest, coordination chemistry, may be in order here. Even for the founder of coordination chemistry, Alfred Werner, only a few short studies were available until recently. It was not until 1966, the year marking the centennial of Werner's birth, that a booklength biography appeared (13). Yet for most of the lesser contributors to the field, names such as Blomstrand, Cleve, Delépine, Frémy, Gros, Howe, Miolati, Peyrone, Pfeiffer, Reiset, and Vortmann, to mention only a few, adequate biographical sketches are still lacking in English.*

* Since this paper was presented, articles on Howe (Kauffman, G. B., *J. Chem. Educ.*, **45**, 804 (1968)) and Miolati (Kauffman, G. B., *Isis*, **61**, 241 (1970)) have appeared, and a biography of Delépine is in preparation,

This is particularly true of Russian chemists who have specialized in the coordination chemistry of the platinum metals although some steps have recently been taken in this direction with studies of Kurnakov (*14*) and Chugaev (*15*).

Regardless of whether or not his completed study is definitive, and by a proper choice of subject its chances of being so can be maximized, the student will at least achieve the satisfaction of having made a contribution to the literature. As he answers the requests for reprints which arrive from all parts of the globe, he will realize how far he has advanced from his initial literature search. His feeling of pride in obstacles overcome and a job well done should sustain him in his later work, whether it be in the history of science, chemistry, or even an entirely unrelated area.

The exact procedure to be followed in writing a biography, of course, cannot and perhaps should not be specified here in detail. A few guidelines, however, may be in order. In so far as it is possible, the student should be allowed to select his own subject. Often his chemical interest will suggest a suitable topic. The biography may be a natural outgrowth of his own experimental research. He may decide to investigate the man beyond a particular "name reaction", law, principle, compound, discovery, or piece of apparatus.

Once the subject is decided upon, the student can proceed from the general to the particular. Articles or monographs reviewing the field in which his subject worked will help him to appraise his work and his place in history. Searching the entries for the biographee in *Chemical Abstracts*, *Chemisches Zentralblatt*, or *Journal of the Chemical Society, Abstracts* under subject (for biographies and obituaries) and under author (for his publications) will provide the basic data. The possible procedures from this point on are limited only by the student's initiative and ingenuity.

Physical limitations such as the lack of an adequate library are not as serious as might at first be imagined. Although this may be anathema to professional historians, respectable short biographical articles can be written with the aid of abstracts rather than the original articles themselves. In those cases where the original article must be consulted, it can usually be obtained *via* interlibrary loan.

Aaron Ihde, in his recent book "The Development of Modern Chemistry" (*16*), lists sources of biographies, and several bibliographies of biographies are available in the literature (*17, 18*). Biographical articles can often be found in the *Journal of Chemical Education*, the *Journal of the Chemical Society*, and the *Berichte der Deutschen Chemischen Gesellschaft*.

One of the frustrating things that the student who has written a biography will find is that he cannot generalize from his data. A knowledge of the life of one chemist does not necessarily give us any insight into the life of another chemist. Yet what appears at first sight to be a shortcoming may actually be an asset, particularly for a young person who is attempting to find himself and his place in the world. A well written biography should lead him to a realization of the uniqueness of every human being, a sorely needed antidote to a science, which, like the world in which it functions, is becoming increasingly mechanistic and depersonalized.

Acknowledgement

The author wishes to acknowledge the financial support of the History and Philosophy of Science Program of the National Science Foundation Division of Social Sciences (Grant GS-1580), the donors of the Petroleum Research Fund administered by the American Chemical Society (Grant 1152-B), the American Philosophical Society (Johnson Grant 876), and the California State College at Fresno Research Committee.

Literature Cited

(1) Sarton, G., "The History of Science and the New Humanism", pp. 43–44, Harvard University Press, Cambridge, Mass., 1936.
(2) Jaffe, B., *J. Chem. Educ.*, **15**, 383 (1938).
(3) Farber, E., ed., "Great Chemists", p. ix, Interscience Publishers, New York, 1961.
(4) Jaffe, B., *J. Chem. Educ.*, **32**, 183 (1955).
(5) Newell, L. C., *J. Chem. Educ.*, **3**, 166 (1926).
(6) Smith, E. F., *J. Chem. Educ.*, **2**, 533 (1925).
(7) Hildebrand, J., "Science in the Making", p. 7, Columbia University Press, New York, 1957.
(8) Snow, C. P., "The Two Cultures: and a Second Look", 2nd ed., Cambridge University Press, Cambridge, Eng., 1964.
(9) "From My Life: The Memoirs of Richard Willstätter", p. 181, trans. by L. S. Hornig, ed. by A. Stoll, W. A. Benjamin, Inc., New York, 1965.
(10) Strachey, L., "Eminent Victorians", Introduction, Putman, London, 1918.
(11) Farber, E., *J. Chem. Educ.*, **30**, 600 (1953).
(12) Fullmer, J. Z., *Science*, **155**, 285 (1967).
(13) Kauffman, G. B., "Alfred Werner—Founder of Coordination Chemistry", Springer-Verlag, Berlin, Heidelberg, New York, 1966.
(14) Kauffman, G. B., and Beck, A., *J. Chem. Educ.*, **39**, 44 (1962).
(15) Kauffman, G. B., *ibid.*, **40**, 656 (1963).
(16) Ihde, A. J., "The Development of Modern Chemistry", pp. 764–766, Harper and Row, New York, 1964.
(17) Fraser, G. L., *J. Chem. Educ.*, **20**, 506 (1943).
(18) Higgins, T. J., *School Science and Mathematics*, **44**, 650 (1944); **48**, 438 (1948).

12. MUSING ON CLIO

Harold G. Cassidy

Department of Chemistry, Yale University, New Haven, Connecticut, U.S.A.

The history of science and technology, exemplified through chemistry and structured as intellectual history, should be taught after the student has built an equity in the discipline. It should have a philosophical component bearing on the recurrent perennial problems, such as the relation between particle and field theories and the roles of theory and practice. It should counter academic arrogance and smugness by giving a sense of the facts that nature is full of surprises; is inexhaustible; and that no limit may be set to the heights of man's ingenuity and inspiration. It should foster creativity by giving the student courage to listen to his own inspirations, and by illustrating that we do not have to pledge the future by what happened in the past.

When I run a reaction that is new to me, I go to "Organic Reactions" or a suitable reference work and get the best available method. I do not care what the history of the reaction might have been. If someone should chide me, saying "But it is an Historical Fact that so-and-so did that reaction, and so-and-so modified it, and so forth, until now it is well worked out and useful", I agree; and I know that so-and-so must have had troubles and problems, and I am thankful to the community of scientists who have made worked-out experiments available, but the history of the reaction is irrelevant to my running the reaction. Especially, history as pure fact or event is not the kind of history that I would defend for a moment, if it were conceived that this should be taught to chemists.

Likewise, I would not defend the teaching of chemistry by an historical method—especially to beginning chemistry majors. It is a waste of time to rehearse the phlogiston theory today. There is too much that needs to be mastered for the hard-pressed beginning-student to spend his time on old wrong theories—he will have enough troubles with modern somewhat less-wrong theories.

The chemistry major should be thoroughly grounded in the symbols, grammar, and reference of his subject: mathematics, physics, and chemistry theory; and he should be introduced in the classroom and laboratory to as many actual chemical substances as possible. This is more than enough to occupy his time in the first years. Then, by the junior or senior year, when he has some equity in the subject, when he has begun to develop what Michael Polanyi (1) calls connoisseurship in his major field, then is the time for a history course. But in my view it should be a special kind of history course.

The history of chemistry should be philosophy of science in action—embodied in chemistry. It should teach, by examples out of the past and by present examples if possible, the cumulative structure of science as

7 Teaching the History of Chemistry

a cooperative search for what is true. In this search a Dalton, a Lavoisier, a Mendeleev, a Gibbs, or a Planck may approach the true, but only because others have gone before. The French philosopher Merleau-Ponty says that a philosophical life bases itself on thinking according to the true, one's self, and others, all three in mutual dependence (2). When all three come together in some manifestation, that moment justifies life. This, I think, might be a central theme of a History of Chemistry and would be part of what I mean by philosophy in action.

A history of chemistry, as I see it, should be in part intellectual history: the student should come from the course with a feeling for the grand structure of science: for its cumulative power and for the sequence of approximate solutions which are superimposed on recurrent perennial problems and which make it so that history does not repeat itself. Problems such as the relation between particle and field have recurred in science since the earliest times, though the names that are used have changed (3).

The student should also have some sense of the impact of science upon the whole culture, and so history of technology should not be slighted. This is particularly important today because there is a danger that theory will be overemphasized, and that the touchstone of theory—namely, whether it works—will be missed. Furthermore, there are problems involving ethical decisions, for example, in matters of governmental action and public policy, for which the holistic historical approach is essential, such as pollution problems of all kinds.

Of course, I am not suggesting that historical facts should be omitted; but they are a basis only—a basis for the kinetics: why did things develop as they did? History is *ex post facto*, but if it includes the kind of analysis of conceptual and technical foundations that I have suggested, it also provides a large predictive component.

I would see a history of science course encouraging the teacher by showing how much the creative chemists have owed to their own teachers, and how a theme of ideas and practice has been dependent on a concatenation of teacher to student to his student. It can play a tremendous role in civilizing the student by countering two prevalent academic sins. One is academic arrogance. How many modern chemists would care to handle the problems that were met by the teachers of their teachers? At one time, the analysis of a naturally occurring fatty acid mixture or of a protein took six months and required forty to a hundred grams of material and a good deal of intuition *cum* careful observation. Yet one chemist announced to a number of his colleagues within my hearing that these people were not chemists. Another sin is that of intellectual smugness. One chemist assured me that quantum theory had solved all problems in principle. Lack of a sense of history, which teaches us neither to set a limit to the surprises that nature has in store with her inexhaustibility, nor to set a limit to the heights of man's ingenuity and inspiration, has made of many clever people educated seminincompoops (as sea Captain Harold Sawyer would have put it).

One aim of a history of science course such as I am describing would be to encourage the student to break through the creative barrier. How many teachers have learned the hard way that ideas are valuable in themselves, that they seldom come as a clap of thunder, but if at all as a still small voice? (The other drum is muffled, but yet may be recognized and followed.) The ability to hear this still, small voice and to follow the new intuition may be helped by specific suggestion from the teacher and by the historical evidence. How often are the experts wrong? How often are the objections of colleagues ill-founded or short-sighted? What tenacity is needed to witness against fashion!

What I have just written may be put in another way. "One can operate with two kinds of assurance: the assurance of ignorance (walking bravely into the forest because no one has told you that there are evil spirits there) or the assurance of knowledge (knowing that the evil spirits are there, one has provided himself with a lethal evil-spirit gun)" (4). In the former state of assurance, what you don't know won't worry you; in the latter, what you don't know worries you a great deal. Much research and other experimentation is done with the assurance of ignorance of the past. This approach is successful in some instances, but in others, such as devising "new" approaches to teaching science, it has been incredibly wasteful: especially where novelty is confused with creativity, or the "new" is worshiped for its own sake.

The value of ideas is generally underrated by the academic. He deals with ideas all the time, and, constantly shuffling them as is our pedagogical habit, he may become expert in dealing new patterns and unable to recognize a new idea except as something to shuffle. ("There are hundreds of Ph.D.'s running around without an idea", said my teacher Harry N. Holmes. "Give them an idea, and they'll run it into the ground; they're trained to. But they are not trained to recognize a new idea or to create one.") History of the technological side of chemistry should help here. One of the things a graduate chemist learns on entering industry is the extraordinary value placed on ideas. Another is the willingness to be wrong—not often taught in competitive academic courses.

But perhaps a history of chemistry course, as intellectual and technological history of science exemplified through chemical examples, could perform its greatest civilizing transformation on the student by illustrating "the contingency of human events" and by showing that we do not have to pledge the future according to what happened in the past. For there are no solutions to human problems, scientific or otherwise. Each solution changes the problem, and a history course of the kind that I describe (which may, for all I know, be taught (5)) would serve its best function in displaying the ambiguities with which we live and in teaching and supporting our unambiguous approach to them.

7*

Literature Cited

(1) Polanyi, Michael, "Personal Knowledge: Towards a Post-Critical Philosophy", Harper Torchbooks, Harper & Row, New York, 1964.

(2) Merleau-Ponty, Maurice, "In Praise of Philosophy", trans. by John Wild and James M. Edie, Northwestern University Press, Evanston, Illinois, 1963.

(3) Cf. Whyte, L. L., "Essay on Atomism: From Democritus to 1960", Harper & Row, New York, 1963 (Wesleyan University Press, 1961).

(4) Patterson, Elizabeth. I wish to thank Prof. Patterson for helpful comments on this paper.

(5) Two authors who approach history of science in somewhat the sense that I try to suggest here (and there may be many others) are the late Norwood Russell Hanson, "The Concept of the Positron: A Philosophical Analysis", Cambridge University Press, London, 1963, and Max Jammer, "The Conceptual Development of Quantum Mechanics", McGraw-Hill, New York, 1966. For example, Jammer traces the influence of the cultural climate, stemming from Kierkegaard, on developments and interpretations of quantum theory by the Copenhagen group.

13. CHEMISTRY AND THE SCIENTIFIC REVOLUTION

ALLEN G. DEBUS

Department of History, University of Chicago, Chicago, Illinois, U.S.A.

The past fifty years have witnessed the professionalization of the history of science, but at the same time there has been evidence of a lessened interest in the history of chemistry. There may well be a reason for this apparent paradox. The Scientific Revolution has generally been interpreted from a twentieth-century viewpoint in which the Newtonian synthesis looms large as the very basis of our modern age. The chemistry of the same period is often either dismissed as superstition or is relegated to a position of secondary importance with the suggestion that it merely shared in the triumphs of seventeenth-century physics through the adoption of the mechanical philosophy. If, however, we look less at the mechanical philosophy of the period and more at the work of the philosophical chemists of the Renaissance, we find a different approach than we might have expected. These men sought a new and universal philosophy of nature based on original observations and experiments. This philosophy was to be a replacement for the scholasticism of the schools, and it was to be founded on the truths of revealed religion—this a matter of no small concern in the period of the Reformation. The influence of this chemical philosophy is evidenced in the writings of accepted giants of the Scientific Revolution—men such as Bacon, Mersenne, Gassendi, Descartes, Boyle, and Newton. We must judge it not as outside the mainstream of sixteenth- and seventeenth-century science but rather as an important influence which helped forge the modern world. When this is more generally accepted, the recently increasing recognition of the importance of the study and the teaching of the history of chemistry will be greatly accelerated.

In his letter of invitation to this Symposium, Professor Kauffman commented that the teaching of the history of chemistry is only now beginning to recover from a half-century of neglect. This statement may not ring as true for Europe as for the United States, but it is interesting that this is the same half-century which has seen the professionalization of the history of science. I would suggest that it may well be that it has been this professionalization which has resulted in the long lack of interest in the history of chemistry. Until quite recently the history of science has been overwhelmingly dominated by historians of the physical sciences, and for them the physical sciences have meant physics, astronomy, and mathematics. The achievement of Newton has been allowed to sweep all else to the side, and as a result, the most penetrating studies of the rise of modern science have been centered around the problems of mechanics and those technical details which resulted in the establishment of the new cosmology. We read of the investigations made at Oxford and Paris in the fourteenth century, and our histories emphasize that great succession of scholars—Copernicus, Tycho, Kepler, Galileo, and Newton. Nor, on the surface, need this seem unfounded. We find Galileo picturing the scientific world of his day in terms of a cosmological conflict—as a dialogue between that proponent of mathematical abstraction and experiment, Salviati, and his opponent, the apologist for Aristotelian-Ptolemaic tradition, Simplicio.

The resultant picture may seem relatively simple, and it surely is extremely appealing. The rise of modern science would appear to have been—with some detours—the gradual triumph of reason coupled with a corresponding decline of superstition. The crowning glory of it all is the Newtonian synthesis. In this interpretation chemistry would seem to have played little part, and the speculations of the chemists have thus largely been relegated to the realm of folklore, magic, and nonsense. It is primarily in those areas where the mechanical philosophy—and thus physics—affected the field that there has been a defense made for seventeenth-century chemistry. In this line Marie Boas Hall has written that

> The amalgamation of chemistry and physics, and the development of rational mechanical theory in chemistry, amply indicate that seventeenth-century chemistry deserves a place in the seventeenth-century scientific revolution. If seventeenth-century chemistry is taken to be either utilitarian iatrochemistry or mystical Helmontian dogma it must properly be held to have no share in the development of rational, mechanical, experimental natural philosophy, and it is fair to think of the scientific revolution in chemistry as postponed until the age of Lavoisier (1).

With this interpretation seventeenth-century chemistry becomes at best a derivative of the mainstream of seventeenth century science and therefore of only secondary importance.

And if Marie Boas Hall seeks salvation for chemistry in terms of physics, more traditional historians of chemistry have often limited their discussions to the progressive description of new discoveries and new techniques in terms of the internal development of the science. The subject matter of this quest, however, does not appear to have the sheer drama of the conceptual change associated with the Copernican revolution, and indeed, it is not immediately evident to most physics-oriented historians of science just what significance should be attached to Renaissance metallurgical assays and lists of new chemically prepared medicines—those subjects which often appear as the prime chemical innovations of the sixteenth and the seventeenth centuries. While none would deny that this is clearly of importance in the technical development of the science, the same facts often seem to have little in common with the major currents of intellectual thought which resulted in the transformation from the medieval to the modern scene.

One may then question on the basis of the research of the past fifty years whether chemistry did play a significant role in the Scientific Revolution. I think that it did, and I believe that this field will become the basis for a new interpretation of the Scientific Revolution. If it does, our debt will be not only to professional historians of chemistry but also to scholars in closely related fields; intellectual historians, historians of medicine, and historians of philosophy. Here Hugh Trevor-Roper's recent essays have pointed to the importance of the occult sciences in the Renaissance (2). Similarly, the recent studies of Frances A. Yates—and especially her book on Giordano Bruno (3)—have emphasized the relation of Herme-

ticism to the rise of modern science. And above all, Walter Pagel has
opened a new chapter in the writing of the history of science—and the
history of chemistry—in his penetrating studies of Paracelsus, van Helmont, and Harvey (4). His work has pointed to the impact of Renaissance
mysticism on major figures of that epoch, and it has shown how that impact
affected their thought. Pagel has remarked on the fallacy of ignoring those
aspects of early science which do not seem to be germane to modern science,
and he has suggested that

> Instead of selecting data that 'make sense' to the acolyte of modern science, the
> historian should therefore try to make sense of the philosophical, mystical or religious
> 'side-steps' of otherwise 'sound' scientific workers of the past—'side-steps' that are
> usually excused by the spirit or rather backwardness of the period. It is these that
> present a challenge to the historian: to uncover the internal reason and justification
> for their presence in the mind of the savant and their organic coherence with his
> scientific ideas. In other words it is for the historian to reverse the method of scientific
> selection and to restate the thoughts of his hero in their original setting. The two
> sets of thought—the scientific and the non-scientific—will then emerge not as simply
> juxtaposed or as having been conceived in spite of each other, but as an organic
> whole in which they support and confirm each other. There is no other way to lay
> the savant open to our understanding (5).

If, indeed, we accept Pagel on this, we will be studying the scientific
revolution in terms of that period rather than our own. In short, we shall
be acting as historians. If we do this, however, we must be willing to seek
our sources not only in the practical discoveries and inventions of the
alchemists and working chemists of that era but also in their philosophical
and medical tracts—texts which contain their theories and stated goals.
There is a special need to plunge into the relatively uncharted wastes of
the somewhat disreputable "occult" literature of the Renaissance and
to find its relationship to those aspects of the Scientific Revolution that
we already know. When we have done this, we shall perhaps find more
similarities with the mechanical philosophers than we might have expected,
and we shall surely note an influence which is greater than we anticipated.
Even on the basis of the limited research in this field to date we begin to
see an entirely new picture of the relation of chemistry to the rise of modern science.

For the Renaissance period we need not tie ourselves to a twentieth-
century definition of chemistry when we speak of a chemical approach to
nature (6). At that time chemistry was most commonly defined as the
Spagyric Art, an art in which the subject matter was primarily the separation of the pure from the impure. It was also an art dedicated to the
perfection of the imperfect in nature. Thus the imperfect metals might
surely be hastened on their slow path to nobility through the skill of the
alchemist. Similarly, the ills of man might well be treated by this art.
The alchemist was both a physician of man and nature. In addition, however, the alchemist thought of himself as a natural philosopher—one to
whom the secrets of nature would be unlocked through the key of chemistry.
Thus, Nicolas Le Fèvre wrote in 1660 that

> Chymistry is nothing else but the Art and Knowledge of Nature it self; that it is
> by her means we examine the Principles, out of which natural bodies do consist and

are compounded; and by her are discovered unto us the causes of their sources of
their generations and corruptions, and of all the changes and alterations to which
they are liable...(7).

This Chemical Philosophy was to be a universal philosophy of nature
founded on new observations and indisputable philosophical precepts.
The teachings of the Schools were rejected as moribund and impious. In
contrast, the true natural philosopher or alchemist was taught to follow
two books, the written record of Holy Scripture and the created book
of nature. If the first of these was to be read as a book, the second was
to be studied through the chemist's own observation and analyses. This
plea for reform stands out in the works of Paracelsus. Idle speculations and
theories are to be rejected in the study of nature. In contrast to the Galenist,
the Paracelsian chemical physician is to be a man who is not afraid to
work with his own hands, a pious scholar who praises God in his work and
who lays aside all the vanities of his tradition-bound competitor and
instead finds his delight in a knowledge of the fire while he learns the degrees
of the science of alchemy (8). If we are to have a new science we must
look on the books of the ancients with considerable distrust. In the "Labyrinthus Medicorum" of Paracelsus (1538) we find no written books discussed
at all. Instead we are told to seek out God through nature. We must turn
to the book of the heavens, the book of the elements, the book of man,
the book of alchemy, and the book of medicine. In effect, published books
are useless for the reform of learning since this must be based on experience
and observation. "Scientia enim est experientia" (9). This was to be an
undeniable maxim of the chemical philosophy, one which was repeated
time and time again throughout the sixteenth and seventeenth centuries.

And if the Renaissance chemist felt that the study of nature was deficient at the Universities because of a reliance on books rather than on
experience, he could complain further that the Aristotelian thought spewed
forth at the Schools could be attacked on other—perhaps more weighty—
grounds. The century of the greatest Paracelsian-chemical influence coin-
cides with the high-point of religious debate in Europe. There was no
doubt that the Aristotelian philosophy had been condemned more than
once on theological grounds, and the chemical philosophers insisted not
only that they performed a divine service in their investigation of nature
by studying the created wonders of the Lord but also, in contrast to the
Aristotelians and the Galenists, that they had founded their philosophy
on the indisputable truths of divine revelation rather than on blind logic.
References to Scriptural passages commenting on nature are cited continually by these authors. Among them one meets most often references to
the Creation account in "Genesis". This was interpreted as a chemical
analogy in which the divine alchemist created the world through an act
of chemical separation. This is the approach found in the widely read
Paracelsian "Philosophy to the Athenians" (10), and it is an interpretation
widely repeated in the literature in the sixteenth and the seventeenth
centuries. The significance of the Creation placed a new emphasis on the
role of the elements in nature since they were among the first products
of the divine separation. For this reason disputes over the Aristotelian

elements and the Paracelsian principles which arose at that time should have more than an antiquarian interest for us today (11). Both systems represented cosmological as well as chemical systems, and as a result of the inadequacies of the elements and the principles which became evident in this fashion a lessened belief in the traditional cosmological system was inevitable.

In addition to the major role played by religion in the chemical philosophy, one meets as well with an insistence on the macrocosm-microcosm analogy. The universe was pictured as small and closely interconnected. Macrocosmic events affected man, and man as the microcosm could in turn affect the great world. The earth itself was thought to be a living body analogous to man in this vast and all-encompassing vitalistic universe. The Creation had been a chemical process on all levels, and it seemed only right to conclude that all nature—the macrocosm, the geocosm, and the microcosm—must continue to operate chemically. For instance, if we examine our earth, we see again the effect of the divine chemistry. Michael Sendivogius, discussing the origin of springs, speaks of the internal fire in the earth which heats subterranean reservoirs of water. The resultant vapor is subsequently cooled at the surface and reduced to the liquid streams so often the point of controversy in this period. In short, here we see the hand of the divine alchemist once more—in this case using the earth as a giant distillation system.

Such therefore is the Distiller, the Maker of all things, in whose hands is this Distillatory, according to the example of which all Distillations have been invented by Philosophers; which thing the most High God himself out of pity, without doubt, hath inspired into the Sons of Men: and he can, when it is his Holy Will, either extinguish the, Central Fire, or break the Vessel, and then there will be an end of all (12).

This was a chemical answer, at the same time natural and divine, which seemed to account for the internal heat of the earth, the generation of metals, and the presence of minerals in mineral waters (13).

Still, the tightly knit universe seemed to reveal its greatest secrets in the relation of man to nature. It was common to insist on the divine analogy of man and the great world. Oswald Crollius stated bluntly that

Heaven and Earth are Mans Parents, out of which Man last of all was created; he that knowes the parents, and can Anotomize them, hath attained the true knowledge of their child man, the most perfect creature in all his properties; because all things of the whole Universe meet in him as in the Centre, and the Anatomy of him in his Nature is the Anotomy of the whole world... (14).

The Doctrine of Signatures and the theory of Sympathy and Antipathy taught the chemist of the interrelation of all things. Indelible signs showed that earthly substances were connected with the microcosm. In past ages men had sought out these signs in the external shapes of plants and minerals which often betrayed their value in resemblances to bodily organs. The chemists of the sixteenth and seventeenth centuries had a more potent tool at their disposal. Through their chemical analyses they could lay bare the occult signs of natural objects (15).

There is no question but that chemistry was pictured as a new key to man's understanding of the universe. New secrets were readily available to anyone who was willing to seek them out, and the truth and beauty of the macrocosm-geocosm-microcosm analogy made the discoveries found on one level a guide to truths on the others. Thus, while man was admonished to seek out nature on his own, it was the expectancy that the fruits of his research would have far reaching results in our understanding of the heavens, the earth, and man. Nature and the Bible with chemistry as a key to it all—this was the answer to a new science. Those who sought a new science through the study of local motion and mathematical abstraction were in reality retrogressing. Logic and mathematics are well and good as far as they go, but they do not go far enough (*16*). In our new interpretation of nature we need devote little time to such Aristotelian fancies and delusions. Rather, we must turn to observation, experiment, and analysis. Here was a plea for a new science which sought truth in the Bible and decried the errors of the Schools. At the same time, it emphasized the importance of man in the eternal scheme of nature and insisted that whatever we learn of nature might be applied to the ills of the human race. It is little wonder that the prime supporters of the chemical philosophy were physicians.

Some iatrochemists reacted with alarm to the etxreme mysticism of this world view taken by some Paracelsians and chemical philosophers. Thus, we find the influential iatrochemist, Andreas Libavius, attacking the Paracelsian philosophers at the close of the sixteenth century. Similarly, his English friend and disciple, Edward Jorden, attacked Peter Severinus for his "Platonicall grandiloquence" (*17*) and for the Paracelsians' constant retreat to the doctrine of Sympathy and Antipathy as a mode of explanation.

If we examine aright what this sympathy and antipathy is, we shall find it to bee nothing but a refuge of ignorance, when not being able to conceive the true reasons of such actions and passions in naturall things, wee fly sometimes to indefinite generalities, and sometimes to this inexplicable sympathy and antipathy: attributing voluntary, and sensitive actions and passions to insensible substances (*18*).

Daniel Sennert lauded the observations of the chemists, but he questioned the validity of their theories, while van Helmont openly objected that

The name of Microcosm or little World is Poetical, heathenish, and metaphorical, but not natural, or true. It is likewise a Phantastical, hypochondriacal and mad thing, to have brought all the properties, and species of the universe into man, and the art of healing (*19*).

Yet, granting all of this, the Helmontians retained the main tenets of the chemical philosophy. The chief science remained medicine, and chemistry was to be its key. The two-book doctrine of revelation remained their guide, and the true student of nature was still told to seek knowledge through observation and experiment rather than logic and mathematics.

It is perhaps unnecessary to continue discussing the views of these chemical philosophers. Their approach to nature was eventually shown to be wrong, and for the most part their hypotheses were relegated to the history of human error rather than to the history of science. And it is a fact that the history of science has largely been a positivistic enterprise with its practitioners wasting little time on anything which the man of the twentieth century would not define as "solid science". The historian of chemistry thus has traditionally paid scant attention to the macrocosm-microcosm analogy, the theory of sympathy and antipathy, the relation of religion to chemical theory, debates over the elements and the principles, and the doctrine of signatures. Instead, in the massive tomes of the iatro-chemists he has sought out specific chemical procedures and those few statements which seem to foreshadow the rational science of a later age.

All of this—although surely not an historical approach—might be condoned if it could rightly be argued that the theoretical basis of the chemical philosophy was of little interest to the man of the Renaissance. This, however, does not seem to be the case. There is strong evidence to show that the Paracelsian world view attracted a large number of well edu-cated and influential scholars. Its influence was clearly the strongest among physicians. In 1608 the prospects for a chemical reform of natural philos-ophy seemed so promising to Oswald Croll that he wrote that Paracelsus' dream of overturning the ancient doctrines of the schools would shortly be an accomplished fact (20).

Perhaps more telling is the evidence supplied to us by the enemies of the chemists. The impact of Robert Fludd's multivolume chemical descrip-tion of the macrocosm and the microcosm (1617–1638) resulted in a running debate with Kepler, Mersenne, and Gassendi (21). The use of chemical analogies, the relation of mathematics to nature, and the recourse to the Bible as a source of truth in science were all topics brought up in the course of this exchange. There was clearly a fear that Paracelsian mysti-cism was attracting too large a share of the learned public for comfort. Hence, Mersenne discussed at length the assertion by his opponents that alchemy is a true science before taking up mathematics, which he felt to be the proper basis for a new learning (22). Mersenne's heated attack was answered in a point-by-point rebuttal by Fludd, and this in turn was answered by Gassendi. This is a significant chapter in the genesis of a new science.

Nor do we find a declining interest in the chemical philosophy in the following decades. In England in the Civil War period serious proposals were made to reform the universities on the basis of the Paracelso-Helmon-tian concept of nature (23). And as late as 1661 Robert Boyle complained that the chemists were thought to have brought forth so many experiments in support of their views "that of those that have quitted the unsatis-factory Philosophy of the schools, the greater Number dazl'd as it were by the Experiments of Spagyrists, have imbrac'd their Doctrines instead of those they deserted" (24). New experiments, he insisted, must be brought forth so that the disenchanted Aristotelians would be lured to the mechan-ical philosophy rather than the chemical philosophy of nature.

Surely, then, on historical grounds we cannot dismiss the theoretical concepts of the Paracelsians. Whether or not they were right, they were influential. The Scientific Revolution therefore cannot be understood unless we try to understand their work. Specifically in what areas, however, can we argue that they affected the growth of key concepts in the rise of modern science? It is still difficult to answer this question since to date so few detailed studies have been carried out in this field. We know that we must trace in greater detail those similarities between Paracelsian and phlogiston chemistry. We know that we must look into the relationship of the element disputes of the Renaissance and the contemporary speculations on the validity of the traditional cosmology. And we must ask further if there is a connection between the *Naturphilosophie* of the nineteenth century and this essentially German, non-mechanical science of an earlier period.

It is true that we have more questions to ask than answers to give, but we can point to the mystical Paracelsian concept of an aerial saltpeter and follow its transformation into the celebrated aerial niter of Boyle, Hooke, and Mayow (25). We can show how Hermetic philosophers tried to remove the atheistic stigma long attached to atomism by associating this concept in its original form with the Old Testament Prophet, Moses (26). We can show the relation of the neo-Paracelsian Rosicrucian movement with the mid-seventeenth-century search for educational reform and independent scientific societies (27). Or we can point to the influence of Hermetic and alchemical thought on such giants of the Scientific Revolution as Francis Bacon (28), René Descartes (29), Robert Boyle (30), Isaac Newton (31), and William Harvey (32).

This influence makes little sense if we wish to think of these men only as modern scientists. It is, however, readily understandable if the Hermetic-alchemical-Paracelsian system is understood as a universal philosophy, proposed and widely accepted as an alternative to the discredited Aristotelianism of the schools. Here was a call for a new science by men who opposed the apparent inactivity of university scholars. Rather, they turned to the Holy Scriptures and nature for a nonmathematical road to a new science—a new science which placed high value on man's ability to understand through his own experience. And the goal of their new chemically oriented science was surely not limited to the compounding of medicines or the artificial production of the noble metals. It was to be more than this, a new key to all nature. In short, there was much in this system of nature for which we generally give full credit to the mechanical philosophy. As historians we should not be asking only how the mechanical philosophy differed from the mystical systems it superseded, but also we should be asking to what extent the mechanical philosophy was indebted to the natural magic and the chemical philosophy of the Paracelsians.

My point has not been merely to describe an outmoded system of thought of interest only to antiquarians. Instead, I have hoped to show that, for the most crucial years—the formative years—of the Renaissance and the Early Modern periods, chemistry can and must be thought of as part of the mainstream of that discontent and reform which led to what we call the Scientific Revolution. As long as the main emphasis of the history of chemistry in this period is placed on metallurgy and practical iatrochemistry —or even the chemical application of the mechanical philosophy practiced by Boyle and his colleagues—then we can do little more than treat the subject as a derivative of that mainstream. This is quite incorrect, and it is surely misleading to students. As the real importance of chemistry in this period becomes more apparent to historians of science, we shall see a greatly increased influx of students into this field on all levels. And if we have seen a renaissance of studies in the history of chemistry in recent years, it is as yet nothing compared to what I believe that it will be in the near future.

Literature Cited

(1) Boas, Marie, "Robert Boyle and Seventeenth-Century Chemistry", p. 231, Cambridge University Press, Cambridge, 1958.

(2) Of special interest is his "Witches and Witchcraft", *Encounter*, **28**, no. 5, 3–25 (1967); **28**, no. 6, 13–34 (1967). Also of interest for historians of English science in the Civil War period is his "Three Foreigners and the Philosophy of the English Revolution", *Encounter*, **14**, 3–20 (1960).

(3) Yates, Frances A., "Giordano Bruno and the Hermetic Tradition", Chicago University Press, Chicago, 1964. Also of special importance is her paper, "The Hermetic Tradition in Renaissance Science", in "Art, Science and History in the Renaissance", ed. by Charles S. Singleton, pp. 255–274, The Johns Hopkins Press, Baltimore, 1968.

(4) The reader is referred particularly to his "Paracelsus: An Introduction to Philosophical Medicine in the Era of the Renaissance", S. Karger, Basel, 1958; "Das medizinische Weltbild des Paracelsus, seine Zusammenhänge mit Neuplatonismus und Gnosis", Franz Steiner Verlag, Wiesbaden, 1962; "Jo. Bapt. Van Helmont: Einführung in die philosophische Medizin des Barock", Julius Springer, Berlin, 1930; "The Religious and Philosophical Aspects of van Helmont's Science and Medicine", Supp. Bull. Hist. Med. No. 2, The Johns Hopkins Press, Baltimore, 1944; "William Harvey's Biological Ideas: Selected Aspects and Historical Background", S. Karger, Basel/New York, 1967.

(5) Pagel, "William Harvey's Biological Ideas", p. 82.

(6) This has been discussed by the present author in "The English Paracelsians", pp. 13–42, Oldbourne Press, London, 1965, Franklin Watts, New York, 1966, and more specifically in "Renaissance Chemistry and the Work of Robert Fludd", in Debus, Allen G., and Multhauf, Robert P., "Alchemy and Chemistry in the Seventeenth Century", pp. 3–29, William Andrews Clark Memorial Library, University of California, Los Angeles, 1966. In slightly modified form this paper has been reprinted under the same title in *Ambix*, **14**, 42–59 (1967).

(7) le Febure, Nicasius, "A Compleat Body of Chymistry", p. 1, trans. by P. D. C., Esq., one of the Gentlemen of His Majesties Privy-Chamber, O. Pulleyn, Jr. for John Wright, London, 1670.

(8) Paracelsus, "Of the Nature of Things", in Sendivogius, Michael, "A New Light of Alchymy", pp. 252–53, A. Clark for Tho. Williams, London, 1674.

(9) Paracelsus, "Labyrinthus Medicorum", in "Opera Omnia", Vol. I, pp. 264–88 (275), 3 vols., Joan. Antonii & Samuelis De Tournes, Geneva, 1658.

(10) In addition to separate printings, the "Philosophiae ad Athenienses" forms the opening selection in the second volume of the widely circulated Huser folio edition of Paracelsus, "Opera Omnia". This was published by Lazarus Zetzner at Strassburg in three volumes in 1603, 1605, and again in 1616, 1618. A translation is conveniently in English in Crollius, Osw., and Paracelsus, "Philosophy Reformed and Improved", two treatises translated by H. Pinnell, London, 1657, and more recently in "The Hermetic and Alchemical Writings of Paracelsus", Vol. 2, pp. 249–81, trans. and ed. by A. E. Waite, 2 vols., London, 1894.

(11) See Debus, Allen G., "Fire Analysis and the Elements in the Sixteenth and the Seventeenth Centuries", *Annals of Science*, **23**, 127–147 (1967).

(12) Sendivogius, "A New Light of Alchymy", pp. 94–95.

(13) This scheme and a rival chemical hypothesis of the structure of the earth have been discussed by the present author in "Edward Jorden and the Fermentation of the Metals: An Iatrochemical Study of Terrestrial Phenomena", in "Toward a History of Geology: Proceedings of the New Hampshire Inter-Disciplinary Conference on the History of Geology, Sept. 7–12, 1967", pp. 100–121, ed. by Cecil J. Schneer, MIT Press, Cambridge, Mass., 1969.

(14) Crollius, Osw., "Discovering the Great and Deep Mysteries of Nature", in "Philosophy Reformed and Improved", p. 24, trans. by H. Pinnell, Lodowick Lloyd, London, 1657.

(15) See the preface to Croll's "Tractatus de Signaturis Internis Rerum, seu de Vera et Viva Anatomia majoris & minoris mundi", in Crollius, Osualdus, "Basilica Chymica", pp. 1–2 (separate pagination), Tampach, Frankfurt [1623]. An English translation exists as "A Treatise of Oswaldus Crollius of Signatures of Internal Things; or, a True and Lively Anatomy of the Greater and Lesser World", sig. A2 verso (separate for this work), John Starkey and Thomas Passenger, London, 1669. ". . .the foot-steps of the invisible God in the Creatures, the Shadow and Image of the Creatour imprest in the Creatures, or that Internal force, and occult vertue of Operation, (which as Natures Gift is insited, and infused by the most high God, into the Plant or Anima, from the Signature and mutual Analogick Sympathy and harmonious concordance of Plants, with the Members of the Human Body), is by the prudent Physitian only inquired into: and thence by the industrious help of *Vulcan*, or *Anatomick Knife*, is drawn out and applied to its proper use, not drousily passed over in noxious Silence, as is by Vulgar *Herbalists* too frequently done." The English translation will be found with separate pagination in the "Bazilica Chymica, & Praxis Chymiatricae or Royal and Practical Chymistry in Three Treatises. . . All faithfully Englished by a Lover of Chymistry", John Starkey and Thomas Passenger, London, 1670. The "Lover of Chymistry" was Richard Russell, as he confessed in his translation of the works of Geber in 1678. See "The Works of Geber", sig. A2 verso, trans. by Richard Russell, William Cooper, London, 1686.

(16) This is discussed in more detail in Debus, Allen G., "Mathematics and Nature in the Chemical Texts of the Renaissance", *Ambix*, **15**, 1–28, 211 (1968).

(17) Jorden, Edward, Dr. in Physick, "A Discourse of Naturall Bathes, and Mineral Waters", p. 69, 2nd edition "in many points enlarged", Thomas Harper, London, 1632.

(18) *Ibid.*, p. 121.

(19) van Helmont, J. B., "Oriatrike or Physick Refined", p. 323, trans. by John Chandler, Lodowick Lloyd, London, 1662.

(20) Crollius, "Philosophy Reformed and Improved", pp. 142–47.

(21) The Fludd–Kepler exchange has been discussed by W. Pauli in "The Influence of Archetypal Ideas on the Scientific Theories of Kepler", in Pauli, W., "The Interpretation of Nature and the Psyche", trans. by Priscilla Silz, Pantheon, New York, 1955. The most recent accounts of the conflict will be found in Yates, F. A. "Giordano Bruno" (cited above, ref. 3), pp. 432–55, and in Cafiero, L., "Robert Fludd e la polemica con Gassendi", *Rivista Critica di storia filosofia*, Part 1, **19**, 367–410 (1964); Part 2, **20**, 3–15 (1965). An older, but basic study is Lenoble, R., "Mersenne ou la naissance du mécanisme", Vrin, Paris, 1943. A discussion of Fludd's defense of the doctrine of sympathy and antipathy in these debates will be found in Debus, A. G., "Robert Fludd and the Use of Gilbert's *De Magnete* in the Weapon-Salve controversy", *Journal of the History of Medicine and Allied Sciences*, **19**, 389–417 (1964).

(22) Mersenne, F. Marin, "La Vérité des Sciences. Contre les septiques ou Pyrrhoniens", du Bray, Paris, 1625. Here the first chapter is titled "Auquel le Septique dispute contre l'Alchymiste, s'efforçant de prouuer que l'Alchimie est une science certaine".

(23) Here the most interesting debate was between the chemist, John Webster, and the mathematician, Seth Ward, in 1654. This conflict has been discussed by the present author in "The Chemical Dream of the Renaissance", Churchill College Overseas Fellowship Lectures, Heffer, Cambridge, 1968, and also in

his "Science and Education in the Seventeeth Century. The Webster-Ward Debate." Macdonald, London, and American Elsevier, New York, 1970,

(24) Boyle, Robert, "Some Specimens of an Attempt to Make Chymical Experiments Useful to Illustrate the Notions of the Corpuscular Philosophy", sig. P5 recto, Henry Herringman, London, 1661.

(25) Debus, Allen G., "The Paracelsian Aerial Niter", *Isis*, 55, 43-61 (1964).

(26) McGuire, J. E., and Rattansi, P. M., "Newton and the 'Pipes of Pan'," *Notes and Records of the Royal Society*, **21**, 108–43 (1966).

(27) Held has discussed the relation of J. V. Andreae's "Christianopolis" (1619) to the founding of the Royal Society in his edition of the text. Andreae, Johann Valentin, "Christianopolis. An Ideal State of the Seventeenth Century", pp. 100–25, trans. with an historical introduction by Felix Emil Held, Oxford University Press, New York, 1916. Andreae seems to have been the author of the Rosicrucian "Fama Fraternitatis", 1st ed., 1614. Considerable attention has been placed on this work also by Margery Purver in her "The Royal Society: Concept and Creation", Routledge and Kegan Paul, London, 1967. See also Armytage, W. H. G., "The Early Utopists and Science in England", *Annals of Science*, **12**, 247–54 (1956); and Turnbull, G. H., "Hartlib, Dury and Comenius, Gleanings from Hartlib's Papers", University of Liverpool Press, Liverpool, 1947.

(28) Rossi, Paolo, "Francis Bacon: From Magic to Science", University of Chicago Press, Chicago, 1968.

(29) Gouhier, Henri, "Descartes et les Rose-Croix", Chap. 5 of "Les premières pensées de Descartes", J. Vrin, Paris, 1958.

(30) Debus, "Fire Analysis..." (see ref. 11 above).

(31) Newton's library catalog has been printed in de Villamil, Lieut.-Col. R., "Newton: The Man", pp. 62–111, foreword by Albert Einstein, Gordon D. Knox, London, n.d. Even the most cursory glance at this will convince the reader that all of the most important chemical texts were present. For a sample of Isaac Newton's alchemical writings the reader is referred to Taylor, F. Sherwood, "An Alchemical Work of Sir Isaac Newton", *Ambix*, **5**, 59–84 (1956). The reader is referred also to the paper by McGuire and Rattansi (see ref. 26 above).

(32) Pagel, "William Harvey's Biological Ideas" (for complete citation, see ref. 4 above).

14. THE ROLE OF THE PRE-BOYLE PERIOD IN THE UNDERSTANDING OF THE CONCEPTUAL DEVELOPMENT OF MODERN CHEMISTRY

DAVID F. LARDER*

Notre Dame University of Nelson, Nelson, British Columbia, Canada

The pre-Boyle period marks the origin of such basic concepts of modern chemistry as those of pure substance, element, compound, molecule, and atom. The fundamental problem of elements in compounds was formulated by the Greeks, and it led to the less strongly rooted Epicurean viewpoint in opposition to the Aristotelian explanation. The Medieval commentators increasingly emphasised the minima theory, which shows in the fusion of Aristotelian and atomistic ideas which followed the printing of Lucretius' "De Rerum Natura" in 1474. Opposition to Aristotle was accompanied by greater emphasis on atomism, which led finally to the triumph of the mechanical philosophy in the works of Boyle. Some justification for teaching this earlier period in the history of chemistry as well as a brief sketch of it is presented.

What we know and what we think is not a new fountain gushing fresh from the barren rock of the unknown at the stroke of the rod of our own intellect, it is a stream which flows by us and through us, fed by the far-off rivulets of long ago (1).

The establishment of the basic concepts and development of modern chemistry has a history of little more than two hundred years (2), and the beginning of scientific chemistry predates this by an additional hundred years, so that most histories of chemistry have heavily emphasised the period from Robert Boyle, or in some cases from Joseph Black, paying much less attention to the pre-1660 period. This is understandable because the nineteenth century in particular has seen the consolidation of modern concepts, and the period is more easily understood by chemists with little historical background and by historians of chemistry attempting to relate the history of the subject to modern twentieth century science. Further, as Crombie has pointed out, "more demands are made on scientific equipment by more recent science, and conversely ancient or medieval science, for example, make more demands on philological and usually also on philosophical equipment" (3). It is these latter demands that make it more difficult for a chemist turning to the history of his discipline to cope with satisfactorily. The education and training of scientists usually emphasise modern rather than classical languages inasmuch as these are more utilitarian in the understanding of today's international scientific literature, and little or no time is spent on philosophy.

But the origins of chemistry must be sought in earlier times (4), and while Walden has drawn attention to ancient ideas in modern chemistry (5), Hughes has considered that the extent to which the four-element theory persisted "provides a good part of our evidence for the survival

* Work done at Department of the History and Philosophy of Science, University of Aberdeen, Aberdeen, Scotland.

into the sciences of the eighteenth and early nineteenth centuries of the ideas and modes of thought which belong to ages antecedent to the rise of modern experimental science" (6). Leicester has considered it necessary to devote nearly half of his book (7) to the period before Boyle in order "to trace the interrelationships of chemical concepts" since "the germ of many modern theories is to be found among the ancient Greeks or even earlier" (8), and Wightman has suggested that "the birth of ideas, like that of persons, does not occur spontaneously, but is a culmination of travail following on, maybe, centuries of gestation" (9).

Opinion, however, in divided as to the importance of the ancient and medieval periods.* In the two great rival seats of learning, Oxford and Cambridge, the emphasis is different; and while for the postgraduate Cambridge Certificate in the History and Philosophy of Science, no paper is required in Ancient Science, and the Medieval Paper is optional (10), for the corresponding Oxford Diploma, papers are required in the General History of Science in Antiquity *and* in the Origins of Modern Science (11).

These earlier periods in the history of chemistry assume a new importance if we consider the much neglected aspect of the historical development of chemical concepts—what it is proposed to refer to as the historico-conceptual approach to the history of chemistry, which should be considered alongside the biographical, chronological, and topical aspects, or rather fused with them into a unified history of chemistry.

R. G. Collingwood and A. N. Whitehead...have, I believe, emphasised the two-fold nature of historical fact, namely that every standpoint is what it is by virtue of its origin from the past and its urge towards the future. In its relevance to scientific ideas this means that no scientific entity—atom, organ, or wave—is *merely* itself, but is constantly evolving in a context of associated ideas. Hence the necessity for a knowledge of history; not to "liberalise" science, but to understand it (12).

The meaning of chemistry becomes clear only in terms of its concepts' which serve as the foundation for the architectonics of the science, and these entities, philosophical though they may be, consequently need some definition. It is generally conceded by historians of science that it is not possible, nor desirable, to separate the historical and philosophical aspects of science (13, 14), and in chemistry particularly, the philosophical developments have been largely ignored.

Furthermore, from the educational standpoint (15) the conceptual importance as well as the cultural background are of particular consequence in chemistry courses taught with historical insight and understanding and in survey courses in the history of chemistry, both of which exist in liberal arts-oriented programmes. Hutchinson has recently consid-

---

* About 25% of the papers in *Chymia* (34 of the 126 papers in vols. 1–11 (1948–1966)) deal with the period before 1650, while about 15% of the historical papers in the *Journal of Chemical Education* (22 out of 152 entries in the cumulative index for vols. 26–35 (1949–1958) under the heading *History of Chemistry*) deal with the same period. The differences between these two figures may reflect the differences in emphasis between professional historians and educators (including historians) interested in the history of chemistry.

ered that "a liberal education attempts . . . to present a balanced view
of man's cultural heritage and the intellectual culture of the present day"
(*16*), while Ashby has insisted that "we must cut the path to a liberal
education *through a man's specialism*, not by by-passing it for an hour
or two a week" (*17*) (my italics). Hutchinson goes on to ask:

I think it proper to ask why courses in a liberal curriculum should be so rich in
the background of ideas on which chemistry rests and why training courses should
be so impoverished. If it is important for the liberally educated student to have
a grasp of the principal abstractions it is surely even more important for the chemical
practitioners to have them (*18*).

If we accept with Caldin (*19*) the fundamental concepts discussed by
him as forming the basic structure of modern chemistry, *viz.*, pure substance, element, compound, molecule, atom, subatomic particle, and energy,
then as historians we are interested in the evolution and development of
these basic ideas. Within the postulated historico-conceptual framework
it is necessary, at least for the first five concepts (*i.e.*, pure substance,
element, compound, molecule, atom), to go back to early Greek thought
and to see something of the origins of these ideas. The atomic concept has
been considered by Lasswitz (*20*) and by van Melsen (*21*), while Paneth
(*22*) and McKeon (*23*) have written important articles on the concept of
the element. Paneth refers to the classic question of Anaxagoras, "How
could hair have its origin in non-hair, or flesh in non-flesh?" (*24*), and
concludes that here "the basic problem of chemistry and its conceptual
difficulty are pointedly presented" (*25*).

The early histories of these concepts discussed by Caldin have developed
along similar lines and may therefore be considered together. It is proposed,
then, to indicate briefly certain facets of the threads of continuity of these
ideas from the time of the Greeks to the establishment of the mechanical
philosophy in the second half of the seventeenth century (*26*). It should,
however, be borne in mind that the Greek and Medieval periods cannot
be adequately separated from a much wider view of contemporary philosophic thought than can here be considered, and such authors as Multhauf
(*4*), van Melsen (*21*), and Taton (*27*), amongst others, should be consulted
in addition.

The Ionian scientific picture represents the first attempt to pass from
the cosmogenic to the cosmological world picture, and we see in the pre-
Socratic period the slow evolution of ideas regarding matter and change
in the world (*28*). Parmenides' (fl. *c.* 504 B. C.) denial of the existence of
change stimulated alternate points of view since, for him, Being "is motion-
less in the limits of mighty bonds, without beginning, without cease, since
Becoming and Destruction have been driven very far away, and true
conviction has rejected them" (*29*). Empedocles (490–430 B. C.) suggested
four qualitatively different constituents or elements, which indicated typical differences between bodies: the primary matters of Thales (640–546
B.C.) (water), Anaximenes (560–500 B.C.) (air), Heraclitus (536–470 B.C.)
(fire), and the earth of the Monists, and at the same time included the
opposites of Anaximander (hot and cold, wet and dry). Empedocles'

coming together of the elements by "mixing and exchange of what has been mixed" (*30, 31*) was seen by Aristotle (384–322 B.C.) as a random process (*32*). He saw a lack of unity, of oneness, in matter formed in this way, and he distinguished what we now call *mixture* from *compound*. Empedocles' 'mixture' he considered to "consist of the elements preserved intact but placed side by side with one another in minute particles" (*33*).

The fundamental problem of the explanation of the formation of one compound from others, accepting that substances are permanent, was accounted for by Anaxagoras (500–428 B.C.) on the basis that flesh could have its origin in non-flesh if non-flesh contained seeds of flesh: "No Thing comes into being or passes away, but it is mixed together or separated from existing Things" (*34*). He added to the Empedoclean view an unlimited number of seeds, qualitatively different and incorruptible, all possible kinds of seed being contained in every substance: "In everything there is a portion of everything except Mind; and some things contain Mind also" (*35*). He accepted at the same time infinite divisibility and the indestructibility of matter. Leucippus (*c.* 450 B.C.) and Democritus (460–370 B.C.) postulated an infinity of particles with a single ultimate nature, hard, unchangeable, and of an infinite number of shapes. Democritus saw a loose complex (*36*) "entangled by their own close locking shapes" (*37*), made up of different shapes, positions, and arrangements of the particles (*38*). These rearrangements of the permanent atoms explained compound formation and chemical change, but because of the random mixing process it was difficult to see how a definite compound could be distinguished and characterised in practice.

Horne has noted, on the basis of Piaget's studies (*39*), that children's atomistic notions follow the same line of development as the ancient Greek conceptual change:

> the atomism of children...resembles the famous 'seed' hypothesis of Anaxagoras...much more closely than it does the true atomism of Leucippus and Democritus... Subdivision [for Anaxagoras] may be continued indefinitely but beyond this point [where "new subdivision fails to reveal new species"] the parts will be homogeneous. The properties of bulk matter are determined by the type of homogeneous part, or 'seed', predominating (*40*).

Piaget sees this evolution from the atomism of Anaxagoras to that of Democritus as a

> progressive evolution of artificialist [anthropomorphic] causality into higher forms of causality... These higher forms, which the child attains spontaneously, are... causality by identification of substance, the form modelled on the notions of condensation and rarefaction, and a certain primitive atomism or synthesis of the elements (*41*).

Plato (427–347 B.C.) is seen as the main villain in the opposition to science by Farrington, who considers that "the development of Natural Philosophy was violently interfered with by considerations that arose in . . . Platonic politics . . ." (*42*), and he argues that "the problem of the failure of ancient science from the point of view of the social structure of ancient society seems the true one" (*43*). Plato's political and religious theories continued to oppress the masses and prevented the assimilation of Ionian

science and its rooting amongst the artisans. The four elements were associated with four of the five regular solids by Plato, who was concerned
rather with the form of solids than with their content or matter and who
seems to have influenced directly the development of science to only a
small degree (44). The interconversion of the elements through their con-
stituent triangles, as envisaged by Plato in the *Timaeus*, occurs again in
Cardanus (1501–1576), who likewise saw transmutation between the
Platonic solids in terms of these planes (45). The tetrahedron appears in
Plato as Empedocles' element of fire (46), as it does later in Davidson
(1593–1669) (47), although Gassendi (1592–1655) associated this shape
with cold or cooling atoms (*atomos frigoris, aut frigorificas*) (48). The
tetrahedron has a long history in the development of chemistry (49). Whyte
has commented:

The satisfying Pythagorean representation of numbers as plane patterns of dots,
and the fascination exerted by regular three-dimensional patterns of points—such
as the vertices of the five regular solids—on such minds as Plato, Leonardo, Kepler,
and many others, led directly to static geometrical atomism, the interest in regular
atomic arrangements in crystals and elsewhere. However, Democritean atomism was
primarily concerned with change and movement, and Huygens, Newton, and Boscovich were respectively led to explore the possibilities of a kinetic, dynamical and
kinematic atomic physics (50).

Aristotle introduced the defining principle of *form* impressed upon
prime matter to characterise a substance, since he was unable to accept
that the random mingling process of the atomists could give rise to definite
and well defined arrangements. While the earlier Greeks had considered
the elements (or atoms) as the starting point and therefore the ordering
principle of matter, Aristotle was more concerned with causes as principles.
A useful summary of Aristotelian science has been given by Dijksterhuis
(51). But Aristotle unwittingly paved the way for atomism, since he left
an undeveloped minima theory (52), which led ultimately to a more organ-
ised atomism, and the medieval commentators were left with the problem
of the persistence of the elements in the compound in terms of these minima:
"the resulting compound being still potentially what it was before they
[the elements] were mixed and not destroyed . . . for their [the elements']
potentiality is preserved" (53).

Epicureanism is seen to be in contrast to the mechanical determinism of
Democritus and in opposition to the Platonic tradition, of a separation
of science from religion, of observed fact from authoritarian control. Not
only does Epicurus (341–270 B. C.) add weight to the atoms, but his views
were widely disseminated in Lucretius' poem "De Rerum Natura" (57
B. C.) in which Epicurus considers that a reciprocal association of move-
ments, *consociare motus* (54), distinguishes a particular *concilium* as a
stable compound. The question of the elements in the compound did not
become a problem in the mechanical atomism of the Epicureans, since
for them the elements were simply juxtaposed and just as readily disband-
ed. But the Stoics, consolidating the Platonic and Aristotelian traditions,
were more influential, and Meyerson sees the Scholastic dichotomy concerning this mixture of the elements to arise "because with some the purely

logical aspect of Aristotelianism prevails, whereas with others its properly
scientific theoretical aspect dominates" (55). At any rate, atomic and
minima theories did not die out, being discussed by Isidore of Seville
(560–636), the Venerable Bede (672–735), Hrabanus Maurus (776–856)
and Vincent de Beauvais (d. c. 1268), but they were not particularly influential (56). The scientific works of Aristotle were translated into Latin
in the twelfth century (57), at the same time as many other Greek and
Arabic sources were being translated, during the awakening of Europe.

For Avicenna (980–1037) the forms of the elements persist in the compound, but a new fused quality arises (58), a view acceptable in medical
circles and not enlarged upon in the *Canon*, which was to be the standard
medical work for some six centuries. Averroës (1126–1198) placed greater
emphasis on the minima of Aristotle as having physical significance, considering the forms of the elements to be fused into the new form of the
compound: "The first thing which becomes or perishes in the generation
or corruption of a substance is the smallest particle of this substance, for
the minimum of all that becomes is of limited quantity" (59).

Although the Averroist and Scotist emphasis on minima were perhaps
more important for science, Thomas Aquinas (1225–1274), the most influential medieval commentator on Aristotle, presented a third viewpoint.
Aquinas considers "some kind of mediant quality which is the quality
characteristic of the compound and which differs in different compounds
according to the different proportions of the combinations" (60). These
mediant qualities, as "grey which lies between white and black and as
does warm which lies between hot and cold" (61), led the Scotist Walter
Burleigh (c. 1275–c. 1345) later to suggest the analogy of the mule, which
has been used in the twentieth century concept of resonance (62). According to Dijksterhuis, Burleigh compared "the relation between a *mixtum*
and the elements . . . to the way in which a mule contains *in virtute* a horse
and a donkey; it resembles both but has the form neither of a horse
nor of a donkey" (63).

The equation of the elements with literal matter, although implicit
in Aristotle, began to be apparent in William of Conches (c. 1080—1145),
who fused together the ideas of Plato and Lucretius: "An element"
therefore, as Constantine says in the "Pantechne", "is a simple and minimum
part of any body, simple with respect to quality, minimum with respect
to quantity" (64). The influential Pietro d'Abano (1250–c. 1316) later
made the same emphasis in almost the same words (65) and added,
"we shall never know the quantities and weights of the elements in
compounds" (66), but he continued to refer to the *specific form* of
compounds in his classification of poisons (66). William of Conches defined
philosophy as "the true comprehensions of things which are and are not
seen, and of things which are and are seen", assuming that invisible
things, both corporeal and incorporeal, can be understood in terms of
the visible, and that causes may be inferred from the consideration of
effects. He distinguished the invisible elements (*elementa*) from an aggre-
gation of elements (*elementata*), water, for example, as we know it, being
elementata, formed from *elementa*. Hence he distinguishes between the

four *invisible* elements and their corresponding visible *elementata* (*67*). Burleigh adopted the view that minima were applicable only to heterogeneous matter, which was infinitely divisible: "We must, therefore, say that in homogeneous things maxima and minima are impossible, but this does not hold for heterogeneous things, such as living beings" (*68*).

The changing emphasis was enhanced by the discovery in 1417 by Poggio Bracciolini of a manuscript of the "De Rerum Natura", which was printed in 1473 and had a wide circulation. At the same time, the Platonist Nicholas of Cusa (1401–1464) supported Greek atomism with new arguments, extending those of the Aristotelian critic, Nicholas of Autrecourt, which led eventually to the atomism of Bruno. The Averroist emphasis on the minima theory had quietly paved the way for the acceptance of a corpuscular theory and the eventual establishment of the seventeenth century atomic mechanical philosophy.

The Paracelsian revival at the beginning of the sixteenth century introduced the three principles, or *tria prima*, from the four elements and heralded in a new critique both of Aristotelianism and of Scholasticism. Criticism of Medievalism came particularly from the point of view

of the development of ideas on scientific method and, in particular, on induction and experiment and on the role of mathematics in explaining physical phenomena, for they gradually led to an entirely different conception of the kind of question that should be asked in natural science, the kind of question, in fact, to which the experimental and mathematical methods could give an answer (*69*).*

Perhaps the foremost critic was Petrus Ramus (1515–1572),** who followed his master's examination with a violent attack on Aristotle in 1543 (*74*), the same year that the works of Copernicus and Vesalius appeared. Publication of these works of Ramus was prohibited, and the following year they were ordered to be burned (*75, 76*). Ramus' contribution to the development of science was to emphasise "the observation of nature instead of the idea of philosophers about nature" (*77*). Not only were the new scientific and philosophic insights significant, but these created the need for pedagogical reexamination, which is what Ramus did. Ong sees the order in the universe existing in the minds of Ramus' contemporaries sustained by a curriculum, rather than in terms of "logically" consistent sciences (*78*). Other opponents of Aristotle of scientific interest are Telesio,

---

* Burtt has drawn attention to the unimportance, for example, of the entities space and time for scholastic science since "spatial and temporal relations were accidental, not essential characteristics. Instead of spatial connexions of things, men were seeking their logical connexions; instead of the onward march of time, men thought of the eternal passage of potentiality into actuality" (*70*).

** Ramus is reputed, on tenuous evidence according to Ong (*71*), to have successfully defended in 1536 the master's thesis: "Quaecumque ab Aristotele dicta essent, commentitia esse". Ong prefers to paraphrase this as "All the things that Aristotle has said are inconsistent because they are poorly systematised and can be called to mind only by the use of arbitrary mnemonic devices" (*72*), rather than "...because they are false". Waddington (*73*) adopts this latter view and emphasises the anti-Aristotelian nature of Ramus' early thinking.

William Gilbert, Basso, and Gassendi, but many philosophers lent support
to both sides, and in 1624 "fourteen theses in opposition alike to the Para-
celsists, cabalists, and dogmatic Peripatetic physicists" (*79*) were suppressed
by the Parlement of Paris.

In the sixteenth century the transition from *minima* to *atom* neared
completion. The very influential Julius Caesar Scaliger (1484–1558) extensively used the minima, "the first particle of the compound" (*80*), *mixis*
or compound formation being an intimate fusion of Aristotelian and atomistic ideas:

> *Mixis* is the motion of the minima of bodies towards mutual contact, so that
> they may form a union. But our particles are not merely touching, as the Epicurean
> atoms, but they form a continuous body, which is a unity. It becomes unity through
> the continuity of its boundaries, which are common to everything in the compound,
> in this way excluding from the compound two classes (*81*).

Toletus (1532–1596) followed a similar emphasis, and in compound formation "the reagents are separated into natural minima, and the individual
minima are close to each other, and act upon each other, until a third
substance results with the form of the new compound" (*82*). Van Melsen
has considered that such sixteenth century opinions "are efforts to express,
without abandoning the Aristotelian unity of form in the compound,
something which we may call a structural concept, the construction of
a compound from its components" (*83*).

Partington has focussed attention on the simple experiment of the
deposition of copper on an iron knife blade from a copper salt solution
(*84*). This apparent transmutation of iron into copper, known since the
time of Pliny (23–79), was explained only about 1600 by van Helmont,
who asserted the existence of copper in the blue salt and its displacement
by iron. Multhauf (*85*) has emphasised the earlier role of the medical chemists, from John of Rupescissa (fourteenth century), and has assigned
to distillation chemistry a central role. Attention was slowly directed to
chemical species, both in terms of the distillates as well as of the residues,
and the preparation of compounds for medicine was beneficial to the development of chemistry.

Atomism continued in the writings of Bruno (1548–1600) and Bodin
(1530–1596), although Libavius (1540–1616) stood out from the atomic
movement by viewing atoms with disfavour. Francis Bacon (1561–1626)
held atomistic ideas from the time of his contact with the Northumberland
Circle (*86*), but changed his views by the time of the "Novum Organum"
(1620). While Partington accepts this change (*87*, *88*), Harrison does not
(*89*), and Boas (*90*) sees Bacon's protest (*91*) merely as a plea against a
purely speculative atomism. The Earl of Northumberland saw that "the
Doctrine of Generation and Corruption unfoldeth to our understandings
the method general of all atomical combinations possible in homogeneal
substances, together with the ways possible of generating of the same
substances ... with all the accidents and qualities rising from these generated substances ..." (*92*). Nicholas Hill's "Philosophia Epicurea" (*93*)
seems to have been the first modern work actively proposing the ancient

atomic theories (*94*), and Hill (*c.* 1570–1610), as Secretary to Edward de Vere, Earl of Oxford, subsequently had some sort of connexion with the Earl of Northumberland (*95*).

Sennert (1572–1637) attempted to weld together the minima and atomic theories, which he derived through Asklepiades (b. 124 B. C.), whose medical theories were influenced by Epicureanism. Sennert's mechanistic outlook was modified by a spiritual principle, *Natura quinta*, while still retaining the four elements of Aristotle and the Paracelsian *tria prima*. There is some evidence that Sennert was acquainted with Basso's atomism (*96*), and he adopts Scaliger's definition of compound formation that "the movement of the minima of bodies towards mutual contact, leads to unity" (*97*), as also did Gorlaeus (1592/1–1612) (*98*).

Sennert's building blocks are "corpora minima naturae, atomi, atoma corpuscula, corpora indivisibilia" (*99*), although an earlier work contains no mention of atoms (*100*). He requires "a higher form of the compound" (*101*) to avoid the formation of mere aggregates, so that "elements and simple bodies preserve their whole nature in compounds [which] is the key to almost all natural science" (*102*). Unlike Sennert, Basso, in the "Philosophia naturalis", which was widely read by his contemporaries, opposed the Aristotelian theory of forms and supposed the constituents of compounds to have an *actual* existence (*103*). He gave the first explicit account that atoms form corpuscles of varying degrees of complexity (*104*).

Jungius (1587–1657), who knew Sennert's "De Chymicorum . . ." (1619), may have had some influence on Boyle's later work, and his views in some respects are very similar to those of Boyle. He considered that mere mechanical juxtaposition was not enough to account for chemical change, which involved a greater cohesion (*105*). Although he considered attraction and cohesion between the atoms in a compound (*106*), he had little direct influence on his contemporaries. He foreshadowed isomerism in terms of differing arrangements of letters which represented atoms (*107*); Gassendi (1592–1655) also used this literary analogy (*108*).

The philosophy of Descartes (1596–1650) shows a complete break with the scholastic tradition, and this resulted in his works being placed on the Index in Rome and Paris in 1671. For him, the nature of a body consists in extension, with features of dimension (including weight and velocity), unity, and figure (*109*). In Descartes we see the mathematisation of matter, and his ideas are important for the understanding of the works of Boyle, Mayow, and Lemery, *inter alia*, chemists who represent the beginnings of the later period.

In 1215 the statutes of the University of Paris had forbidden the teaching of Aristotle's "Physica" and "Metaphysica", though at the same time Albertus Magnus (1206–1280) was basing his scientific work on Aristotelian principles (*110*). However, in 1624 the Parlement of Paris confirmed the censure of the medical and theological faculties and decreed that no one should hold or teach any doctrine contrary to Aristotle, on penalty of death (*111*, *112*). Gassendi's anti-Aristotelian work (*113*) was suppressed. He held atomic and molecular views based on Epicureanism (*114*) and referred specifically to molecules: "Thus the elements of things are atoms, from which the smallest first concretions or molecules are constructed" (*115*). The importance of Gassendi for atomism is indicated in the title of a work by Charleton (*116*).

In the work of Boyle (1627–1691) is found the consolidation of the new experimental mechanical philosophy and the integration of chemistry with natural philosophy (*117*). Partington sees the first application of atomism to chemistry in the writings of Boyle, Mayow, Lemery, and Hartsoeker (*118*). The crude Greek atomism has been moulded into a more sophisticated system, which is adaptable to the later trends of the eighteenth and nineteenth centuries. An early terminology, which had been largely based on physical properties such as colour, crystalline form, taste, and smell (*119*), had, in the hands of Boyle, a new *chemical* basis, the typical and characteristic reactions of a compound. The purification and isolation of substances, developed particularly during the sixteenth century, necessitated consideration of chemical as well as physical characteristics.

In "The Origine of Formes and Qualities" Boyle distinguished the atoms, *Minima*, or *Prima Naturalia* from a coalition of several of these, "Primitive Concretions or Clusters of Particles" (*120*).

> For if we assign to the corpuscles, whereof each element consists, a peculiar size and shape, it may easily enough be manifested, that such differingly figured corpuscles may be mingled in such various proportions, and may be connected so many several ways, that an almost incredible number of variously qualified concretes may be composed of them (*121*).

While chemists were ready to accept the mechanical philosophy, they were reticent about using it in chemical theory. As Boas has remarked, "Eighteenth-century chemists nearly always distinguished between physical principles—ultimate particles—and chemical principles—elements . . . One could, that is, accept as physically true a particulate structure of matter . . . without necessarily making any use of it in discussing chemical composition or chemical reaction" (*122*). This is the emphasis placed by Cullen, in a number of his extant manuscripts, that the notion of atoms was so speculative and ill-defined that they were of little use in chemistry (*123*). Lavoisier likewise avoided discussing these particles that could not be discovered experimentally, although he was cognisant of atomic explanation.

In the history of ideas the continuity of thought about many modern concepts has a long history which should not be ignored nor left untaught. Particularly in a liberal arts framework this earlier period can be richly explored in order to see the interactions of many disciplines which are considered separately today. In this paper only one aspect has been considered.

Acknowledgements

The author is very indebted to Dr. W. P. D. Wightman, F. R. S. E., for suggestions and comments and to Notre Dame University of Nelson, British Columbia, Canada, for a sabbatical leave spent at the University of Aberdeen.

Literature Cited

(1) Foster, Sir M., "Lectures on the History of Physiology", p. 1, Cambridge, 1901
(2) Ihde, A. J., "The Development of Modern Chemistry", Harper, New York, 1964, covers largely the period from about 1750.
(3) Crombie, A. C., *Hist. Sci.*, **1**, 59 (1962).
(4) Multhauf, R. P., "The Origins of Chemistry", Oldbourne, London, 1966 is the best account. See also Stillman, J. M., "The Story of Early Chemistry", Appleton, New York, 1924; Partington, J. R., "A History of Chemistry", 4 vols., Macmillan, London; Vol. 1, unpublished to date, will deal with chemistry to 1500, Vol. 2 (1961) includes the period from 1550 to Boyle.
(5) Walden, P., *J. Chem. Educ.*, **29**, 386–391 (1952).
(6) Hughes, A., *Ann. Sci.*, **8**, 323 (1952).
(7) Leicester, H. M., "The Historical Background of Chemistry", John Wiley and Sons, New York, 1956.
(8) *Ibid.*, Preface, p. vi.
(9) Wightman, W. P. D., "The Growth of Scientific Ideas", p. 3, Oliver and Boyd, Edinburgh and London, 1950.
(10) Buchdahl, G., *Hist. Sci.*, **1**, 62–6 (1962).
(11) Crombie, A. C., *Hist. Sci.*, **1**, 57–61 (1962).
(12) Wightman, W. P. D., ref. (9), preface, p. vi.
(13) Crombie, A. C., and Hoskin, M. A., in "Scientific Change", ed. by A. C. Crombie, pp. 757–64, Heinemann, London, 1963; and also in the ensuing discussion, pp. 768–88.
(14) de Milt, Clara, *J. Chem. Educ.*, **29**, 340 (1952).
(15) Larder, D. F., *Improving College and University Teaching*, **XV**, 76–9, 86–7 (1967).
(16) Hutchinson, E., *J. Chem. Educ.*, **44**, 261 (1967).
(17) Ashby, E., *Impact*, **9**, 45 (1958).
(18) Hutchinson, E., *loc. cit*, p. 263.
(19) Caldin, E. F., "The Structure of Chemistry", p. 5 *et passim*, Sheed and Ward, London, 1961.
(20) Lasswitz, K., "Geschichte der Atomistik", 2 vols., Verlag von Leopold Voss, Leipzig, 1926.
(21) van Melsen, A. G., "From Atomos to Atom: The History of the Concept Atom", Duquesne University Press, Pittsburgh, 1952.
(22) Paneth, F. A., *Brit. J. Phil. Sci.*, **13**, 1–14, 144–160 (1962); trans. by H. R. Paneth from *Schriften der Königsberger Gelehrten Gesellschaft*, Naturwissenschaftliche Klasse, 1931, Heft 4.
(23) McKeon, R., in "The Dignity of Science", ed. by J. A. Weisheipl, O. P., pp. 75–120, The Thomist Press, 1961.
(24) Anaxagoras, fragment 10, in Diels, H., "Die Fragmente der Vorsokratiker", Vol. 1, p. 403, Weidmannsche Buchhandlung, Berlin, 1922; translations below from Diels taken from Freeman, K., "Ancilla to the Pre-Socratic Philosophers", Basil Blackwood, Oxford, 1952.
(25) Paneth, F. A., *loc. cit.*, p. 9.
(26) Boas, Marie, *Osiris*, **10**, 412–541 (1958).
(27) Taton, R., ed., "Ancient and Medieval Science", trans. by A. J. Pomerans, Thames and Hudson, London, 1963.
(28) Multhauf, R. P., *op. cit.*, particularly ch. 2, pp. 39–51.

(29) Parmenides, fr. 7, 8 in Diels, *op. cit.*, p. 153 *f*.

(30) Empedocles, fr. 8, in Diels, *op. cit.*, p. 226.

(31) Aristotle, "De Gen. et Corrupt.", 314b, 7. Aristotle's works are taken from the Loeb Classical Library, William Heineman, London (Greek-English editions) and are cited with reference to the Berlin text of I. Bekker, 1831; Oxford, 1837; by page, column, and line. "De Gen. et Corrupt.", trans. by E. S. Forster; "De Caelo", by W. K. C. Guthrie; "Physica", (2 vols.), by P. Wicksteed and F. M. Cornford.

(32) *Ibid.*, 333b, 17–21.

(33) *Ibid.*, 334a, 26–30.

(34) Anaxagoras, fr. 17, in Diels, *op. cit.*, p. 407.

(35) *Ibid.*, fr. 11, in Diels, *op. cit.*, p. 404.

(36) Aristotle, "De Caelo", A. 10. 279.

(37) Lucretius, "de Rerum Natura", ii, 1. 102; in "T. Lucreti Cari, De Rerum Natura, Libri Sex", trans. by H. A. J. Munro, 4th ed., Cambridge, 1891.

(38) Aristotle, "De Gen. et Corrupt.", 314a, 23–26.

(39) Piaget, J., "The Child's Conception of the World", *passim*, Harcourt, Brace and Co., New York, 1929.

(40) Horne, R. A., *J. Chem. Educ.*, **35**, 561 (1958).

(41) Piaget, J., *op. cit.*, in Horne, R. A., *loc. cit.*, p. 560.

(42) Farrington, B., "Science and Politics in the Ancient World", p. 14, Unwin University Books, London, 2nd ed., 1965.

(43) *Ibid.*, p. 24.

(44) Benfey, O. T., and Fikes, L., in "Kekulé Centennial", pp. 111–128, American Chemical Society, Washington, 1966 (Advances in Chemistry Series No. 61).

(45) Cardani, Hieronymi, "De Rerum Varietate libri XVII", *Lib.* XIII, *Cap.* LXIII, Basileae, 1557. For a note on the editions of this work see Larder, D. F., *Isis*, **59**, 74–77 (1968).

(46) Plato, "Timaeus", 56a.

(47) Davidson, W., "Les Elemens de la Philosophie de l'Art du Feu ou Chemie", pp. 627–9, Paris, 1651; trans. by J. Heleot from the Latin of 1633–5.

(48) Gassendi, P., "Physica", *Sect.* I, *Lib.* VI, *Cap.* VI; in "Opera Omnia", 6 vols., edited by C. N. Averanio, Florence, 1727; Vol. I, p. 349.

(49) Larder, D. F., *J. Chem. Educ.*, **44**, 661–6 (1967).

(50) Whyte, L. L., "Essay on Atomism: From Democritus to 1960", p. 39, Thomas Nelson and Sons, London, 1961.

(51) Dijksterhuis, E. J., "The Mechanisation of the World Picture", pp. 17–42, Clarendon Press, Oxford, 1961; trans. by C. Dikshoorn from the Dutch ed. of 1950.

(52) Aristotle, "Physica", 187b, 30 to 188a, 1.

(53) Aristotle, "De Gen. et Corrupt.", 327b, 24–31.

(54) Lucretius, "de Rerum Natura", ii, 1, 111; in Munro, *op. cit.*

(55) Meyerson, E., "Identity and Reality", p. 327, Dover Publications, Inc., New York, 1962; trans. by Kate Loewenberg from the 3rd French ed., 1926.

(56) Stones, G. B., *Isis*, **10**, 445–65 (1928).

(57) Crombie, A. C., "Augustine to Galileo: The History of Sciences A. D. 400–1650", pp. 27–8, Falcon Press, London, 1952.

(58) Multhauf, R. P., *op. cit.*, pp. 122, 149.

(59) Averroës, "Physica", VI, comm. 32; in van Melsen, ref. (21), p. 60.

(60) Aquinas, Thomas, "De mixtione elementorum", trans. by Larkin, V. R., in *Isis*, **51**, 67–72 (1960); p. 72 cited.

(61) *Ibid.*, p. 71.

(62) Wheland, G. W., "Resonance in Organic Chemistry", p. 4, John Wiley and Sons, Inc., New York, 1955.

(63) Dijksterhuis, E. J., *op. cit.*, p. 203.

(64) William of Conches, "De Philosophia Mundi", I, 21, PL172, 48D–9A; in McKeon, *loc. cit.*, p. 99; see also Lasswitz, *op. cit.*, Vol. 1, p. 74, note.

(65) Pietro d'Abano, "Conciliator Controversiarum..." (1565), *Differentia* XI, Bibliographical detail in Wightman, W. P. D., "Science and the Renaissance", Vol. 2, pp. 191–2, Oliver and Boyd, Edinburgh and London, 1962.

(66) Pietro d'Abano, "Libellus de Venenis", ch. 1, attached to "Conciliator", ref. (65). "de Venenis" probably dated 1316 (Thorndike, L., "History of Magic and Experimental Science", Vol. 2, pp. 935–8, Columbia University Press, New York, 1923).
(67) McKeon, R., loc. cit., pp. 96–7, 101.
(68) Burlaei, Gault, "De Physica Auscultatione Commentaria", p. 70A, Venetiis, 1589; in van Melsen, ref. (21), p. 62.
(69) Crombie, A. C., "Augustine to Galileo...", op. cit., p. 212.
(70) Burtt, E. A., "The Metaphysical Foundations of Modern Physical Science", p. 13, Harcourt, Brace and Company, Inc., New York, 1925.
(71) Ong, W. J., "Ramus, Method, and the Decay of Dialogue", pp. 36–41, Harvard University Press, Cambridge, Massachusetts, 1958.
(72) Ibid., pp. 45–7.
(73) Waddington, C., "Ramus, sa vie, ses écrits, et ses opinions", p. 29, Paris, 1855.
(74) Ramus, Petrus, "Dialecticae Institutiones", and "Aristotelicae Animadversiones" (1543); facsimile ed. with introduction by W. Risse, Friedrich Frommann Verlag, Stuttgart-Bad Cannstatt, 1964.
(75) Stones, G. B., Isis, 10, 449 (1928).
(76) Hooykaas, R., "Humanisme, Science et Réforme. Pierre de la Ramée (1515–1572)", p. 3, E. J. Brill, Leyden, 1958.
(77) Ibid., p. 126.
(78) Ong, W. J., op. cit., p. 306.
(79) Thorndike, L., op. cit., Vol. 6, p. 388 (1941); also chap. 42, pp. 363–389.
(80) Scaliger, J. C., "Exotericarum Exercitationum Libri XV de Subtilitate ad Hieronymum Cardanum", Exerc. 16, Paris, 1557.
(81) Ibid., Exerc. 101.
(82) Toleti, D. Francisci, "Commentaria, una cum Quaestionibus, In Lib. Arist. de Gen. et Corrupt.", Lib. I, cap. 10, q. 9, Cologne, 1577.
(83) van Melsen, A. G., op. cit., p. 72.
(84) Partington, J. R., Chymia, 1, 110 (1948).
(85) Multhauf, R. P., op. cit., particularly pp. 201–236.
(86) Kargon, R. H., "Atomism in England from Hariot to Newton", pp. 43–53, Clarendon Press, Oxford, 1966.
(87) Partington, J. R., "A History of Chemistry", Vol. 2, pp. 395–6, Macmillan, London, 1961.
(88) Partington, J. R., Ann. Sci., 4, 267 (1939).
(89) Harrison, C. T., Harvard Studies and Notes in Philology and Literature, XV, 191–218 (1933).
(90) Boas, Marie, Osiris, 10, 439 (1958).
(91) Bacon, Francis, "Novum Organum", Aphorism lxvi; "The Works of Francis Bacon", ed. by J. Spedding, R. L. Ellis, and D. D. Heath, Vol. IV, pp. 66–8, London, 1858.
(92) Percy, Henry, "Advice to His Son" (1609), ed. by G. B. Harrison, p. 70, Ernest Benn, Ltd., London, 1930.
(93) Hill, N., "Philosophia Epicurea, Democritiana, Theophrastica, proposita simpliciter, non edocta", Paris, 1601; Geneva, 1619.
(94) McColley, G., Ann. Sci., 4, 390–1 (1939).
(95) Ibid., p. 392.
(96) Partington, J. R., op. cit., Vol. 2, p. 273.
(97) Sennert, D., "De Chymicorum...", cap. XII; in "Operum Omnia", Vol. 3. p. 779, Lyons, 1650.
(98) Gorlaeus, D., "Exercitatione Philosophiae...", p. 248, Lugd-Batavorum, 1620; and his "Idea Physicae...", pp. 38, 42, Utrecht, 1651.
(99) Sennert, D., "Physica Hypomnemata", Hypomnema III, cap. I, p. 81, Lyons, 1637.
(100) Sennert, D., "Epitome Naturalis Scientiae", 1633; 1st ed., 1618.
(101) Sennert, D., "Physica Hypomnemata", Hypomnema III, cap. II, p. 112.
(102) Ibid., pp. 112–3.
(103) Basso, S., "Philosophia Naturalis adversus Aristotelem Libri XII", Lib. II, Intentio III, Art. I, pp. 26f, Geneva, 1621.

(104) *Ibid., Intentio* I, *Art.* I, pp. 79, 126.

(105) Jungius, J., "Doxoscopiae Physicae Minores", Part II, Sect. I, *cap.* 16, *Assert.* XXV, Hamburgi, 1662.

(106) *Ibid., cap.* 17, *Assert. passim.*

(107) Jungius, J., "Disputationum de principus corporum naturalium", *Disputatione* I, 76, Hamburg, 1642; trans. into German in E. Wohlwill, "Joachim Jungius und die Erneuerung atomischer Lehren im 17. Jahrhundert", *Abhandlung aus dem Gebiete der naturwissenschaftlichen Verein in Hamburg*, X, 1–66 (1887).

(108) Gassendi, P., "Physica", *Sect.* I, *Lib.* V, *Cap.* VII; in "Opera Omnia", *op. cit.*, Vol. 1, p. 322.

(109) Descartes, R., "The Philosophical Works of Descartes", trans. by E. S. Haldane and G. R. T. Ross, Vol. 2, pp. 61 *ff.*, University Press, Cambridge, 1911.

(110) Greenwood, T., *Archeion*, **14**, 69–70 (1932).

(111) Lasswitz, K., *op. cit.*, Vol. 1, pp. 482–7.

(112) Thorndike, L., *op. cit.*, Vol. 7, *passim* (1958).

(113) Gassendi, P., "Exercitatione Paradoxicae Adversus Aristoteleos", 1624; in "Opera Omnia", *op. cit.*, Vol. 3, pp. 99–193.

(114) Gassendi, P., "Philosophiae Epicuri", *Sect.* I, *cap.* XVII; in "Opera Omnia", *op. cit.*, Vol. 3, p. 23.

(115) Gassendi, P., "Physica", *Sect.* I, *Lib.* V, *Cap.* VII; in "Opera Omnia", *op. cit.*, Vol. 1, p. 322 *et passim.*

(116) Charleton, W., "Physiologica Epicuro-Gassendo-Charltoniana: or A Fabrick of Science Natural upon the Hypothesis of Atoms", London, 1654.

(117) Boas, Marie, "Robert Boyle and Seventeenth Century Chemistry", University Press, Cambridge, 1958.

(118) Partington, J. R., *Ann. Sci.*, **4**, 247 (1939).

(119) Crosland, M. P., "Historical Studies in the Language of Chemistry", pp. 65–78, Heinemann, London, 1962.

(120) Boyle, R., "The Origine of Formes and Qualities", 2nd ed., p. 47, Oxford, 1667.

(121) Boyle, R., "The Sceptical Chymist", p. 32, Everyman's Library ed., J. M. Dent and Sons, Ltd., London, 1911.

(122) Boas, Marie, in "Critical Problems in the History of Science", ed. by M. Clagett, p. 500, University of Wisconsin Press, Madison, 1959.

(123) Wightman, W. P. D., personal communication. See also his second Cullen article in *Ann. Sci.*, **12**, 194 (1956).

15. USES OF THE PAST

Henry A. Bent*

Department of Chemistry, North Carolina State University at Raleigh,
Raleigh, North Carolina, U.S.A.

Teaching chemistry from an historical point of view has a number of attractive features. Because it focuses attention on the creative side of science—on science in the making, on the invention of concepts rather than their formal mathematical manipulation, on controversies and misconceptions, and (not least of all) on people—and because (therefore) it is relatively nonmathematical (in the conventional sense of the word), it appeals to a broad spectrum of students, particularly those with creative abilities. It presents opportunities to use facts agressively—to capture hypotheses—rather than passively—to illustrate theories. It seeks to resolve complexity, not to conceal it. It offers for study genuine examples of inductive-deductive reasoning. Probably it is the only way to illustrate fully the "scientific method". It is simple and inexpensive to administer, requires relatively little class time, and is a sure guarantee against an incorrect or illogical procedure. Yet it is little used today, partly, perhaps, because it is felt that, as Dirac once said, all of chemistry is in principle solved (therefore the past is uninteresting, scientifically), but chiefly, probably, because it is more difficult than less scholarly treatments—for the teacher, not the student.

Teaching elementary chemistry from an historical viewpoint has a number of attractive features. Most importantly,

It is Interesting

During a lecture on chemical thermodynamics several years ago to a large class of sophomore engineers, a power-failure plunged our windowless classroom into darkness. After the initial laughter had subsided somewhat and further discussion of heat engines had been boisterously voted down, the class elected to listen to an informal account of the lives of the founders of thermodynamics. Probably they wished to feel free to leave the room— or to sleep there—in peace. When the lights came on a quiet half-hour later, however, they were mostly still present—wide awake. Evidently, in small doses, the historical approach is interesting, even to engineers. And that is important. "For amusement is a good preparation for study", observed Mark Twain, "and a good healer of fatigue after it" (1).

Generally, the success of a lecture is gauged by the factual information "covered" in class. Yet seldom does a student spend as many hours in class as he does outside it. What he learns in class may be important. What he learns (or does not learn) outside class is more important. Does he study

* Work done at Department of Chemistry, University of Minnesota, Minneapolis, Minnesota, U.S.A.

two hours a week or ten? That is the question. Covering half as much material, interestingly, in class may stimulate the student to cover five times as much, eagerly, outside class *"Less may be More"* (*2*).

Thinking Creatively

The historical approach has another attractive feature not possessed in equal measure by a nonhistorical, deductive, orderly and logical, safe and non-controversial, dogmatic, here-it-is-boys-and-girls-now-learn-how-to-use-it approach, which, in its extreme form, views science as merely "a collection of mathematical theories adorned with a few facts" (*3*).

The historical approach can develop skill in creative thinking. It can offer genuine examples of inductive reasoning, of reasoning divergently, analogically, and innovatively, of guessing and making plausible inferences, "which is the only kind of reasoning for which we care in everyday affairs" (*4*), because, in fact, it is the only kind of reasoning that leads to essentially new knowledge. "Pure logical thinking cannot yield us any knowledge of the empirical world" (*5*). To be useful, logic must have something to be logical about; it must have axioms, postulates, premises, or hypotheses to work on. But how does one secure, invent, discover, or "catch" an axiom or hypothesis? There is no logical way, Einstein has said. For hypothesis-catching, pure logic is like Lewis-Carroll's map for catching snarks, "A perfect and absolute blank" (*6*).

Put another way, the historical approach can encourage creative thinking by offering for emulation concrete examples of generalizing, of searching for similarities among differences, of reasoning from facts to ideas, which is important, for "generalization can only be reached from details" (*7*) by induction, for which there are no formal rules.

Reverence for Facts

The previous remarks may be put still differently. The historical approach views chemistry as an inductive-deductive system based upon experimental facts. It uses facts aggressively to "capture" hypotheses. The nonhistorical approach views chemistry as (ideally) a deductive system based upon the laws of physics. It uses facts indifferently to illustrate captive hypotheses. The historical approach seeks modestly to interpret nature. The nonhistorical approach seeks boldly to anticipate nature. It is one-upmanship on nature. Theories, it implies, are "the source of information instead of the receptacle for it" (*8*). Take Bohr's theory, however. Bohr did not predict that atoms would be stable and that the ionization potential of hydrogen would be 13.61 volts. He assumed the former and interpreted the latter.

With time, the historical approach produces "a certain preference for the matter of fact" (*4*), but, at the same time, a dissatisfaction, possibly even, as with Darwin, "a fine contempt for work that merely describes things without showing their connections" (*9*). Not least of all, the historical approach fosters a critical attitude toward scientific hypotheses. That is important, particularly in the physical sciences, where "training in the art of reasoning is likely to produce nothing but overrefinement, which accepts indifferently postulates foolish and wise" (9).

Handling Complexity

Generally, a nonhistorical approach tends to conceal complexity (10). The historical approach seeks to resolve complexity. That is one of its more attractive features. Through concrete examples,

The historical approach can illustrate how to work creatively within the "actual disorder of experience" (11).

An excellent example, in biology, is Darwin's work; in chemistry, Mendeleev's. Such work requires a willingness, and ability, to seek solutions to separate problems while keeping an eye on a larger goal.

Guarded Optimism

To work many years with a great store of partially processed data under the "checks and balances of earthly reality" (12) and under the constant tensions of unsolved paradoxes and unanswered, and perhaps unanswerable, questions, requires deep-rooted optimism tempered with restraint. Sometimes, Berzelius has said, it may be necessary "to leave that which is incomprehensible unexplained until the explanation comes of itself from facts so clear that divided opinions concerning them can scarcely remain" (13).

Similarly, Dirac has said, "I should like to suggest that one not worry too much about this controversy [in quantum mechanics]. I feel very strongly that the stage physics has reached at the present day is not the final stage. . . . The present stage of physical theory is merely a stepping stone toward the better stages we shall have in the future. One can be quite sure that there will be better stages simply because of the difficulties that occur in the physics today" (14).

Selection and Classification

Specifically,

The historical approach can show how to reduce complexity through intelligent classification of facts.

Lavoisier's nomenclature and the nomenclature of organic chemistry, Goldschmidt's work on crystal structures, and again, the works of Darwin and Mendeleev, are excellent examples of inspired classifications. G. P. Thomson asserts that, "performed consciously or unconsciously, the act

9 Teaching the History of Chemistry

of classification is indispensible to and accompanies every scientific infer-
ence" (*15*).

Even more fundamental than classification is the prior act of screening,
sorting, and evaluating. Kekulé supported his wide-sweeping generalization
regarding the valence of carbon, for example, with eight carefully selected
examples (*16*).

> *The history of scientific discoveries shows that "selection is essential [in
> science] as in all arts"* (*15*).

Still, what guides selection? How can one know whether he is selecting
wisely?

Ideally, a selector should be "intimately familiar both with the subject
matter and with the techniques employed to supply the relevant information" (*17*). Practically, such selectors do not exist, simply because

> there is much more to know than any of us are ever going to catch up with; and
> this is not just the trivial fact that we don't work hard enough; it is not the trivial
> fact that things are difficult to learn. It is that any form of knowledge really precludes
> other forms; that any serious study of one thing cuts out some other part of your
> life (*18*).

A good description of the Problem of Selection, whose solution determines the success of an interpretive study, has been given by Mulliken,
in recent remarks regarding the interpretation of internuclear distances
in chemical compounds:

> The greatest difficulty of all may be that it is almost impossible for any one
> individual to collect and to keep in view all at once the now extremely large and
> very varied mass of both experimental and theoretical evidence, all of which must
> be most cautiously and critically and simultaneously evaluated if he is to reach
> sensible conclusions (*19*).

Still, a problem's charm lies in such difficulties. The beauty of a scientific
generalization, like the beauty of any artistic creation, lies in the order
achieved compared with the complexity summarized (*11, 20*).

Tremendous Trifles

But if students have no sense of the underlying complexity, if they
have no knowledge of the facts of life, scientific generalizations such as
the Second Law of Thermodynamics, for example, or the equations of
quantum mechanics may appear more monstrous than beautiful. Again,
the historical approach can help. In its emphasis on facts as the source
of ideas,

> *The historical approach can help students discover—or rediscover—the "divin-
> ity in simple things"* (*11*).

It can help them "to recognize a miracle [the absolute irreversibility of
natural events, for example, or the stability of molecules] even if [they]
see it everyday" (*7*).

Indeed, "It is the greatest discovery in method which science has made", writes G. P. Thomson, "that the apparently trivial, the merely curious, may be clues to an understanding of the deepest principles of Nature" (*15*). Of Darwin it has been said, similarly, that

the noblest lessons [he] left to the world is this, —which to him amounted to a profound, almost religious conviction, —that every fact in nature, no matter how insignificant, every stripe of color, every tint of flowers, the length of an orchid's nectary, unusual height in a plant, all the infinite variety of apparently insignificant things, is full of significance. For him it was a historical record, the revelation of a cause, the lurking place of a principle (*9*).

"Like every other endeavor, the beginning [in science] is in small things" (*21*).

The Invisible Method

These "small things", so important to science, are usually invisible to outsiders. What philosophers, logicians, and young students of science usually see in science are its broad generalizations. As with artistic creations, generally, the beginnings—and the processes by which, gradually, the beginnings become objects of public interest—are seldom seen. Short of actually participating in a research problem,

The only way an outsider can gain an appreciation of the scientific method is through a study of specific examples drawn from the historical record.

How else can one see, outside the laboratory, the differences between a highly dynamic, unsettled, research science like chemistry and an apparently more nearly static, finished: fossilized science like planetary mechanics, geometrical optics, or classical thermodynamics?

The examples selected to illustrate the "scientific method" may be ancient or modern (*22, 23*). Usually the latter are easier to present interestingly to young, semisophisticated students. Either type of example will generally illustrate that science changes, although seldom in a straight line. Probably,

The historical approach is the only approach that can illustrate fully the slow (24), crooked (25) course of scientific progress.

This approach will not appeal to students who want to know right off that "the butler did it". Its appeal is more to those who, like Robert Frost, "enjoy the straight crookedness of a good walking stick" (*26*).

Relation to Physics

Interestingly,

The historical approach shows that progress in theoretical chemistry has generally not followed the conventional pattern often prescribed by philosophers of science.

Chemical progress has been more evolutionary than revolutionary (*27*). The physicist asks, "How frequently must our ideas about the structure

9*

of matter be revolutionized?" (*28*). The chemist asks, "What will be the
next approximation?" (*29*).

Since 1860 chemists have not been *testing* the atomic hypothesis. They
have been *refining* it. Gradually, the atom has acquired definite mass,
affinity hooks, directed valencies, electric charges, charged corpuscles,
a serial number, a kernel, a valence shell, shared electrons, unshared
electrons, wave-like electrons, and spinning electrons. It has been a very
adaptable atom, to some an "indecently changeful atom" (*30*).

For every advance was unexpected. Every advance was directly contradictory to the physics of the time. How could two similar, uncharged atoms
attract each other, as Avogadro postulated? How could the direction of an
attractive force be independent of the position of the attracted body, as
van't Hoff seemed to postulate? (*31*). (Worse yet, how could the attractive
forces in unsaturated compounds not even be directed toward the attracted
bodies? (*32*).) How could Werner's coordination compounds stick together?
(*33*). How could Lewis's electrons stay in place? One comes to feel that,
perhaps,

*The great psychological lesson of history for chemists is the realization that
every important step forward in structural theory has violated accepted physical
principles.*

To violate accepted principles and yet to be "right", *i.e.*, "useful", is the
touchstone of an important advance.

Newton's Advice

"One does not get anywhere simply by going over the successes again
and again", Dirac has said (*14*). Yet scientists have always tried to account
for chemical phenomena in terms of known physical forces. That may be
putting the cart before the horse. Until recently, at least,

*History has supported Newton's view that "We must learn from the Phaeno-
mena of Nature what Bodies attract one another, before we enquire the Cause
by which the Attractions is perform'd"* (*34*).

"And although the arguing from Experiments and observations by
Induction be no Demonstration of general conclusions", Newton continues,
"yet it is the best way of arguing which the Nature of Things admits of . . ."

Controversy's Contribution

Of course, when Demonstration is lacking, and even when it is not
(*35*), there may be differences of opinion. Although not usually discussed
in textbooks,

Controversy, history shows, has always played an important part in science
(*36*).

Through repetition of arguments and multiplication of communications, it insures that the message gets through (*37*). With good theories, any publicity is good publicity. Official attacks on Laviosier's nomenclature (*38*), Dalton's condemnation of Berzelius's chemical shorthand (*39*), Kolbe's tirade against van't Hoff's three-dimensional formulas (*40*), and Henry Armstrong's fulminations against Lewis's "love-pair" (*41*), "bigamous hydrogen", Arrhenius's ions (*42*), and the Braggs' model of sodium chloride helped to bring these useful ideas to the attention of the scientific community.

The Human Side

As a by-product of discussions of controversies,

The historical approach can show young students that even the chiefs of science make mistakes.

Certainly it can do the self-confidence of young scientists no harm to discover that to the end Priestley believed in phlogiston (*23*) and Lavoisier in caloric (*38*); that Dalton disbelieved Gay-Lussac's law on combining volumes (*43*); that Mendeleev and Werner believed in the existence of elements lighter than hydrogen (*44*); that as a student van't Hoff, by his own admission, was never able to understand the real import of Avogadro's law (*45*) and that later he based his famous laws of solution upon a false analogy (*46*); that Ostwald did not believe in atoms into the twentieth century; that Kelvin had great difficulty in accepting Joule's results on the mechanical equivalent of heat (*47*); and that, initially, Bragg, through a misinterpretation of the atomic volume curve for the elements, concluded that an alkali ion was larger than the neighboring halogen ion. "Looking back . . . over the long labyrinth ion path which finally led to the discovery [of the quantum theory]", writes Planck, "I am vividly reminded of Goethe's saying that men will always be making mistakes as long as they are striving after something" (*35*).

Nor can it help but interest young students contemplating careers in science to learn that as a student Darwin received "no inspiration and very little knowledge" from his medical courses; that he felt there were "no advantages and many disadvantages in lectures compared with reading" (*9*); and that in his own view he had "no great quickness of apprehension or wit", that his power "to follow a long and purely abstract train of thought [was] very limited", and "So poor in one sense is my memory", he wrote, "that I have never been able to remember for more than a few days a single date or a line of poetry . . ." (*48*).

By such citations,

The historical approach can balance the traditional commitment in science courses "to orderly reasoning and the rhetoric of intelligence, which dehumanizes its subject" (11).

In addition,

The historical approach may provide students with critically important biographical and autobiographical information.

"Clearly the desire for a short autobiographical essay of his heroes is legitimate in one about to devote his life to a continuation of the work they began" (*49*). Students of chemistry may be interested to learn, for example, that van't Hoff, one of the founders of physical chemistry, "with no great mathematical or experimental attainment, with no striking gift as a teacher"—and with a dislike for his university studies, which, he complained, "were too matter-of-fact" and under which, he declared, "he would have become a dried and shrivelled scientific conglomerate"—nevertheless "influenced and moulded the current thought, and even much of the practice, of chemistry for decades" (*50*).

"One of the charms of the scientific enterprise", Oppenheimer has noted, "is how deficient we can be in many . . . qualities and still play some meaningful part in it" (*51*). Einstein, Klein writes,

> had been a slow child; he learned to speak at a much later age than the average, and he had shown no special ability in elementary school. . . . [Later] he spent most of the time in his room studying the original works of the masters of nineteenth-century physics and pondering what they set forth. The lectures on advanced mathematics did not hold him, because in those days he saw no need or use for higher mathematics as a tool for grasping the structure of nature. He knew that he did not have and could not, or perhaps would not, acquire the traits of the outstanding student: the easy facility in comprehension, the willingness to concentrate one's energies on all the required subjects, and the orderliness to take good notes and work them over properly (*52*).

Brilliance, in the usual sense of the word, is not required for scientific work. "To be extremely intelligent is not the same thing as to be gifted in creative work" (*53*).

One does not need to have an extraordinarily high I.Q., history shows, to be a productive scientist.

One does need enthusiasm ("Nothing great is achieved without passion" (*54*)), optimism ("With active optimism, even in the absence of more than average knowledge, useful discoveries are almost sure to be made" (*55*)), and an appetite for hard work ("My only strength lies in my tenacity" (*56*).)

Depth of Commitment

Newton has described the importance in creative work of steadily intending one's mind in a given direction. Asked how he made his discoveries, he replied, "By *always* thinking onto them. I keep the subject *constantly* before me and *wait* till the first dawnings open *little by little* into full light" (*57*) (italics added). Similarily, Pavlov, when asked by his pupils, in jest, what they should do to become "a master" answered, in all seriousness: "Get up in the morning with your problem before you. Breakfast with it. Go to the laboratory with it. Eat your lunch with it. Keep it before you after dinner. Go to bed with it in your mind. Dream about it" (*58*). And

Gauss said, "I think anybody could have made my discoveries if he had applied himself as I did".

Duhem cites the example of Napoleon. "The good position of my armies", Napoleon said, "comes from the fact that I concentrate on it every day . . . and when they send my monthly reports on the conditions of my troops and ships, which form a score of thick booklets, I stop everything else I am doing in order to read them in detail." Thus it is, Taine recorded, that

> Returning from the camp at Boulogne, Napoleon meets a squad of lost soldiers' asks them for the number of their regiment, figures out the day of their departure, the route they have taken, the road they should be on, and says to them:—'You will find your battalion at such and such a stopping point.'—Now, the army then consisted of 200,000 men (59).

Many such examples could be cited. The *New Yorker* has described in detail the commitment required to become a basketball star of the first magnitude (60). Kekulé cites Liebig's advice: "If you want to be a chemist, you will have to ruin your health; no one who does not ruin his health with study will ever do anything in chemistry nowadays". "I faithfully followed the advice", writes Kekulé. "During many years I managed to do with four and even three hours' sleep. A single night spent over my books did not count; it was only when two or three came in succession that I thought I had done anything meritorius" (61). From such examples the young student may sense, correctly, that, while one need not be a genius,

To be a productive scientist, one must work hard.

On Failing

Still, to accomplish things you have to be lucky, Monet has observed, but to be lucky you have to work hard, "Because if you don't work hard, you won't *see* your luck when it comes" (62). The discovery of x-rays was narrowly missed by several physicists, notes Whittaker. "An Oxford physicist, . . . having found that photographic plates kept in a box near a Crookes tube were liable to be fogged, told his assistant to keep them in another place" (63). Yet, though luck is important, observes Thomson, "If a man goes on trying promising things throughout a working life-time he is really unlucky if he does not get one good thing." As Kettering says, "In research and invention work you fail hundreds and even thousands of times and if you succeed once you are in" (15). In research, failure is the rule, success the exception that justifies that rule. It is said that Leonardo da Vinci was unlucky for thirty years (64). Kepler made nineteen hypotheses with regard to the motion of Mars and calculated the results of each before he made his great discovery that the planet's path is an ellipse (24). W. L. Bragg cites a favorite saying of his father, that "After a year's research, one realizes it could have been done in a week" (65). In her Nobel Award Address, Dorothy Crowfoot Hodgkin said, "I seem to have spent much more of my life not solving structures than solving them" (66). And, near the end of his life, Lord Kelvin wrote:

One word characterizes the most strenuous of the efforts for the advancement of science that I have made perseveringly during fifty-five years, and that word is FAILURE. I know no more of electric and magnetic forces or of the relation between ether, electricity and ponderable matter, or of chemical affinity, than I knew and tried to teach to my students of natural philosophy fifty years ago in my first session as Professor (67).

Yet it should be remembered that the triumphs of twentieth-century physics sprang directly from the failures of nineteenth-century physics. "The most important of my discoveries", Davy has said, "have been suggested to me by my failures".

Unfortunately, students today are constantly cautioned against making mistakes—especially when there are several hundred of them working in one laboratory. Learning to avoid "mistakes" may develop a faculty for following directions, but it will never lead one to discover *why* those directions should be followed.

We must help students learn that to learn they must make mistakes.

Panic of error is the death of learning. "The educated person must be taught that it is not a disgrace to fail and that he must analyze every failure to find its cause", Kettering has said. "He must learn to fail intelligently. For failing is one of the greatest arts in the world."

Erroneous Impressions

Unfortunately, though understandably, the authorized versions of science, the textbooks, record only happy endings—or what are believed to be happy endings. This is science fiction. It produces the erroneous impression that science marches along logically and objectively from one crucial experiment to the next, predicting and explaining the unknown in terms of the known, while, regretably, individual scientists become progressively more specialized in their interests and their fields of competence. Fortunately,

The historical approach can correct many misconceptions about science.

It can show that science is not objective. "Science in the making, science as an end to be pursued", said Einstein, "is as subjective and psychologically conditioned as any other branch of human endeavor".

It can show that in science there are no crucial experiments. "A 'crucial experiment' ", said Duhem, "is impossible in physics" (59).

And it can show that prediction is not the only way of testing hypotheses (68). "No single instance of evolution has ever been observed" (69), for example.

Additionally, the historical approach can show that science does not explain the unfamiliar in terms of the familiar. It does precisely the opposite: it explains the familiar in terms of the unfamiliar. It "explained" planetary motion, which was familiar, in terms of action-at-a-distance, which was unfamiliar; it explained combustion, which was familiar, in terms of union with oxygen, which was unfamiliar; and so forth. It explained weight relations (familiar) in terms of atoms (unfamiliar); isomers (familiar) in terms of the arrangements of atoms in space (unfamiliar); directional affinities (familiar) in terms of electrons (unfamiliar); and the chemical bond (familiar) in terms of quantum physics (unfamiliar). As Whewell has so aptly said,

In advancing to a Science of Cause in any subject, the labour and the struggle is, not to analyze the phenomena according to any preconceived and already familiar ideas, but to form distinctly new conceptions, such as do really carry us to a more intimate view of the processes of nature (24).

But in carrying us to a more intimate view of nature, specialization need not lead to "a progressive limitation of the specialist's field of interest and competence" (70). George Wald, recent Nobel Prize winner in physiology, once compared his work in an exceedingly specialized field, the visual pigments of the eye, to "a very narrow window through which at a distance one can see only a crack of light" but through which "as one comes closer the view grows wider and wider, until finally through the same narrow window one is looking at the Universe" (71).

Indigenous Concepts

But in looking at the Universe through the window of a particular discipline, such as chemistry, those "distinctly new conceptions" that provide us with a more intimate understanding of nature must be *appropriate* (24).

History demonstrates that "the symbolism and calculus developed for a subject must be indigenous" (72).

There is nothing quite like chemistry (73). It is not, for example, a branch of applied physics. One need consider only the simplest synthetic procedure to see that. It is a natural science to which, sometimes, physics may be applied. But it is well to remember that chemists had to invent atoms and molecules and structural formulas well before those concepts were found useful in other disciplines.

Admittedly, owing to the complexities of their subject and to the nature of their evidence that, though voluminous, is usually indirect, chemists have generally entertained a healthy skepticism toward their concepts, until some use has been found for them elsewhere. The concept of the tetrahedral atom was not widely accepted by chemists until it was shown to be useful in interpreting a physical effect, the rotation of the plane of polarized light (74). The wisdom of the atomic hypothesis itself was questioned by a succession of well-known chemists, until it was shown to be useful in interpreting Brownian motion. As for the "chemical bond", since physicists have not yet found a use for that concept, chemists view it with mixed feelings. They are not sure if they should believe it, but they cannot do without it.

Knowledge Claims

Typically, physicists have been more forward in their knowledge claims—possibly because mechanical principles always seem to be universally applicable to matter, even though, or perhaps because, they do not concern themselves with what it is that moves (75), being totally dependent, in applications, on initial conditions (76). Dirac has asserted, for example, that, with the discovery of quantum mechanics, most of physics and all chemistry was in principle solved. Yet quantum mechanics, like its predecessor, Newtonian mechanics, has had about as much impact on the art of chemical synthesis as the theory of relativity has had on bridge-building.

Inevitably, when a field such as physics impinges upon a field such as chemistry or when chemistry impinges upon biology, the field of lesser complexity (physics or chemistry, as the case may be) selects for study its own problems—which may not be (indeed, usually are not) the central problems of the more complex field—and, rather arrogantly, declares that these problems are "fundamental", i.e., "interesting", i.e., "tractable", i.e., "not too hard", while modestly allowing that all other problems—usually those of practical importance—are "applied", "uninteresting", that is to say, "too hard". In such situations,

The historical approach may provide the practicing scientist (and student) with a useful perspective from which to judge the knowledge claims of other disciplines.

If the physicists had always been right, the chemists could not have had atoms or directed affinities or (semi-)localized electron pairs. Still, it was impossible to ignore Dirac, particularly with regard to valence theory, and many chemists capitulated, only to be hauled back full circle after a third of a century to many of their original conceptions.

Relation to Mathematics

One reason for the deference shown to physics by other scientists is the belief inculcated by Lord Kelvin, that "when you cannot express it in numbers, your knowledge is of a meagre and unsatisfactory kind; it may be the beginning of knowledge, but you have scarcely, in your thoughts, advanced to the stage of *Science*, whatever the matter may be" (77). Taken seriously, this admonition would dismiss from science the theory of evolution (which Kelvin disliked) and most of structural theory (which physicists from Helmholtz (78) to Pauli (79) have found intellectually uncongenial). Clearly, quantification is not necessary —nor sufficient (80). The physicists may make excellent use of mathematics and still be "hopelessly and . . . arrogantly wrong" (81).

"They do it smartly", said Bohr of an argument by three physicists, "but what counts is to do it right" (82). Admittedly "right is hard to define. Bohr got the right numerical answers for the ionization potentials of hydrogen and helium, when almost no one else had come close; and Newton got the right answer for the relation between pressure and volume of a Boyle-fluid (*83*). Yet neither Bohr's model nor Newton's model is considered "right" today. With such simple examples,

> *The historical approach can help students see that being mathematically correct and quantitatively precise is no guarantee that one has said the last—or even the "right"—word.*

Moreover,

> *The historical approach can show students that it is incorrect in chemistry to equate "theoretical" with "mathematical".*

The fundamental papers on valence theory by Frankland (*84*), Couper (*84*), Kekulé (*84*), van't Hoff (*84*), Mendeleev (*85*), Werner (*86*), Lewis (*87*), Goldschmidt (*88*), Sidgwick and Powell (*89*), Gillespie and Nyholm (*90*), and Linnett (*91*) contain not a single mathematical equation, which is not altogether surprising. For it was, Goedel said, purely an historical accident that mathematics developed along quantitative lines (*80*); and, indeed, modern mathematics, like modern chemistry, contains numerous important results that cannot be expressed in conventional "mathematical" form. But, more importantly, theoretical chemistry, like theoretical mathematics, is concerned in the first place with the invention of concepts, rather than with their formal manipulation. The importance of concepts arises from the fact that, in G. P. Thomson's words, "They determine the questions one asks and so the answers one can get. They are more fundamental than the theories, which are stated in terms of them" (*15*).

Advantages to Teachers and Authors

Because it focuses attention on the inventive side of science—on science in the making, on controversies and misconceptions, and (not least of all) on people—and because (therefore) it is relatively nonmathematical (in the conventional sense of the word),

> *The historical approach appeals to a broad spectrum of students.*

It appeals not only to those students with a high interest in mathematical and mechanical problems who plan research careers in science but also to those students with high literary interests or high artistic interests or high interests in interpersonal relations. In being concerned, however, more with the drama of ideas than with a battery of techniques, the historical approach, while it may have considerable appeal for potential scientists and science-appreciators, probably has limited appeal for students training to become science-technicians.

In addition, says Lowry,

> *The historical method has also been found to provide a complete solution of the difficult problem of teaching mixed classes of students, some absolute beginners and others with considerable knowledge of elementary text-books . . . (92).*

In passing, it may be noted, in these days of mounting enrollments and limited civilian budgets, that, because its chief vehicle is the printed word,

The historical approach is relatively simple and inexpensive to administer.

Beyond a wise selection of text(s), all that is required of an institution is a generous collection of books for collateral reading, and the courage to allow their students the time to read these books.

There is another advantage for teachers and authors:

The historical approach is a "sure guarantee against an incorrect or illogical sequence" (92).

Textbooks often say, for example, Boyle showed that for gases PV = constant. This is rather like saying that Columbus showed that men could live aboard ship for long periods of time. It misses the point of Boyle's J-tube experiment and that experiment's most significant result: the introduction into science of a new variable, *viz.*, pressure (*83*). Is it surprising that students tend to picture physical scientists as somewhat dull folk, who merely go about measuring things? Columbus would seem dull, too, if we never mentioned his ideas on the earth's shape and the geographical discoveries to which they led him.

Finally, while any gradually unfolding story of a growing science will from time to time require additions to keep it up to date and deletions to keep it within bounds (which is possible, without loss of rigor, since each part of a coherent science supports and is supported by other parts, irrespective of the time of their discovery), carefully executed,

The historical approach does not require major revisions.

For example, Millikan wrote in the preface to a late edition of his classic work "Electrons",

I have been pleased and somewhat surprised to find that the historical mode of presentation originally adopted has rendered radical changes even today both unnecessary and undesirable. ...Believing profoundly in the historical approach both in science and in its teaching, I have made no changes in the first 400 pages save those necessitated by new knowledge, mostly in the values of units... (*93*).

The Past, Present, and Future

Many authors have echoed Millikan's belief that, in Boring's words,

"A knowledge of history . . . has a huge capacity for adding significance to the understanding of the present" (36).

Writes Hund: "We study the history of science for better understanding of science itself" (*94*); and van der Waerden: "In my opinion, a thorough understanding of a physical theory can be reached only by the historical method" (*95*); and C. N. Yang: "It is of course true that an idea, especially a scientific idea, does not have full meaning unless defined against a background of knowledge from which the idea originated and developed" (*96*). F. A. Paneth had a particular love for the historical way of explanation. "Yet, Paneth was not a historian of science but *a chemist who used history as a teaching aid*", writes Dingle. "He was not committed to recreating what *was*, but in using the historical record to illuminate what *is*"(*97*).

There is less agreement among authors on the relation of history to the future. "A knowledge of history . . . fails miserably to foretell the future", holds Boring (*36*). Yet, "Those that do not study history may have to repeat it", remarked Yost (quoting Santayana) at the first conference on noble gas compounds (*98*).

Probably history makes most sense to those who have a passion for the future, said Valery. For the future *is* in the past. The trick is to see where.

Disadvantages

The feeling that in practice there are too many antecedents to make the past a useful guide to the future is no doubt one reason why the historical approach is not more widely used in science teaching and research.

A more important reason, probably, is that most people, not least of all young students, are content to gain knowledge—if not wisdom—second hand. "The process of obtaining new conceptions [the heart of the historical approach] is, to most minds, far more unwelcome than any labour in employing old ideas", writes Whewell. "The effort is indeed painful and oppressive [at first]; it is feeling in the dark for an object which we cannot find." Most students would prefer "a means of talking and writing upon all subjects without thinking . . . [so that] both exertion of thought, and knowledge of facts, become superfluous" (*24*).

The historical method also places a burden on the teacher and writer. "One has to consider one paper after another, to explain the problem of the paper and the situation in which it was written, to state what was known at that time and what attempts had been made before", observes van der Waerden. "Notations may be modernized, proofs may be left out, but the essential ideas must be explained in every case" (*95*). Ideally in elementary courses,

No conception or principle [should be given] at all, unless, in its most elementary aspects, it can be made clear to a beginner; and unless it is capable of numerous applications in elementary [laboratory] work; and, finally, unless a knowledge of it is of material use in organizing and unifying the results of such elementary work (*99*).

These requirements, like those of rhyme and meter in poetry, could be more of a blessing than a burden. They can produce a tension and unity in a treatment that would otherwise be missing. As Robert Frost has said of poetry, working without rhyme and meter is "like playing tennis with the net down".

It is often said that the historical approach is too time-consuming. One wonders whose time is being referred to, the students' or the teacher's? "[For] it does not require a large fraction of total class time to change the atmosphere of a program of study" (*100*).

Kekulé's Advice

And are present programs of study so very economical of student-time? We know how little chemistry students remember, even less, understand. Even a small increment in retention and comprehension would be significant. Is it not important, too, for science majors particularly, to see the personal and creative side of science, early and often? Perhaps we should relax and realize that "One cannot explore new countries in express trains nor will a study of even the best text-books qualify a man to become a discoverer ... Whoever wishes to train himself as an investigator must study the travellers' original works ...", advised Kekulé, "He must follow the Pathfinders" (61). They may be outmoded technically, but not so much in method, and not at all in the spirit that guided their work (101).

Telling

Of course, it always seems much easier and quicker to tell students those things that we want them to know. And that, Piaget asserts, is the great mistake of education. Telling students something forever denies them the joy of discovering it for themselves. Students need a new freedom: the freedom of discovery.

"No scheme for education, and least of all for scientific education, can be complete without some facility and encouragement for browsing", argues Whitehead. "The dangers of our modern efficient schemes remind one of Matthew Arnold's line 'For rigorous teachers seized my youth'. Poor youth!" (102).

The Soft Option

Finally, there is the question of the "soft option". In chemistry departments at many schools, the historical approach is used, if at all, in the first-year, "low-level" course for nonscience majors. If the historical approach is to be more widely used, we shall need, in addition to intellectually stimulating text- and laboratory-materials, a broad selection of philosophically, historically, and scientifically interesting, concrete, concisely stated, short-answer-type problems. The problems below, unfortunately but necessarily out of context, have been used in recent years in discussions of the development of structural theory with honors students in general chemistry at the University of Minnesota. Though often falling short of the requirements above, they may illustrate some of the things one hopes to achieve with the historical approach.

Problems

"How can we distinguish whether the processes we contemplate be composition or decomposition?" (24). ·

"The blade of grass consists of a finite number of discrete particles. These can at most be arranged in a finite number of ways. Therefore there is a number N of possible blades of grass. If we examine carefully N+1 blades of grass, at least two must be alike. But we *never* find two alike. Therefore there cannot be atoms", reasoned Leibnitz (*103*). Comment.

At what point in the development of science was it worthwhile to consider the variability of the masses of atoms? Of the masses of the atoms of a given element?

Axiomatize classical structural theory.

What refinements are needed to bring up to date van't Hoff's theory of carbon compounds?

What aspect of a molecule's structure does classical structural theory give exactly?

Is it surprising that a nonarithmetical theory can predict the precise symmetry of a molecule?

The idea of catenation helped the development of what concept? Later, it hindered the development of what concept?

"Darwin made strenuous efforts to connect extreme instances by gradations of character" (*9*). Who did this for chemistry?

Why is hydrogen often placed in Group I? In what Group(s) should it be placed?

In the 1890's physicists in Europe and in England observed that the properties of cathode rays—their deflection in electric and magnetic fields, *e.g.*—were independent of the chemical nature of the cathode and the residual gas. While their observations were identical, their conclusions were different (*104*). Suggest what these conclusions might have been.

"Long live the electron! May it never be of use to anyone" was a yearly toast to J. J. Thomson at the Cavendish Laboratory's Christmas party during approximately what period?

In what sense did the distribution of charge in Thomson's model of the atom foreshadow the current picture of the charge distribution in atoms?

Who introduced the number 2 into valence theory?

How were effects now attributed to the Exclusion Principle and the self-energy of electrons handled in classical structural theory? In the ion-packing model of heteropolar compounds?

What statement of an electron exclusion principle might Lewis have given in 1916, based upon his identification of the valence-strokes of classical structural theory and the fact that it had never been found useful to represent molecules by structural formulas with crossed valence-strokes? When was supporting evidence from physics forthcoming for this *chemical exclusion principle?*

What questions did the structural theories of van't Hoff, Werner, Lewis, and Linnett answer? What new questions did they raise?

The development of structural theory may be viewed as a search for concepts that can be transferred from one substance to another. What are the items transferred in: Lavoisier's theory of acids; Dalton's atomic theory; the radical, substitution, and type theories of organic chemistry; Werner's coordination theory; Rutherford's atomic model; Lewis's model of electronic structure; ion-packing models of heteropolar and homopolar compounds; Schroedinger's equation; the Pauli Principle?

What do we mean when we say there is "oxygen" in a compound?

Atoms, electrons, photons, and water can be obtained, respectively, from molecules, nuclei, excited states, and sulfuric acid. Does that mean there are atoms, electrons, photons, and water in molecules, nuclei, excited states, and sulfuric acid?

Is there "water" in the ocean? In Na_2SO_4 10 H_2O? In Na_2O H_2O? In SO_3 H_2O? In NH_4NO_3?

Illustrate the remark that "the only complete formula of a substance is its structure". (Why, for example, is the formula of "sodium peroxide" not written simply NaO?)

Give two examples of "theories of great importance which are consistent with known facts but on which there is as yet no direct evidence".

Show with illustrations that "a model supplies primarily a terminology".

Illustrate that, to be useful, a model must be wrong (in some respects) or else (in some respects) neither right nor wrong (*105*)—and that the trick, therefore, is to see where it is right.

Wigner raises this question (attributed to F. Werner) concerning the limited factual basis of theories: "How do we know that, if we made a theory which focuses its attention on phenomena we disregard and disregards some of the phenomena now commanding our attention, we could not build another theory which has little in common with the present one but which, nevertheless, explains just as many phenomena as the present theory?" (*76*). Has this happened in chemistry?

The Hard Option

More exciting are problems (not illustrated above) that permit students to participate, if even only in a modest way, in the invention of new concepts Ideally, a course of study should be a continuous sequence of such problems. Perhaps that is attempting to play the game with the net too high. The real problem of the "soft option" is not that it is too easy for the students but that it is too hard for their instructors.

Literature Cited

(1) Twain, M., Letter to Andrew Lang, "The Portable Mark Twain", p. 773, Viking Press, Inc., New York, N. Y., 1955.

(2) Morrison, P., *Am. J. Phys.*, **32,** 441 (1964).

(3) Klein, M., "Mathematics and the Physical World", Thomas Y. Crowell Co., New York, N. Y., 1959.

(4) Polya, G., "Induction and Analogy in Mathematics", Princeton University Press, Princeton, N. J., 1954.

(5) Einstein, A., "Essays in Science", p. 14, Philosophical Library, New York, N. Y., 1934.

(6) Carroll, L., "The Hunting of the Snark", Fourth Stanza, Second fit.

(7) Szent-Györgyi, A., *Science*, **146,** 1278 (1964).

(8) Scott, A. F., *Chem. Eng. News*, 86 (March 29, 1965).

(9) Cramer, F., "The Method of Darwin. A Study in Scientific Method", A. C. McClurg and Co., Chicago, Ill., 1896.

(10) Smith, C. S., *Phys. Today*, **18,** no. 12, 1 (1965).

(11) Arrowsmith, W., *Key Reporter*, **31,** no. 3, 1 (1966).

(12) Matthew, W. D., quoted by G. G. Simpson, *Science*, **143,** 769 (1964).

(13) Söderbaum, H. G., "Jons Jacob Berzelius", p. 180, trans. by O. Larsell, The Williams and Wilkins Co., Baltimore, Md., 1934.

(14) Dirac, P. A. M., *Sci. Am.*, **208,** no. 5, 45 (1963).

(15) Thomson, G., "The Inspiration of Science", Oxford University Press, New York, N. Y., 1961.

(16) Kekulé, F. A., *Ann. Chemie Pharm.*, **106,** 129 (1858); Trans. by O. T. Benfey, "Classics in the Theory of Chemical Combination", Dover Publications, Inc., New York, N. Y., 1963.

(17) Dunitz, J. D., and Ibers, J. A., ed., "Perspectives in Structural Chemistry", Vol. I, p. viii, John Wiley and Sons, New York, N. Y., 1967.

(18) Oppenheimer, J. R., Address to Undergraduates at California Institute of Technology, *ca.* 1955.

(19) Mulliken, R. S., *Tetrahedron*, **17,** 247 (1962).

(20) Birkhoff, G. D., "Aesthetic Measure", Harvard University Press, Cambridge, Mass., 1933.

(21) Ramsay, W., "Essays, Biographical and Chemical", p. 116, E. P. Dutton and Co., New York, N. Y., 1909.

(22) Conant, J. B., "On Understanding Science. An Historical Approach", Yale University Press, New Haven, Conn., 1947.

(23) "Harvard Case Histories in Experimental Science", J. B. Conant and L. K. Nash, ed., Harvard Univ. Press, Cambridge, Mass., 1957.

(24) Whewell, W., "The Philosophy of the Inductive Sciences", Vol. 2, D. Appleton and Co., New York, N. Y., 1882.

(25) Koestler, A., "The Sleepwalkers", Grosset and Dunlap, New York, N. Y., 1963.

(26) Frost, R., in "Complete Poems of Robert Frost", p. vii, Holt, Rinehart and Winston, New York, N. Y., 1964.

(27) Caldin, E. F., *Brit. J. Phil. Sci.*, **10,** 209 (1959).

(28) Toulmin, S., in "Quanta and Reality", p. 9, American Research Council, 1962.

(29) See Lewis, G. N., "The Anatomy of Science", p. 7, Yale University Press, New Haven, Conn., 1926.

(30) Gregory, J. C., "A Short History of Atomism, From Democritus to Bohr", A. C. Black, Ltd., London, England, 1931.

(31) Sementsov, A., *Am. Sci.*, **43,** 97 (1955).

(32) Lossen, W., *Ber.*, **20,** 3309 (1887).

(33) Soddy, F., "The Interpretation of the Atom", p. 266, G. P. Putnam's Sons, New York, N. Y., 1932.

(34) Newton, I., "Optics", Book Three, Part I, Quest. 31.

(35) Planck, M., "Scientific Autobiography", trans. by F. Gaynor, Philosophical Library, New York, N. Y., 1949.

(36) Boring, E. G., "History, Psychology, and Science", John Wiley and Sons., Inc., New York, N. Y., 1963.

(37) Schultz, J., *Science*, **157**, 296 (1967).
(38) Davis, K. S., "Priestley and Lavoisier: The Cautionary Scientists", p. 175, G. P. Putnam's Sons, New York, N. Y., 1966.
(39) Jorpes, J. E., "Jac. Berzelius", p. 58, Almqvist and Wiksell, Stockholm, Sweden, 1966.
(40) See Wheland, G. W., "Advanced Organic Chemistry", 2nd ed., p. 132, John Wiley and Sons, New York, N. Y., 1949.
(41) Armstrong, G. E., *Nature*, **117**, 553 (1926).
(42) Armstrong, G. E., *Chem. Ind.*, **43**, 1101 (1924).
(43) Greenaway, F., "John Dalton and the Atom", Heinemann, London, England, 1966.
(44) Kauffman, G. B., in "Werner Centennial", p. 41, R. F. Gould, ed., Advances in Chemistry Series No. 62, American Chemical Society, Washington, D. C., 1967.
(45) van't Hoff, J. H., "Physical Chemistry in the Service of the Sciences", p. 17, University of Chicago Press, Chicago, Ill., 1903.
(46) Kendall, J., *Trans. Faraday Soc.*, **33**, 2 (1937).
(47) Bent, H. A., "The Second Law", p. 15, Oxford University Press, New York, N. Y., 1965.
(48) "The Life and Letters of Charles Darwin", Vol. I, Chap. 2, F. Darwin, ed., Basic Books, Inc., New York, N. Y., 1959.
(49) Ewald, P. P., in "Fifty Years of X-ray Diffraction", p. 3, P. P. Ewald, ed., International Union of Crystallography, Utrecht, Netherlands, 1962.
(50) Walker, J., *J. Chem. Soc.*, **103**, 1127 (1913).
(51) Oppenheimer, R., *Science*, **142**, 1143 (1963).
(52) Klein, M. J., *Phys. Today*, **18**, no. 1, 38 (1965).
(53) Getzels, J. W., and Jackson, P. W., "Creativity and Intelligence", John Wiley and Sons, New York, N. Y., 1962.
(54) Russell, B., "The Autobiography of Bertrand Russell", Little, Brown and Co., Boston, Mass., 1967.
(55) Whitney, W. R. (source unknown).
(56) Vallery-Radot, R., "The Life of Pasteur", trans. by R. L. Devonshire, Doubleday, Doran and Co., Inc., New York, N. Y., 1928.
(57) Andrade, E. N. da C., "Sir Isaac Newton. His Life and Work", p. 35, Doubleday and Co., Inc., Garden City, N. Y., 1958.
(58) Cited by Polanyi, M., "Personal Knowledge", p. 127, University of Chicago Press, Chicago, Ill., 1958.
(59) Duhem, P., "The Aim and Structure of Physical Theory", trans. by P. P. Wiener, Princeton University Press, Princeton, N. J., 1954.
(60) McPhee, J., *New Yorker*, 40 (Jan. 23, 1965).
(61) Quoted by Japp, F. R., *J. Chem. Soc.*, **73**, 97 (1898).
(62) Cited in *New Yorker*, 89 (Sept. 29, 1962).
(63) Whittaker, E., "A History of the Theories of Aether and Electricity", Vol. I, p. 358, Harper and Brother, New York, N. Y., 1960.
(64) Vallentin, A., "Leonardo da Vinci", The Viking Press, New York, N. Y., 1938.
(65) Bragg, L., *Proc. Roy. Soc.*, **A262**, 145 (1961).
(66) Hodgkin, D. C., *Science*, **150**, 979 (1965).
(67) Thompson, S. P., "The Life of William Thomson", Macmillan, London, England, 1910.
(68) De Beer, G., *Science*, **143**, 1311 (1964).
(69) Bailey, O. T., *Phil. Sci.*, **15**, 1 (1945).
(70) Odegard, P. H., *Key Reporter*, **27**, no. 4, 2 (1962).
(71) Quoted by Carlson, R., *New Yorker*, 35 (June 30, 1962).
(72) Coler, M. A., *Chem. Eng. News*, 84 (Aug 15, 1966).
(73) Black, J., "Lectures on the Elements of Chemistry", ed. by J. Robison, M. Carey, Philadelphia, Penna., 1807.
(74) Hein, G. E., in "Kekulé Centennial", pp. 10–11, R. F. Gould, ed., Advances in Chemistry Series No. 61, American Chemical Society, Washington, D. C., 1966.
(75) Kompaneyets, A. S., "Basic Concepts in Quantum Mechanics", p. 132, trans. by L. F. Landovitz, Reinhold Publishing Corp., New York, N. Y., 1966.

(76) Wigner, E. P., "Symmetries and Reflections", Indiana University Press, Bloomington, Indiana, 1967.

(77) Quoted by Holton, G., and Roller, D. H. D., "Foundations of Modern Physical Science", p. 229, Addison–Wesley Publishing Co., Inc., Reading, Mass., 1958.

(78) Koenigsberger, L., "Hermann von Helmholtz", p. 340, trans. by F. A. Welby, Dover Publications, Inc., New York, N. Y., 1965.

(79) Casimer, H. B. G., in "Theoretical Physics in the Twentieth Century", p. 137, M. Fierz and V. F. Weisskopf, ed., Interscience Publishers, Inc., New York, N. Y., 1960.

(80) Rosenblith, W. A., *Phys. Today*, **19**, 23 (1966).

(81) Eiseley, L., "Darwin's Century", Chap. 9, Doubleday, Garden City, New York, 1958.

(82) "Niels Bohr", p. 129, S. Rozental, ed., John Wiley and Sons, Inc., New York, N. Y., 1967.

(83) Brush, S., "Kinetic Theory", Vol. I, Selection 2, Pergamon Press, New York, N. Y., 1965.

(84) See Benfey, O. T., Ref. (16).

(85) See Mendeleev, D., "The Principles of Chemistry", trans. by G. Kamensky, Longmans, Green and Co., London, England, 1891.

(86) See Werner, A., "New Ideas on Inorganic Chemistry", trans. by E. P. Hedley, Longmans, Green and Co., New York, N. Y., 1911.

(87) Lewis, G. N., *J. Am. Chem. Soc.*, **38**, 762 (1916).

(88) Goldschmidt, V. M., *Trans. Faraday Soc.*, **25**, 253 (1929).

(89) Sidgwick, N. V., and Powell, H. M., *Proc. Roy. Soc.*, **A176**, 153 (1940).

(90) Gillespie, R. J., and Nyholm, R. S., *Quart. Rev.*, **11**, 339 (1957).

(91) Linnett, J. W., *J. Am. Chem. Soc.*, **83**, 2643 (1961).

(92) Lowry, T. M., "Historical Introduction to Chemistry", The Macmillan Co., Ltd., London, England, 1915.

(93) Millikan, R. A., "Electrons", p. v, University of Chicago Press, Chicago, Ill., 1947.

(94) Hund, F., *Phys. Today*, **19**, 23 (1966).

(95) Ref. (79), p. 199.

(96) Yang, C. N., "Elementary Particles. A Short History of Some Discoveries in Atomic Physics", Princeton University Press, Princeton, N. J., 1962.

(97) Dingle, H., *Science*, **149**, 1363 (1965).

(98) Yost, D. M., in "Noble-Gas Compounds", p. 22, H. H. Hyman, ed., University of Chicago Press, Chicago, Ill., 1963.

(99) Smith, A., "Introduction to General Inorganic Chemistry", The Century Co., New York, N. Y., 1907.

(100) Kemble, E. C., "Physical Science. Its Structure and Development", p. x, M.I.T. Press, Cambridge, Mass., 1966.

(101) Weiss, P., *Science*, **136**, 468 (1962).

(102) Whitehead, A. N., "The Interpretation of Science", ed. by A. H. Johnson, Bobbs-Merrill, Indianapolis, Ind., 1961.

(103) Morrison, P., *Am. J. Phys.*, **26**, 258 (1958).

(104) Thomson, J. J., "Recollections and Reflections", p. 340, The Macmillan Co., New York, N. Y., 1937. Friedman, F. L., and L. Sartori, L., "The Classical Atom", p. 57, Addison-Wesley Publishing Co., Inc., Reading, Mass., 1965.

(105) Zwicky, F., *Phys. Rev.*, **43**, 1030 (1933).

16. LOOKING IT UP IN THE ENCYCLOPEDIA—AN EXERCISE WITH AN OBVIOUS SOURCE

ELIZABETH C. PATTERSON

Albertus Magnus College, New Haven, Connecticut, U.S.A.

Based on an examination in the bicentennial year of successive editions of the "Encyclopedia Britannica", from the first in 1768 to the present, especially of the articles on *chemistry*, *atom*, and *sulfur*, a bounteous source of material is demonstrated, readily available to any student in touch with a library, either through xeroxing or on microforms. The development of scientific ideas through the past crucial two centuries is dramatically shown, and the style, usage, and flavor of these decades presented directly to the interested student who may, in many cases, have no other direct access to a primary source of material.

The "Encyclopedia Britannica" offers an excellent source of material to the historian of science. The first volume of the "EB" appeared in 1768. Its editor, William Smellie, wrote in his Preface (*1*):

To diffuse knowledge of Science is the professed design of the following work. What method, it may be asked, have the compilers employed to accomplish this design? Not to mention original articles, they have had recourse to the best books upon almost every subject, extracted the useful parts, and rejected whatever appears trifling or less interesting. Instead of dismembering the Sciences, by attempting to treat them intelligently under a multitude of technical terms, they have digested the principles of every Science in the form of systems or distinct treatises, and explained the terms as they occur in the order of the alphabet, with reference to the Sciences to which they belong... We will... venture to affirm that any man of ordinary parts may, if he chuses, learn the principles of Agriculture, of Astronomy, of Botany, of Chemistry, &c., &c., from the *Encyclopedia Britannica*.

Smellie was an able young Edinburgh journalist interested in natural philosophy. The new encyclopedia had been conceived in that city and would for many years continue to be chiefly an Edinburgh product, profiting from the great surge of intellectual and artistic vitality that began in Scotland after the mid-eighteenth century. Science—both theoretical and practical—in the forefront of Scottish achievements from the days of Joseph Black, Thomas Thomson, James Watt, Thomas Telford, and others, could rightly expect a prominent place in such an undertaking.

In the editions that followed, from the second in 1777 to the present,[1] this

---

[1] In the early history of the "EB", the volumes of a single edition were published over a span of years, as each was completed; for example, the third and final volume of the first edition appeared in 1771. This edition contained no biographies. These were introduced in the second edition (1777–1784), along with a number of other new entries to accompany the material of the first. The third edition (1788–1797) was largely made up of new material. The fourth (1801–1810) was for the most part a reprint of the third; it contained some new articles on mathematics and natural history, including chemistry. Both the fifth (1815–1817) and the sixth (1823–1824) editions may be considered little more than reprints of the fourth, although the

original policy of full and systematic treatment of science has not been materially altered. Definitive articles by first-rate contributors have been the rule. The principles and practices of a science at the time of publication have in each edition been examined and often explained at length and in some detail. General criticism of the encyclopedia has sometimes been directed toward omissions in biography, too great an emphasis on matters British or matters American, and slowness in bringing articles up to date or in adding new entries, but never toward the substance of the scientific articles. Those on chemical matters have fared remarkably well. Even so outspoken a critic as Harvey Einbinder (3) praises the high caliber of the chemical entries and faults only their plethora of detail and too frequent use of chemical symbols as confusing to the general reader.

As an easily available source of information any encyclopedia is an obvious choice. The "Encyclopedia Britannica" has acquired and maintained a high reputation for reliability and usefulness in the English-speaking world. All of its editions are readily accessible by library loan through xeroxing or on microforms and offer a rich lode of material for making chronological comparisons on any included subject or for studies centered in any one period of publication. With the thought in mind that an examin-

---

innovation of Continental contributors (Arago and Biot) and of book-length dissertations on the history of science were included. The seventh edition (1830–1842) multiplied the number of dissertations (among them one on the history of mathematical and physical science) and reprinted all articles that the editor, Macvey Napier, considered of value in past editions and supplements, many of them corrected, altered, and extended by their original authors. The eighth edition (1853–1860) again was almost wholly a reprint; a few new contributors and a continuation of the dissertation on mathematics and physical science were added. The ninth—"the famous ninth"—shamelessly pirated in the U.S.A. by Allen—though still a Scottish product had for the first time an English-born editor, the philosopher T. S. Baynes of the University of St. Andrews. Appearing between 1875 and 1889, its material was almost wholly rewritten and reflects the "modern" spirit of Victorian times, especially in the contributions of such men as T. H. Huxley, J. C. Maxwell, Rayleigh, Swinburne, and W. R. Smith. The tenth edition (1902–1903) added ten supplementary volumes, dealing mainly with current persons and events, to the twenty-five volumes of the ninth. The eleventh (1910–1911) was the first edition aiming for popular consumption; it was designed as a useful, reliable reference work for the general reader rather than directed as previously toward the scholar and educator. Its editorial offices were in London not Edinburgh; an Oxford man, Hugh Chisholm, was its editor; and its volumes were printed by the Cambridge University Press. Topics were no longer presented in long treatises but broken into short, simply written articles—a format that was to persist—and much use was made of current materials. A three-volume supplement added to the eleventh comprised the twelfth edition (1922). The thirteenth (1926), edited by J. L. Garvin, added three volumes to the twelfth and included a good deal of material from American contributors. The fourteenth edition (1929), also under the direction of Garvin, was the last numbered edition and the last edition produced principally in Britain. Its material—almost all new—would for a long period form the core of subsequent editions. After 1932 and the move to Chicago, a policy of "continuous revision" was adopted: all articles were scrutinized at scheduled intervals by experts and alterations made. The schedule adopted for scientific articles calls for more frequent examinations than does that for nonscientific ones. In line with this policy, editions are no longer numbered but simply carry the date of printing; annual printings are the rule. For a history of the "EB", see Herman Kogan's "The Great EB" (2).

ation of successive editions of the "EB" could reveal material both easily overlooked and easily helpful in teaching the history of a science, the author has undertaken a study of three different entries related to chemistry as a demonstration of the usefulness of this obvious primary source. In each case, the entries were read with the following points principally in mind: (1) How much information does the article contain, and what is its quality? (2) How authoritative is its author, and to what degree does his contribution represent the views of his contemporaries? (3) Can anything more than straight information be gained from reading the entry? Has it a covert value in teaching the history of chemistry? (4) What is its worth to the beginner and to the advanced student?

This examination, the essence of which is presented below, reveals, among other things, a fascinating panoramic view of the development of the subject over a 200-year interval; permits the retrieval of material forgotten, mislaid, or misinterpreted through the years; gives at any one period a general contemporary impression of the subject, useful especially in assessing the significance then accorded various ideas; makes available to the interested student a fuller treatment of old material than is generally afforded; offers both beginner and expert the chance to savour the style and language of a different age; and, to the inevitable amusement of present-day scientists, discloses some suggestions of cyclical trends in certain fashionable historical scientific ideas.

The entries examined were chosen arbitrarily but thoughtfully: *chemistry* (later limited, to keep within manageable bounds, to *history of chemistry*), as the chief topic under consideration; *atom*, on the ground that this entry must show radical change between 1768 and 1967; and *sulfur*, on the chance that it might show relatively little change. Each entry is dealt with separately and some general conclusions drawn.

Chemistry

This topic from the first is treated at great length; in the 1768 edition, for example, it continues over 112 quarto pages (around 150,000 words), while in the 1967 printing the entry is almost as long, though many of its aspects have been placed in separate articles. The author of the first discourse was probably Smellie; he was devoted to science and adept with scissors and paste pot. The chemistry he describes is Aristotelian and casual:

...the principal (elements) are earth, water, air and fire ...as we know by experience, that our senses cannot possibly discover the principles of which they (the elements) are themselves composed, it seems more reasonable to fix upon them, and consider them as simple homogeneous bodies and the principles of the rest than to tire our minds with vain conjectures about the parts or elements of which they may consist (*4*).

Phlogiston and these four principles are considered in detail under "chemical theory", which in turn is followed by a general view of affinities or elective attractions, already a worrisome problem. The remainder of the article deals with the various substances classified at the time under the principles already noted (*e.g.*, saline substances have an affinity with earth and water, the simplest saline substance is called an acid, *etc.*), their properties, analyses, sources, and uses as then known. The latest authority quoted is Robert Boyle; Glauber, du Hamel, Homberg, Rouelle, Geoffroy, Lemery, D'Henouville, DuFay, Malouin, and Kunckel are also mentioned, giving an overpowering indication of Continental authority. The tone of the article is complacent.

A far more professional touch shapes the entry in the third edition, which must be ranked as extraordinary among all the contributions on this topic. Its author is Thomas Thomson (5), then Professor of Chemistry at the University of Glasgow; its length is almost 400,000 words, and it is the precursor of his famed textbook, "A System of Chemistry", which was published five years later, in 1802. The article is a wonderfully complete account of late eighteenth-century chemistry, showing both the influence of the past and the vigorous beginnings of a new era. The language is still that of the old chemistry—"the element of fire", "marine acid", "argillaceous and anomalous earths", "ardent and acetous spirits"—the theory is not yet firmly Lavoisier's, the classifications are shaky, but the emphasis is heavily on quantitative studies. Chemical theory and chemical practice are accorded equal length. It is in the latter section that detailed and quantified (always in grains!) directions are given for the preparation and use of hundreds of substances, their properties described—often numerically (as specific gravity)—and chemical apparatus and procedures presented both in words and in copperplates. A valuable 15-page summarizing table considers "Natural bodies in a chemical view", dividing them and their substances into classes and describing their properties and preparations. The historian of chemistry is struck not only by the vast amount of eighteenth-century chemistry in the article but also by its clear organization, its remarkable and uncommon 20-page (30,000-word) index, and the beautifully drawn copperplates of chemical apparatus. It is notable also for its inclusion of 136 chemical characters or symbols as well as a table of the "chemical language" introduced only the year before (1787) by de Morveau, Lavoisier, Berthollet, and De Fourcroy in France.

Thomson, who would in 1830 also publish a history of chemistry, devotes the opening pages of his article to tracing the development of the science from Tubal Cain, the eighth man from Adam, down through the Egyptians, Greeks, Arabs, alchemists, and seventeenth-century philosophers to Isaac Newton, who "alone has done more to the establishing a rational chemical theory than ever was done before". Throughout this long article, in describing substances or equipment or in discussing processes, short historical notes are introduced. But the bulk of the entry is devoted to the work of contemporary chemists: the Frenchmen above, the Scottish school of Black, Crawford, and Irvine, the Englishman Priestley and the Irishman Kirwan, the Continental chemists Boerhaave and Margraf, and many others. Detailed reference is made to their work, many of their experiments fully described, their failures noted, and their conclusions carefully included, often in their own words. A 22-page appendix "Containing such DIS-

COVERIES as have appeared since the Compilation of the Article, and which could not be inserted in their proper Place" presents recent work, principally on acids and alkalies, by Higgins, Lavoisier, Cavendish, Proust, Priestley, Thouvenal, Tychson, Baumé, Scheele, Bergman, Berthollet, and lesser lights. An aura of change, of almost daily revision, prevails.

A heightened sense of excitement, of witnessing the birth of a new science, pervades Thomson's 250,000-word article for the fourth edition a decade later. Of chemistry he writes (6):

As an art it has been in some measure coeval with the human race. ....As a science, it can hardly be dated farther back than the middle of the 17th century; but since that time it has advanced with a rapidity altogether unprecedented in the annals of philosophy. Newton laid its foundations; and since his days an almost incredible number of the most distinguished names in Europe have enlisted under its banners. So rapid has this progress been, that though the article CHEMISTRY in the *Encyclopedia Britannica* was written only about ten years ago, the language and reasoning of chemistry have been so greatly improved, and the number of facts have accumulated so much, that we find ourselves under the necessity of tracing over again the very elements of the science.

Both the arrangement and vocabulary show radical alteration from the preceding edition. New developments in theory make possible tighter organization and neater categorization. The four main sections of the article are indicative of the changes taking place in the science: (1) of simple bodies (oxygen, simple combustibles, metals, earths, caloric, and light); (2) of compound bodies (water, alcohol, oils, alkalies, and acids); (3) of doubly compound bodies (soap, neutral fats, and hydrosulphures); and (4) of bodies "as they are presented to us by nature in the mineral, animal and vegetable kingdoms". In the last category, the discussion deals almost exclusively with Haüy's theory of crystal structure, which he was then in the very process of elucidating. Words never found in the third edition— such as oxygen, hydrogen, oxides, oxidation, gas, muriatic acid, phosphates—are used easily and familiarly. Whereas the 1788 edition had indicated some unease over the question of phlogiston, saying the dispute must soon be settled, this 1801 edition reports that its existence has been disproved. Caloric, unmentioned in the third, is referred to in several connections in the fourth and questions raised as to whether or not it is substance and the "same as light". Throughout the article a great deal of experimental work is carefully reported, and quantitative results are given in detail, along with conclusions drawn by the experimenters; it is, for the most part, very recent experimental work, including some with gases and with electricity. The copperplates accompanying the text show pneumatic equipment and crystal structure. A history of chemistry is omitted. Again, a magnificent index completes the article.

Thomson continued to contribute the "chemistry" entry through the fifth, sixth, and seventh editions, as well as writing articles on related subjects—baking, brewing, brickmaking, bleaching, and distillation. His chemistry treatise (7) in the seventh edition is typical of the direction in which his interest lay: again a respectable fraction—about one-tenth— of the 200,000-word entry is given over to a detailed history of chemistry ending with a consideration of the work of Davy, Wentzel, Richter, and

Dalton, the last receiving the most marked attention. Thomson had, of course, been the first to call attention to Dalton's atomic theory when he wrote of it in 1807 in the third edition of his textbook, "A System of Chemistry". His enthusiasm for the atomic theory and for Dalton's work is unabated almost forty years later, but he does point out that further investigations will be necessary to resolve the difference between the English and Continental schools as to the weight of oxygen (8 *vs.* 16). Again the remainder of the article is divided into four main sections, and again these categories reflect the changes in chemistry: (*1*) of the laws of combination and decomposition; (*2*) of the chemistry of inorganic bodies; (*3*) of the chemistry of vegetable bodies; and (*4*) of the chemistry of animal bodies. Reports of recent experimental work and quantitative results make up the bulk of these sections. Under each category the preparation, analysis, properties, and uses of most of the substances mentioned are given; the article serves as a valuable handbook on chemistry and chemical processes of the date. Both copperplates and index have disappeared. Significantly, a note at the bottom of the last page of the entry, markedly separate from it, reads: (CALORIC, or HEAT, will be treated of under the article HEAT).

The Dissertations oft he seventh and eighth editions direct their attention to mathematical and physical matters, though that of Dr. John Playfair (*8*) does mention that the "absurd and extravagant" dreams of the alchemists and iatrochemists resulted, after many decades, in the lasting benefit of the application of chemistry to pharmacy and the development of theories of elastic fluids. He uses, too, Lavoisier's experiments on calcination as an example of *instantia crucis* in inductive investigations, and he speaks of Berthollet's work with the bleaching industry.

Beginning with the ninth edition, the chemistry article is divided into sections written by different authors, each one a specialist in the topic that he treats. In this edition, three sections are found, none by an author so well-known as Thomson was or as some of the successors to these three London chemists would in future be: (*1*) historial introduction by F. H. Butler; (*2*) inorganic chemistry by the redoubtable H. A. Armstrong; and (*3*) organic chemistry by R. Meldola. For the first time our present conventional chemical symbols are used, chemical equations are written, and chemical substances are given names familiar to modern ears. Considerably shorter (150,000 words) than the previous article, this 1875 treatment is written with a remarkable tone of assurance and optimism—any points unknown or in doubt can in almost every case be given an explanation that is "not improbable". Its historical introduction—about 10,000 words—disposes of the Egyptians, Greeks, and alchemists in less than a page, moves through the sixteenth and seventeenth centuries in even fewer lines, devotes about the same amount of space to a group of individuals —Boyle, Kunckel, Becher, Stahl, and Hoffmann—but with Newton begins to give a somewhat fuller sketch. The work of the second half of the eighteenth century—phlogiston theory and its displacement by Lavoisier, pneumatic studies, and theoretical developments—are described, along with Dalton's atomic theory, Gay-Lussac's law of combining volumes,

Avogadro's hypothesis, and Berzelius' dualism. The remainder of the article is given to noting developments in contemporary organic chemistry and in "the electro-chemical science". Partly because of its brevity the account lacks both the drama and color of Thomson's historiography.

In the eleventh edition the entire chemistry article is much shortened (60,000 words), again has only one author (Charles Everitt, Fellow of the Royal Chemical Society) (9), and its section dealing with the history of the science, sadly contradictory to Smellie's original design "not to dismember the Sciences", shows changes best indicated by its own words:

> This section is confined to tracing the general trend of the science from its infancy to the foundations of the modern theory. The history of the alchemical period is treated in more detail in the article ALCHEMY, and of the iatrochemical in the article MEDICINE. The evolution of the notion of elements is treated under ELEMENT; the molecular hypothesis of matter under MOLECULE; and the genesis of, and deductions from the atomic theory of Dalton receives detailed analysis in the article ATOM.

From this date forward, a minimally adequate treatment of the history of chemistry is the rule. Now and then a new name or a different spelling appears, or an old one drops out, but arrangement and emphasis stay fairly constant: one column of the whole history given to pre-alchemical times, one and a half to alchemy and iatrochemistry, one to Boyle, one to the phlogiston controversy, one to Lavoisier, one and a half to sundry figures and events, one to Dalton and his atomic theory, and three to the work of the past century, ending with some mention of work in progress.[2] In the 1967 printing this arrangement has taken the form of two large sections: prescientific practical chemistry (from the Greeks through alchemy and iatrochemistry) and "chemistry as a science" (from 1597 through the early twentieth century). Its author, H. M. Leicester (12), is an outstanding historian of science and has used his assignment to give, in terms of the change and growth of concepts and in chemical organizations, a concise summary of a voluminous topic. His tone and subject matter, however, are too familiar to offer much to today's student in the history of chemistry that cannot easily be found in more detail and better arrangement elsewhere.

From the ninth edition onward, as might be anticipated, the significant points for the historian are in the "EB" points of detail, such as its failure to mention Mendeleev or his periodic table in the 1875 edition and his inclusion as an historical figure in the 1910 edition; the increasing number of substances identified as belonging to one or another category through the centuries; the rise of chemical industries and the development of chemical education; the formation of chemical societies and institutions; the explosive growth of organic and biochemistry from the late 1870's. The early editions, especially Thomson's articles in the third, fourth, and seventh, are elaborately useful sources for the student, not only in content

---

[2] In the 1929 edition (14th), H. B. Dixon (10) of the University of Manchester closes his article with mention of Rutherford and Bohr, while in 1959, A. J. Berry of Cambridge (11) has extended the Dixon article to include the Joliot-Curies and Chadwick.

but also in language, vocabulary, references, and as a mirror of the views and problems of the times. These articles involve him directly with phlogiston, antiphlogiston, caloric, affinities, classifications, preparations, and uses of chemical elements and compounds—all the worrying chemical questions of the past two hundred years—and with the triumphs of their resolution. In a way that no mere description can convey, they give the flavor of the past and a sense of the evolving science.

Atom

Changes of a different sort are demonstrated by this entry. It enlarges itself, for example, from the mere definition that was its total content for the first five editions (1768–1815)

ATOM, in philosophy, a particle of matter so minute as to admit of no divisions. Atoms are the *minima naturae* and are conceived as the first principle or component of all physical magnitude.

to the thousands of words that, beginning in 1875, make up the entry. The first edition (4) carried at the end of the above definition the directions "See Chemistry", but for a period in the nineteenth century "atom" belonged firmly to the physicists. "Atomic theory" in the modern sense did not appear until 1815 (fifth edition) when Thomas Thomson included Dalton's atomic views in his article on "Chemistry". In the third and fourth editions he had made no mention of them, and the entry in the fifth edition is merely "ATOMIC theory, see Chemistry".

No important change appears in the "atom" entry until the appearance in the seventh and eighth editions of Professor John Leslie's dissertation on mathematical and physical science. In the section of this paper on dynamics, Leslie (13) describes atoms as the "ultimate portions . . . [whose] . . . various combinations constitute the particles of matter". His discussion of atoms, some 1400 words in length, deals wholly with Boscovichean atoms.[3] He includes a brief and laudatory biography of "the ingenious Boscovich",[4]

---

[3] Boscovich theorized that matter was made up of three-dimensional aggregates of geometrical point-masses surrounded by force fields. Surrounding each point was a field of intense repulsive force, which, from a physical point of view, insured the impenetrability of each minute body. Alternate attractive and repulsive forces explained the physical and chemical properties displayed by matter in various forms. Mass was a function of the number of points in a given space, not a primary quality. Boscovich's theory, which is currently of much interest to historians of science, received serious support in many quarters. Both Priestley and Faraday found it more congenial than Newton's hard, massy, and impenetrable atoms. Philosophically, it continues to be an attractive theory.

[4] As early as the fourth edition, a 15,000-word account of Boscovich and his work appeared in the "EB", more than half of which deals with his System of Natural Philosophy (theory of matter). In the 1967 printing the entry on Boscovich is quite short, describes him as an astronomer and cosmologist, makes no mention of his atomic ideas but does drop the anglicized form (Roger Joseph) of his Croatian given name for the italianized version (Ruggiero Guiseppe). Boscovich was born in Dbrovnik in 1711 and as a Jesuit mathematician, astronomer, and natural philosopher spent productive years in Italy, France, and England. He died in 1787.

and, though regretting that this philosopher had "obscured his fine theory by an infusion of scholastic metaphysics", he states clearly his satisfaction with the theory and voices his concern that it has not yet been more widely accepted.

Almost fifty years later, another graduate of the University of Edinburgh included Boscovich's theory in his article on "atom" for the ninth edition. For this entry James Clerk Maxwell (14) wrote some 15,000 words. His piece is of exceptional interest not only because in it he explains his kinetic theory of gases, developed a few years earlier, but also for a number of other reasons: (1) his treatment of theories of continuity and discontinuity—both historically and in their applications to space, matter and time; (2) his long discussion of the Boscovichean theory as "an example of the purest monadism"; (3) his full account of the theory of vortex atoms, including its mathematical definition through differential equations; (4) his analysis of the significance of some current experimentation, especially spectroscopic studies; and (5) his comments upon the import of atomic theory applied to, among other things, the aether, the theory of heredity, the uniformity of physical constants, and the fundamental properties and creation of matter. He omits any mention of John Dalton and his atomic theory in a striking demonstration of the distinction current at the time between the "chemical" and the "kinetic" atom. Maxwell points out, in speaking of Gay-Lussac's work on gases, the difference between the definition of the word "molecule" as the chemists use it and as he himself uses it in his kinetic theory: the former arises from "purely chemical reasoning, not dynamical reasoning" and is "founded on chemical experience, not on the laws of motion". His references to the work of others are frequent and cogent—Joule, Clausius, Helmholtz, William Thomson, Boltzmann, Stoney, Loschmidt, Lesage, Prevost, and Galton are so treated.

Beautifully written, the article conveys unmistakably the quality of Maxwell's mind: open, daring, lucid, widely acquainted with the works of the past and the present, fair in presentation and careful in judgment, adept at verbal formulations of mechanical models, dextrous with mathematical and experimental data, unwilling to generalize without at the same time noting difficulties and exceptions, taking a patent delight in aesthetically satisfying mathematics. His account of vortex atoms, for example, illustrates splendidly his approach: after setting out the necessary conditions and developing the theorems for the formulation of "a correct mathematical theory of a material system", he shows how vortex tubes meet these conditions, subjects the vortex atom to scrutiny as regards its adequacy in doing the same for conditions arising from sensible matter, and concludes with an assessment of the possible validity of the theory:

> ...it is ingenious... it is the only theory of the cause of gravitation which has been so far developed as to be capable of being attacked and defended... it does not appear... to account for the temperature of bodies remaining moderate while their atoms are exposed to bombardment.

Far different in tone and different in caliber is the "atom" entry appearing in the eleventh, "the popular", edition. Written by F. H. Neville (15), its words are simple, its examples graphic and commonplace, its descrip-

tive adjectives frequent, and its higher mathematics nonexistent. Like
Maxwell's article, it begins with a brief historical survey of the subject,
but, unlike his, only the Greeks, Lucretius, and Boyle are mentioned. No
reference is made anywhere to Boscovich's atomic ideas or to vortex
atoms; however, almost two-thirds (4,000 words) of the article is devoted
to the work of John Dalton, the development of his atomic laws and theory,
and their verification in the work of Berzelius, Stas, and other experimenters. Weight ratios derived from experimental data are frequently quoted
and their significance in sustaining the laws of chemical combination
pointed out. Atomic weights, symbols, and formulae are discussed; the
reader is referred to the articles on *radioactive* and *element*. Clearly, he has
become the layman seeking capsule information rather than a scholar
seeking a learned summary of a subject. Clearly too, "atom" has moved
from the realm of the physicist to that of the chemist.

Not until the notable fourteenth edition was this article changed to any
degree. The author of the 1929 article was Niels Bohr (*16*). Bohr makes
no mention of atomic history beyond reminding his readers that "experimental discoveries of the second-half of the 19th century" had made it
clear that atoms were not indivisible but were made of aggregates. His
account carries all the excitement of immediate discovery; its concern
is with the present and the future. He tells of the work of Stoney, J. J.
Thomson, Zeeman, Lorentz, and Rutherford, launching into a discussion
of the properties of elements and the relations between them. Once
again, as in the days of Maxwell, mathematical formulae appear—the
Balmer equation, the Rydberg equation, Moseley's frequency relation.
Quantum theory, the spectra of hydrogen and higher weight elements are
considered, as well as the link between atomic constitution and the periodic
table (unmentioned by Maxwell, though both Mendeleev's and Lothar
Meyer's works had appeared in German and English in the early 1870's).
Approximately one-fourth of the 8,000-word article deals with "Recent
Progress"—developments since 1925, especially the wave mechanics of
De Broglie, Schroedinger, Pauli, Dirac, and others and the experimental
support that it was receiving. The reader is advised not only to "See chemistry" and "See element" but to look also at isotope, conduction of
electricity in gases, quantum theory and transmutation of elements. The
style is forthright and clear, but the material is taxing for the general
reader. A brief paragraph on atomic numbers by G. T. Morgan (*17*) of
London and a longer piece by T. W. Richards of Harvard (*18*) on atomic
weights follow this entry. The latter author, stressing the historical approach, begins with a description of Dalton's work and, unlike Neville,
mentions also Avogadro's hypothesis, Cannizzaro's paper, and Mitscherlich's crystal studies. Dalton's theory, firmly established since early in
the century, is buttressed by other theoretical and experimental work;
not even a faint shadow is cast upon present-day atomic concepts, even
by hinting at any awkwardnesses or alternatives—Boscovichean, vortex,
or Ostwaldian.

The Bohr article continued to be the hard core of subsequent entries
for over thirty years. Minor stylistic changes were made, a new introduc-

tion written, "recent work" updated, and sections on new developments
continued to be added in annual printing after annual printing. In the
1967 printing, however, a wholly new article is used. Its author is K. F.
Smith (*19*) of the University of Sussex, who had previously written some
of the added sections on new developments. In addition to the factual
information that it contains, the article shows some interesting evolutions
in emphasis. Bohr's atom has taken its important place in atomic history,
along with those of the Greeks, Dalton, and Rutherford. Once again,
increasing interest in the history of science reappears, to judge from the
space accorded atomic history. Six of the fifteen sections of the article
are allotted to it; the remaining nine are devoted to topics stemming
from the work of Rutherford and Bohr—atomic numbers, nuclear charge,
isotopes, energy levels, electron states, unstable atoms and so on. Dia-
grams are frequent; mathematics relatively simple. The article mirrors
a period in which knowledge in consolidated, in which reassessments of
the significance of past work are made with assured hindsight, and one
in which, satisfying progress having been rapid, future promise is measured
with happy confidence.

In summary, one may fairly say that successive editions of the "Encyclopedia Britannica" show, in the case of the entry "atom", a vast enlarge-
ment of that concept in science, its changing significance, and its wander-
ings from the purlieu of the philosopher to that of the physicist to that
of the chemist and now to a territory shared by the latter two. The caliber
of the articles is often extremely high. Those of Maxwell and Bohr are
of particular value in conveying a sense of their approaches to science
and in indicating their assessments of significant points in the atomic
concept. The contrast between the gradual penetration of Dalton's ideas
into the general topic "atom" and the rapid penetration of those of J. J.
Thomson, Rutherford, Bohr, and the quantum mechanicians is the measure
of the changing pace in theoretical development and acceptance of new ideas.
Fashion in ideas is demonstrated by the disappearance of Boscovich from
the place of prominence that he held in the nineteenth century; his reap-
pearance in the history of atomic theory may be anticipated in future
printings.

Sulfur

The greatest change shown in successive articles on sulfur is the change
in its spelling that took place some thirty years ago—*sulphur* to *sulfur*.
In contrast to the changes in "chemistry" and "atom", the general outline
of "sulfur" has remained remarkably fixed, reflecting primarily changes
in technology. Not until the eleventh edition did a separate entry appear;
until then the material was included in the "chemistry" article. The material covered, edition after edition, include the recognition that "brim-
stone" and its uses in bleaching and medicine had long been known to
the ancients; a description of its common properties —color, smell, taste,
texture, electrical conductivity, behavior when heated and when exposed

to air and water; a listing of some of its common forms, as flowers of sulfur, hepar of sulfur, and the like, and its common compounds (sulfuric acid, sulfates) and their preparations and properties; and some discussion of its occurrence and of its use in gunpowder. Even in early editions quantitative information is often given; specific gravities, melting points, and temperatures at which various changes are visible are listed. The discussion in the fourth edition by Thomson (6) of Stahl's idea that sulfur was composed of sulfuric acid and phlogiston and its disproof by Lavoisier is an interesting account of a then recent chapter in chemistry. Even as early as this edition the acids of sulfur are considered in sections separate from "sulfur", and their importance is increasingly recognized in subsequent editions. Thomson's description of the "modern" method of obtaining sulfuric acid by burning sulfur and niter in lead chambers as done in France is but one of the detailed narrations of processes in his article.

Although the crystallization of sulfur into different forms had long been included in the entry and the geometrical forms identified, not until the ninth edition does the term "allotropic forms" appear, along with the suggestion that they may have something to do with the "molecular structure" of sulfur. The ninth edition groups sulfur, selenium, and tellurium into one section for discussion in the "chemistry" entry but also has a separate "sulphur" entry (20) dealing primarily with its mineralogy and compounds.

The listing of geographical areas in which sulfur is mined lengthens through the years from "in the vicinity of volcanoes in the Mediterranean" (4) to include deposits discovered in other parts of Europe, in the United States, Japan, and South America. In the same way, the number of uses of sulfur and its compounds augments; from the first its importance in gunpowder, medicine, bleaching, and as an insecticide is noted, and dozens of other uses added year by year. Processes involving sulfur and its compounds multiply. An important chemical industry with far-reaching implications economically, socially, and politically develops rapidly from mid-nineteenth century. One indication of this change is the authorship of the "sulfur" entry, which in the 1967 printing is done by the research manager of the world's largest sulfur company (21).

In brief, a consideration of the entries on "sulfur" is useful primarily in illustrating the changing interpretation of data which have been long known. Technological changes—the development of new processes, new compounds, and new uses—the rise of a chemical industry that is central to the operation of a modern industralized state—these overshadow the acquisition of new and improved data and interpretations. The economist, the engineer, and the technical specialist may well find more of significance in successive "sulfur" entries than the beginner in the history of chemistry.

What, then, does the "Encyclopedia Britannica" really offer the historian of chemistry? Some of its benefits have been pointed out along the way; others await each specific searcher, often as a surprise. Some of its merits are obvious: (1) factual information, but factual information made more valuable because it reflects in its vocabulary, its arrangements, and its emphases the context of the time in which it is written; (2) fuller treatments in certain editions of topics which have for a variety of reasons become of lesser importance with the passing of years; and (3) an evolving picture of the development of a variety of concepts and concrete entities, treated expertly at each stage of their development. But its chief advantage may well be a hidden one—its assistance in avoiding some of the pitfalls that are always lying in wait for the student of history: (1) mistaking the context of his own time for the context of previous times; (2) distorting older vocabularies and usages by unconscious substitution of this contemporary vocabulary and usage; (3) the unintentional blinding from view of meanings and implications which theories and events carried in their own day but which have become lost or awkward in the intervening years; and (4) attributing to theories and events convenient nuances truly apparent only through hindsight. Direct, immediate contact with the work of the past is the happiest protection against such snares. This shield the "EB" can easily provide.[5,6]

[5] A growing number of primary sources are scheduled to become available to both beginners and experts in a few years. Already, all books printed in America before 1820, including numerous "pirated editions", and all books printed in England before 1614 are on microforms. Special microfilming services for out-of-print books are available. Potential services for uses of scientific information are now under study by the federal libraries, many private libraries, and library organizations. When combined with already available services—interlibrary loans, duplicating and reproducing devices, and reprints—these new services may well put primary sources in the hands of every interested student.

[6] The author has not included in the foregoing discussion any reference to an article by W. T. Brande, Professor of Chemistry at the Royal Institution, which, according to a personal communication from the Editorial Offices of "Encyclopedia Britannica", appeared as one of three dissertations in a supplement issued between the sixth and seventh editions of the "EB". Efforts to date to find this supplement have been fruitless, nor does such a dissertation appear in the numbered editions which the author has seen. A small volume (120 pages) catalogued as published in Boston by Wells and Lilly in 1818 and whose title page reads

Dissertation Third: Exhibiting a General View of the Progress of Chemical Philosophy, From the Early Ages to the End of the Eighteenth Century. By William Thomas Brande, Secretary of the Royal Society of London, Fellow of the Royal Society of Edinburgh, Professor of Chemistry in the Royal Institution of Great Britain, and Professor of Chemistry and Materia Medica to the Society of Apothecaries of the City of London.

has been examined.

Nowhere in it is reference made to the "Encyclopedia Britannica", and the date is troubling, since the sixth edition was published in 1823 and the seventh in 1830. Otherwise it fits very well the description given of the Brande dissertation.

This little book, about 40,000 word in length, surveys in its first quarter chemistry from the time of Tubal Cain through the seventeenth century. Its remaining five sections are devoted: one, to the work of Becher, Stahl, Rey, Mayow, Hales, and Boerhaave; another to the Scottish school of Black; a third to the pneumatic studies of Rutherford and Priestley; a fourth to Scheele and Cavendish; and the book closes with a brief résumé of the investigations of Lavoisier. Its material is descriptive, not quantitative, and the writing is florid, faintly polemical, and nationalistic in the praise given Scottish chemists over English chemists and both over foreigners. Many brief biographies are included, and the numerous footnotes are frequently interesting (as the one on the steam engine, pages 72—94) and often amusing (as the one about Robert Hooke's penuriousness, page 25).

11 Teaching the History of Chemistry

Literature Cited

(1) Smellie, William, "Preface", in "Encyclopedia Britannica", 1st ed., Vol. 1 London, 1773.

(2) Kogan, Herman, "The Great EB", Chicago, 1958.

(3) Einbinder, Harvey, "The Myth of the Britannica", p. 247, Grove Press, Inc., New York, 1964.

(4) "Encyclopedia Britannica", or a Dictionary of Arts and Sciences Compiled upon a New Plan in which the Different Sciences and Arts are digested into distinct Treatises or Systems and the various Technical Terms, &c. are explained as they occur in the order of the Alphabet. Illustrated with One Hundred and Sixty Copperplates. By a Society of Gentlemen in Scotland. In Three Volumes. London. Printed for Edward and Charles Dilly, in the Poultry, 1773. (A reprint of the first edition prepared for export to the American colonies.)

(5) Thomson, Thomas, "Chemistry", in "Encyclopedia Britannica", 3rd ed., Vol. 4, pp. 374–635, Edinburgh, 1797.

(6) Thomson, Thomas, "Chemistry", in "Encyclopedia Britannica", 4th ed., Vol. 1, pp. 210–403, Edinburgh, 1801.

(7) Thomson, Thomas, "Chemistry", in "Encyclopedia Britannica", 7th ed., Vol. 6, pp. 341–505, Edinburgh, 1842.

(8) Playfair, John, "Dissertation Fourth: Exhibiting a General View of the Progress of Mathematical and Physical Science, Since the Revival of Letters in Europe, Section II. Experimental Investigation. 2. Novum Organum", in "Encyclopedia Britannica", 8th ed., Vol. 1, pp. 570, 581–582, 589–590, Edinburgh, 1853.

(9) Everitt, Charles, "History of Chemistry", in "Encyclopedia Britannica", 11th ed., Vol. 6, pp. 33–39, Cambridge, 1910.

(10) Dixon, H. B., "History of Chemistry", in "Encyclopedia Britannica", 14th ed., Vol. 5, pp. 355–360, New York, 1929.

(11) Berry, A. J., and Dixon, H. B., "History of Chemistry", in "Encyclopedia Britannica, 1959", Vol. 5, pp. 361–367, Chicago, 1959.

(12) Leicester, H. M., "History of Chemistry", in "Encyclopedia Britannica, 1967", Vol. 6, pp. 387–441, Chicago, 1967.

(13) Leslie, Sir John, "Dissertation Fifth: Exhibiting a General View of Progress of Mathematical and Physical Science, chiefly during the Eighteenth Century. Section II. Applicate Science. I. Dynamics", in "Encyclopedia Britannica", 8th ed., Vol. 1, pp. 721–723, Edinburgh, 1853.

(14) Maxwell, J. C., "Atom", in "Encyclopedia Britannica", 9th ed., Vol. 3, pp. 36–49, H. G. Allen & Co., New York, 1888.

(15) Neville, F. H., "Atom", in "Encyclopedia Britannica", 11th ed., Vol. 2, pp. 870–874, Cambridge, 1910.

(16) Bohr, Niels, "Atom", in "Encyclopedia Britannica", 14th ed., Vol. 2, pp. 642–648, New York, 1929.

(17) Morgan, G. T., "Atomic Number", in "Encyclopedia Britannica", 14th ed., Vol. 2, p. 648, New York, 1929.

(18) Richards, T. W., "Atomic Weights", in "Encyclopedia Britannica", 14th ed., Vol. 2, pp. 648–651, New York, 1929.

(19) Smith, K. F., "Atom", in "Encyclopedia Britannica, 1967", Vol. 3, pp. 702–717, Chicago, 1967.

(20) Dittmar, W., "Sulphur", in "Encyclopedia Britannica", 9th ed., Vol. 22, pp. 634–637, H. G. Allen Co., New York, 1890.

(21) Duecher, W. W., "Sulfur", in "Encyclopedia Britannica, 1967", Vol. 22, pp. 391–395, Chicago. 1967.

17. THE TEACHING OF THE HISTORY OF CHEMISTRY IN SCOTLAND—PAST LESSONS FOR THE FUTURE

Owen Hannaway

Department of the History of Science, The Johns Hopkins University,
Baltimore, Maryland, U.S.A.

Attention is drawn to the long and vigorous tradition of teaching and research on the history of chemistry in the Scottish universities. Three representative figures, William Cullen (1710–1790), Thomas Thomson (1732–1852), and John Ferguson (1837–1916), are chosen to illustrate the motives which prompted this historical activity of Scottish chemists. Three uses for the history of chemistry emerge: firstly, to proclaim the status and dignity of chemistry itself by an appeal to its long history; secondly, to act as a framework for the teaching of descriptive chemistry at an elementary level; and thirdly, to give the young professional chemist an appreciation of the historical development of chemical concepts and theories. The implications of these approaches for the historiography of chemistry are briefly discussed. It is argued that the rise of theoretical chemistry has seen a concomitant decline in the historical approach to the teaching of chemistry. The resurgence of the subject stems largely from the emergence of the history of science as a discipline in its own right. Within this new context, the history of chemistry has new functions to perform in relation to history rather than to chemistry. An appeal is made for fresh emphasis on the social and economic impact of technical chemistry, and a warning is given against the dangers of a certain exclusiveness seen to be developing in the subject.

"According to the custom long established in this University, we shall begin with a history of Chemistry; and though this was introduced only probably to fill up the time allowed to public Lectures, yet it is of great service to the young student if properly attended to..."

William Cullen (1)

These comments, addressed by William Cullen to his chemistry class at the University of Edinburgh in 1756, are a forceful reminder of the very old tradition of the teaching of the history of chemistry in Scottish chemistry departments. Indeed, the history of chemistry has been taught in Scotland for as long as the science of chemistry itself. All four of the oldest Scottish universitites have produced or harboured chemists who have taught and written on the subject. Some of the names which come to mind are Thomas Thomson, James Ferguson, M. M. Pattison Muir, T. S. Patterson, Andrew Kent (all of Glasgow University); Alexander Crum Brown and Leonard Dobbin (Edinburgh University); A. N. Meldrum and Alexander Findlay (Aberdeen University); and John Read (St. Andrews University). In most cases, the work of these men was not just the product of an intellectual hobby which provided relief from the serious study of chemistry; but rather, reflected a sincere conviction that the history of chemistry had a valuable contribution to make to chemical education. Nor has activity been restricted to teaching. As long ago as 1904, Aberdeen University awarded its D.Sc. degree to A. N. Meldrum for a thesis on "Avogadro and Dalton, The Standing in Chemistry of their Hypotheses" (2). John Ferguson, throughout the period in which he held the Regius Chair of Chemistry at Glasgow (1847–1915), devoted his research interest

11*

to the history of chemistry, mainly on the compilation of his "Bibliotheca Chemica". His erstwhile assistant and colleague, T. S. Patterson, continued these research interests, publishing several important contributions to the history of chemistry, notably on Beguin (4) and Mayow (5). It was Patterson, who subsequently as Gardiner Professor of Chemistry at Glasgow University, introduced a course on the history of chemistry as part of a new honours curriculum in chemistry in 1924 (6). After Patterson's retirement in 1942, this course was continued by Dr. Andrew Kent, who brought the long Glasgow tradition down to the recent past, being the present author's mentor. Glasgow University Chemistry Department has supported two Ph. D. degrees in the history of chemistry (7).

It is not intended, however, to present just a list of past Scottish personalities and achievements: the present state of the teaching of the history of chemistry is our proper concern. Nevertheless, if we are to place the present situation in perspective, we should attempt to understand the work and aims of our predecessors. There are some valuable lessons to be learned. An attempt will be made to analyse the present position, *vis-à-vis* the past and the future, with illustrations drawn from earlier Scottish historians of chemistry.

Why have chemists lectured and written so profusely on the history of chemistry for their fellow chemists? As far as the Scottish scene is concerned—and this probably applies equally to other national situations—the reasons seem to vary in a subtle manner with the state and status of chemistry in particular periods and situations.

William Cullen's reasons for teaching the history of chemistry were quite straightforward and readily understandable. In the mid-eighteenth century, Cullen was pioneering a new subject on the academic scene in Scotland. Novelty has never been a particular recommendation in any academic circles, and it was Cullen's aim to demonstrate, both to his students and to the administration, that chemistry had as old an history as any other university discipline. As he said himself in his lectures:

> Professors in every Science take a pride in endeavouring to prove that Science as ancient as possible, whether they think that this antiquity will make it be more esteemed, or that they will shew its great usefulness by the esteem in which it has been for many ages: The Chemists have not been behind in this... (8)

This was not a new ploy devised by Cullen; here he was consciously imitating the example of Herman Boerhaave (1668–1738), who prefaced his "Elements of Chemistry" with an historical section (9), and even Boerhaave had his antecedents in this respect (10). Cullen's example was imitated by his successor in both Glasgow and Edinburgh, Joseph Black (1728–1799) (11).

A somewhat similar objective motivated Thomas Thomson to write his "The History of Chemistry" in 1830 (12). In his introduction he writes:

> It is natural to feel a desire to be acquainted with the origin and the progress of such a science; and to know something of the history and character of those numerous votaries to whom it is indebted for its progress and improvement. The object of this little work is to gratify these laudable wishes, by taking a rapid view of the progress

of chemistry, from its first rude and disgraceful beginnings till it has reached its present state of importance and dignity (*13*).

Thomson's effort, however, was aimed at a much wider public than Cullen's purely academic exercise. Chemistry by 1830 had grown beyond its largely medical confines of Cullen's period and had begun to show its potentialities in industrial and agricultural spheres. Thomson himself was actively involved in the instruction of a new type of laboratory-trained specialist (*14*): his "History" was a propaganda effort for this new profession directed at the general public. It is interesting to note how Thomson in this work almost apologises for what he regards as the shady origins of the science in alchemy.

Thomson, however, had another use for the history of chemistry, and this is exemplified in his textbook "A System of Chemistry" (*15*). Faced with a mountain of factual and empirical data which no longer fitted into the framework set by Lavoisier, Thomson adopts the simplest form of systematisation, the historical:

> The object of this Work was to facilitate, as much as possible, the progress of chemistry, by collecting into one body the numerous facts which lay scattered through a multiplicity of writings, by blending with them the history of their gradual development... (*16*).

In this respect, Thomson's "System" has some affinity with such earlier 'Histories' of sciences as those of Joseph Priestley (1733–1804) (*17, 18*). But the "System" was something more than a stimulus to the further study of chemistry—it was also intended as un up-to-date textbook. Thomson gives further justification for the historical approach in that "... by thus blending the history with the science, the facts will be most easily remembered, as well as better understood" (*19*). This use of the history of chemistry for pedagogical purposes has perhaps been the main justification for the concern of chemists with the history of chemistry. It has certainly coloured the approach to writing it.

Some forty-five years after Thomson published his 'History of Chemistry", John Ferguson, his successor in the Glasgow Chair of Chemistry, lamented the fact that his lead had not been followed up in Britain. In what was an *apologia* for his own cultivation of the history of chemistry, delivered to the Glasgow Philosophical Society in 1875, Ferguson contrasts British indifference to the subject, with the vigorous activity which was taking place on the Continent (*20*). At the time of Ferguson's address, Hermann Kopp (1817–1892) was still active in Germany (*21, 22*); in France C. A. Wurtz had produced his provocative essay on the history of chemistry (*23*), and F. Hoefer's "Histoire de la chimie" (*24*) was still a fairly recent work.

Ferguson justifies his historical interests by an appeal to the need for historical perspective in the assessment of current chemical theories. He regrets the disappearance of an historico-theoretical element in contemporaneous textbooks. He was not, however, advocating a return to the

chronological arrangement of facts; he was explicitly opposed to the inductive method in both science and history. "It is not so much", he states,
"that the facts of the history—or, as they may be called, chemical antiquities—are in themselves more or less interesting than any other mere
facts, but that they have not been made to yield results which are of permanent interest in the science of laws, in the general development of
thought" (25). Ferguson's appeal was directed towards chemists who,
he felt, were so absorbed in the facts of their science and in their theoretical
constructs that they had no sense of the transience of scientific hypotheses.
Thus "when a change comes, and every foundation seems to be giving
way, [they] are incapacitated by habit from estimating correctly the amount
and the character or direction of the alteration. The corrective for the
narrowness of such thinking is to be found in historical study . . ." (26).
This is a justification for the teaching of the history of chemistry to active
chemists in order to improve the quality of their chemistry. But it is one
of the several odd facts of Ferguson's career that he himself, in spite of
long years of research, never made any significant contribution in his
writings to the history of chemical ideas and theories: his research contribution was, in the main, to chemical antiquities. It is easy to be generous;
the skill and erudition which he devoted for thirty years to the compilation
of his "Bibliotheca Chemica" (3) has left students of early chemistry greatly
in his debt, but looking back on the somewhat privileged position which
he enjoyed for so long as a Scottish professor, one cannot but feel that
Ferguson's was an opportunity not fully grasped.

But if Ferguson himself did not contribute directly to his own ideal
of the history of chemistry, many of his contemporaries did. M. M. Pattison
Muir, praelector in chemistry at Gonville and Caius College, Cambridge,
who was a fellow undergraduate of William Ramsay (1852–1916) at Glasgow
when Ferguson was just beginning his career in the chemistry department,
attempted a survey of chemical ideas in his "History of Chemical Theories
and Laws" (27); A. N. Meldrum wrote on the significance of Dalton's
and Avogadro's hypotheses in chemistry (1904) (2); and in Edinburgh,
Leonard Dobbin (who described himself as a lecturer on chemical theory
and history) translated A. Ladenburg's "Lectures on the History of the
Development of Chemistry Since the Time of Lavoisier" (28) as well as
launching the Alembic Club reprints of classical chemical papers in cooperation with his Professor, Alexander Crum Brown, and other members of
the Edinburgh chemistry faculty. Alexander Findlay, among Scottish
historians of chemistry, continued this genre of chemical history in his
"A Hundred Years of Chemistry" (29).

When Ferguson's protégé in the history of chemistry, T. S. Patterson,
introduced a course in the history of chemistry into the honours chemistry
curriculum at Glasgow, it was partly his intention to overcome the narrowness of increasing specialisation in chemical education which his predecessor
had so decried. Unfortunately, Patterson was too faithful a pupil, and
he tended to fall into the bibliographical trap which his master had set.
It was left to Andrew Kent to give a course in the history of chemistry
in Ferguson's old department, which did indeed concentrate on the devel-

opment of chemical ideas and methodology as opposed to chemical antiquities. This course was the author's introduction to the history of chemistry,
and it was a provocative and stimulating one.

Thus there appears to have been three motives wich prompted the long
tradition in Scotland of teaching the history of chemistry. The first was
concerned with establishing the status and dignity of chemistry; the second
was the use of the history of chemistry in providing a framework for the
factual presentation of chemistry; and the third was to provide the young
professional chemist with some historical perspective of chemical ideas
and theories. The author personally experienced the last two approaches
in Scottish high school and university; and traces of the first motive can
still be found in modern histories of chemistry as, for instance, in the following tendentious statement by J. R. Partington in his "A History of
Chemistry": "Stahl has a high opinion of physical chemistry, which he
regarded as a separate branch of chemistry as distinct from common physics" (30). Partington was a physical chemist.

Understanding something of the objectives of our predecessors, we are
now in a position to evaluate our inheritance. Almost without exception,
the historians of chemistry discussed here were teaching or writing history
of chemistry for chemists, with the object of improving chemical education
in some form or another. Whether as a propaganda or as a pedagogic
device, the history of chemistry has remained mainly an internal concern.
The charge of parochialism is the one most commonly levelled at the subject, and it is largely justified. Even those works which purport to deal
with the history of chemical ideas and theories are noticeably lacking in
any appreciation of intellectual currents outside of chemistry, including
those of its sister sciences. Physics does not seem to have had a history
for many chemist-historians; but then, when you are writing for fellow
chemists, why bring in irrelevancies! Also, when the history of chemistry
was used for the teaching of chemistry or as a means of enlarging the chemical insight of students, it required considerable historical awareness to
avoid a history which justified current positions in the science itself. This
awareness too often was absent, and the history of chemistry frequently
deteriorated to a story of correct techniques and ideas triumphing over
erroneous ones.

A new situation, however, has arisen. Chemistry itself in recent years,
has undergone nothing short of a revolution. The emergence of theoretical
chemistry in the last four decades has broken down departmental barriers
between chemistry, physics, and applied mathematics. This new mathematisation of the science has not yet entirely eclipsed classical chemistry,
but it has affected teaching methods down to the lowest level. Whereas
former generations began with Dalton, the present generation picks up
from Bohr. This eliminates much classical chemistry from the start.
Chemical educators are now much more concerned with increasing their
students' mathematical competence than with providing them with a
sense of the historical development of a chemistry that is regarded as out-
dated. The history of physics would now appear to be of much relevance
to the young chemist. In short, amongst chemists themselves, the history

of chemistry is associated with an old-fashioned teaching approach which, it is felt, lingered too long in the classrooms and lecture halls.

This transformation of attitudes towards the history of chemistry on the part of chemists themselves may prove, in the long term, beneficial to the subject, if it forces the present generation of historians to grasp the opportunities presented by development of the history of science as an academic discipline in its own right. Freed from the old professional constraints, it is to be hoped that concentration can now be focussed on teaching and writing a history of chemistry which will be a genuine contribution to intellectual, economic, and social history in general. While it is true that purely chemical theories have not had the profound philosophical repercussions of, say, the Newtonian synthesis or the Evolutionary Theory in biology—chemical paradigms have not been drawn on such large canvases—no science has had such a direct effect on the material welfare of man. The social and economic impact of applied chemistry would appear to be areas in which the historian could make a valuable contribution in both teaching and research. To cite a Scottish example, A. and N. Clow's study of the role of chemical technology in the Industrial Revolution in Scotland is the type of work which could profitably be imitated (*31*).

The comparative neglect of the historical implications of chemical technology is all the more regretable when it is considered how much intellectual effort has been devoted to questions of priority in discovery and to elaborate and ingenious reconstructions of the genesis of certain chemical ideas. It may be important in some of these matters to set the historical record aright—where this can be done with recourse to extant sources—but these questions should not become ends in themselves. If there is one form of the history of chemistry which has *no* future, it is history of chemistry for historians of chemistry. This would be replacing an old form of internalism by a new and much more stifling one. Those of us who are engaged in teaching the history of chemistry in independent History of Science Departments must be on guard against the danger of just talking to ourselves. While an important part of our function is to train future historians of chemistry with sound, critical, historical judgement, our students in general and our wider public will expect something more than historical niceties. It is as well we appreciate that the new situation has its attendant dangers, as well as the old.

In conclusion, a study of the long tradition of the teaching of the history of chemistry in Scotland reveals that it was primarily connected with the teaching of chemistry itself. This tradition produced much valuable teaching and research, which was limited and coloured, however, by the motives which prompted it and by the restricted audience for which it was intended. Now that the history of science has gained academic status in its own right, the history of chemistry has entered a new phase. Freed from professional obligations to chemistry, it can now realize its potential as a legitimate branch of history, particularly in relation to social and economic history. To accomplish this, the historian of chemistry must resist the temptation of turning the subject into yet another discipline. Within a new academic context the history of chemistry has fresh roles to play in relation to history rather than in relation to chemistry. Surely we do not need to turn the wheel full circle and seek to justify the history of chemistry as a legitimate academic interest by appealing to the dignity and status of chemistry.

Literature Cited

(1) Kent, A., ed., "An Eighteenth Century Lectureship in Chemistry", p. 15, Jackson, Son and Co., Glasgow, 1950.

(2) Meldrum, A. N., "Avogadro and Dalton, The Standing in Chemistry of their Hypotheses", William F. Clay, Edinburgh, 1904.

(3) Ferguson, J., "Bibliotheca Chemica", 2 vols., Maclehose, Glasgow, 1906.

(4) Patterson, T. S., Ann. Sci., **2**, 243 (1937).

(5) Patterson, T. S., Isis, **15**, 47 and 504 (1931).

(6) Obituary notice, J. Chem. Soc., **1949**, 1667.

(7) Dr. A. Kent's and the author's.

(8) Ref. (1), p. 16.

(9) Boerhaave, H., "Elementa Chemiae", Leiden, 1732.

(10) Hannaway, O., Ambix, **14**, 103 (1967).

(11) McKie, D., Ann. Sci., **16**, 1 (1960) (published 1962).

(12) Kent, A., Brit. J. Hist. Sci., **2**, 59 (1964).

(13) Thomson, T., "The History of Chemistry", 2. vols., Colburn and Bentley, London, 1830–1.

(14) Kent, A., Proc. Chem. Soc., **1959**, 111.

(15) Thomson, T., "A System of Chemistry", 5 vols., 3rd ed., Bell, Bradfute and Balfour, Edinburgh, 1807.

(16) Ibid., p. viii.

(17) Priestley, J., "The History and Present State of Electricity", Dodsley, Johnson, Davenport and Cadell, London, 1767.

(18) Priestley, J., "The History and Present State of Discoveries relating to Vision, Light, and Colours", J. Johnson, London, 1772.

(19) Ref. (15), p. 13.

(20) Ferguson, J., Proc. Phil. Soc., Glasgow, **10**, 27 (1875).

(21) Kopp, H., "Beiträge zur Geschichte der Chemie", 3 pts., Druck und Verlag von Friedrich Vieweg und Sohn, Braunschweig, 1869–75.

(22) Kopp, H., "Die Entwicklung der Chemie in der neueren Zeit", R. Oldenbourg, München, 1878.

(23) Wurz, C. A., "Histoire des Doctrines Chimiques depuis Lavoisier jusqu'à nos jours", Hachette, Paris, 1869. First published as an introductory essay to the author's "Dictionnaire de Chimie pure et appliquée", 3 vols. in 5, Hachette, Paris, 1868–78.

(24) Hoefer, J. C. F., "Histoire de la chimie", 2 vols., 2nd ed., Didot, Paris, 1866–69 (1st ed., 2 vols., Paris, 1842–3).

(25) Ref. (20), p. 31.

(26) Ibid., p. 31.

(27) Muir, M. M. P., "A History of Chemical Laws and Theories", Wiley, New York, 1907.

(28) Ladenburg, A., "Lectures on the History of the Development of Chemistry since the time of Lavoisier", trans. from the 2nd German ed. by L. Dobbin, rev. ed., James Thin, Edinburgh, 1905.

(29) Findlay, A., "A Hundred Years of Chemistry", 3rd ed., rev. by T. I. Williams, Gerald Duckworth and Co., Ltd., London, 1965.

(30) Partington, J. R., "A History of Chemistry", vol. II, p. 664, Macmillan, London, 1961.

(31) Clow, A., and Clow, N. L., "The Chemical Revolution, A Contribution to Social Technology", The Batchworth Press, London, 1952.

18. HISTORY OF CHEMISTRY AT THE UNIVERSITY OF WISCONSIN

AARON J. IHDE

Department of the History of Science, University of Wisconsin,
Madison, Wisconsin, U.S.A.

History of chemistry became a curricular subject in 1908 when Edward Kremers offered the course. Between 1920 and 1940, it was taught by Louis Kahlenberg. It languished during the war years but was revived by the writer in 1946 and has been given continuously since that time. Graduate work in the subject soon became possible, and the first Ph. D. was granted to Robert Siegfried in 1952. Research in the history of chemistry has been stimulated at Wisconsin by acquisition of the Thordarson Collection in 1948, the Duveen Collection in 1950, and the Sinclair Collections in 1953. The library has also been active in filling gaps in the university's holdings in the history of chemistry.

Courses in the History of Chemistry

Courses in the history of chemistry have a long record at the University of Wisconsin. The first such course was offered in 1908 by Edward Kremers, Professor of Pharmaceutical Chemistry and Director of the Pharmacy Course, who met ten students in his home one evening per week during the fall semester. Kremers had already started a similar course in the history of pharmacy the previous year. These two courses were given at regular intervals during the next decade, and they gradually became more formal in character. By 1914, history of chemistry carried two credits, was listed as Chemistry 107, and was given every fall. In 1920, when Kremers was on leave of absence for the year, Chemistry 107 was entrusted to Louis Kahlenberg of the Chemistry Department. To Kremers' dismay, Kahlenberg refused to give up the course and continued to offer the subject in fall semesters until his retirement in the spring of 1940. During much of this period, Chemistry 107 was a required course for chemistry majors, but the requirement was dropped in 1937.

Kahlenberg also introduced a second course, Chemistry 209, "The Lives of Great Chemists", which was taught on an intermittent basis and was organized in the form of a seminar, with students studying and reporting on the lives of assigned chemists. Generally, after such a report, Kahlenberg held forth for the remainder of the period, discussing the work, personality, and foibles of the chemists under consideration.

Following Kahlenberg's retirement, Chemistry 209 was dropped, but Chemistry 107 remained in the college catalog. It was assigned to Professor N. F. Hall, but during the war years the course was never given. In the summer of 1946, with the encouragement of the Chairman of the Chemistry Department, J. H. Mathews, the course was revived by me and was given regularly in the spring semester.

In 1963, Chemistry 107 was abandoned, being replaced by two courses, Chemistry, 501 and 502. Chemistry 501, "The Foundations of Chemistry", deals with the developments in technological arts, Greek philosophy, alchemy, and medicine which laid the foundations for the modern science of chemistry. This course begins with antiquity and ends in the last quarter of the eighteenth century with the Chemical Revolution.

Chemistry 502, "The Development of Modern Chemistry", picks up the subject with the work of Lavoisier and brings the discipline up to the present day, emphasis being placed on the growth of chemical concepts, the rise of specialization in chemistry, and the impact of chemical knowledge on other sciences and on industry. Although the two courses follow a chronological pattern, they are independent of each other and may be taken separately (See Appendix for the content of these three courses).

These courses are offered at the upperclass level, a course in analytical and organic chemistry being a prerequisite. As a result, it is possible to presuppose a reasonably advanced knowledge of basic chemistry in the educational background of the students. It is not necessary to develop scientific background but the students' historical background is generally weak, and time must be taken to relate the development of chemistry to the major events in political and social history.

Very soon after I began teaching the history of chemistry it became apparent that there was no textbook adequate for the kind of course that I wished to give. As a consequence, I spent many years seeking to create a book that would be suitable for the course. This ultimately led to the publication of "The Development of Modern Chemistry" by Harper and Row in 1964. This book differs from the earlier histories of chemistry in that all chemical activities before 1750 are summarized in the first chapter, and the rest of the book deals with chemistry since that time. Almost all histories of chemistry have failed to deal significantly with the twentieth century. My book is unique in devoting ten chapters to developments of the last sixty years, a period in which chemistry has progressed further than it had during the entire previous history of man.

Within the next year, I shall publish a book which will carry the title, "The Down of Chemistry", and will serve as a text for Chemistry 501. This book will deal with man's activities in the manipulation of matter from ancient times to the Chemical Revolution. It will also examine philosophical concepts regarding the nature of matter and will show the technological, medical, and alchemical roots of modern chemistry.

Rationale for the History of Chemistry Course

Perhaps a few words are in order with respect to the place of the history of chemistry in the curriculum. It is my feeling that the principal rationale for the course lies in the opportunity which it provides to bring the areas of chemistry together and to make the subject a coherent whole. The present-day chemistry major takes a sequence of courses labeled general, analytical, organic, physical, and perhaps advanced inorganic chemistry, instrumental analysis, and biochemistry. The average professor feels harassed by the need to keep his course up-to-date. This pressure has caused him ruthlessly to discard historical material, biographical allusions, and rejected concepts in an effort to remain abreast of current knowledge and points of view. The result is a compartmentalized look at the status of present-day chemistry, without an appreciation for the interrelations between the several specialties, and a failure to see the growth of chemical knowledge as a human activity.

Ideally, history of chemistry should be a part of every course in the subject. Since history is the one facet of chemistry that most professors consider expendible, the senior course in the history of chemistry is essential if chemistry majors are to be sent out into the working world without a grossly distorted view of the nature of the subject. It offers an opportunity for the student to see the growth of chemistry out of philosophy, technology, medicine, and alchemy; to see the testing of hypotheses; the problems associated with the determination of atomic weights; the proofs of structure; the role of tools; the practical application of knowledge; the involvement of human beings and institutions; the influence on commerce and government. History of chemistry makes it possible for the student to see that chemistry is a creation of human beings and that it is a part of human activity. It brings about the realization that chemical knowledge is not static, that ideas are frequently wrong, and that even good ideas must be reexamined continually. Through a study of history the student gains an understanding of the real nature of chemistry, rather than moving into the profession with the conviction that present-day knowledge represents the science of matter.

The Graduate Program in the History of Chemistry

Although the history of chemistry preceded the study of general history of science at Wisconsin, the development of the History of Science Department from 1941 has significantly stimulated the growth of the history of chemistry. The History of Science Department was founded at Wisconsin with the coming of Henry Guerlac, who had recently received his doctoral degree in history at Harvard. Guerlac taught courses in introductory history of science and initiated research work, but his stay at Wisconsin was cut short when he was called to Washington in connection with wartime historical studies. When the war ended, he accepted a chair at Cornell University and has developed the history of science program there.

Robert C. Stauffer, also a Harvard Ph. D. in history, came to Wisconsin in January, 1947 and revived the history of science program. He was joined in September of that same year by Marshall Clagett. About that same time Erwin Ackerknecht was appointed to a chair in the history of medicine and George Urdang to a chair in the history of pharmacy. This group accepted me into their midst where I was close to the development of these various disciplines and was encouraged by them to expand work in the history of chemistry. Chemistry 107 was cross-listed as History of Science 107, and a seminar in the history of chemistry was started in 1957.

Toward the end of the 1940's, graduate students began to show an interest in certain fields of the history of science, and a Ph. D. program was developed. The Graduate School, as is commonly done with young departments, permitted work toward the doctorate when the work was done as a joint major with one of the established departments. In due time, the history of science department was granted the privilege of granting degrees directly.

The first student to complete requirements for a history of science doctorate was Robert Siegfried, who received the degree with a joint major in chemistry and history of science in 1952. The second doctorate went to Glenn Sonnedecker shortly thereafter, jointly in pharmacy and history of science. Dr. Sonnedecker remained at Wisconsin, taking over Dr. Urdang's chair in the history of pharmacy upon Urdang's retirement in 1952. Sonnedecker later succeeded Urdang as Director of the American Institute of the History of Pharmacy, which Kremers and Urdang founded in 1941. The third doctorate in history of science went to Erwin N. Hiebert in 1953, jointly in chemistry and history of science.

It may be of interest to list students who have received Ph. D.'s in the history of science on the basis of dissertations dealing with the history of chemistry or a closely related field. Their dissertation title follows immediately after their name.

Robert Siegfried, "A Study of Chemical Research Publications from the United States before 1880" (1952). Dr. Siegfried subsequently taught at Boston, Arkansas, and Illinois before returning to Wisconsin in 1963. He is a member of the History of Science Department.

Erwin N. Hiebert, "The Development of the Concept of Mechanical Work to 1750" (1953 under Professor Clagett). Dr. Hiebert subsequently taught at San Francisco State College, the Max Planck Institute at Göttingen, and Harvard, and he has done research at the Institute for Advanced Study in Princeton. In 1957 he became a member of the History of Science Department at Wisconsin.

Frederick A. White, "Significant Contributions of American Industrial Research Laboratories in the Development of Analytical Instruments for the Physical Sciences, 1900–1950" (1959 under Professor Hiebert). Dr. White is now jointly employed by the General Electric Company and Rensselaer Polytechnic Institute.

Albert B. Costa, "Michel Eugène Chevreul and the Chemistry of Fatty Oils" (1960). Dr. Costa is presently a member of the History Department at Duquesne University, Pittsburgh.

Victory A. Triolo, "Systems of Renal Physiology before Malpighi" (1962). Dr. Triolo is now at the Temple University Medical School, Philadelphia.

Ollin J. Drennan, "Electrolytic Solution Theory, Foundations of Modern Thermodynamic Considerations" (1961 under Professor Hiebert). Dr. Drennan is now Director of General Studies in Science and Associate Professor of Physics at Western Michigan University, Kalamazoo.

Clifford F. Maier, "The Role of Spectroscopy in the Acceptance of an

Internally Structured Atom, 1860–1920" (1964 under Professor Hiebert). Dr. Maier is Chairman of the Science Department of Monteith College, Wayne State University, Detroit.

A. Albert Baker, Jr. "The Development of Understanding of Unsaturation in Organic Chemistry in the Nineteenth Century" (1964). Dr. Baker, a participant in this symposium (Paper 6), is Chairman of the History of Science Department of Grand Valley State College, Allendale, Michigan.

Reese V. Jenkins, "Some Interrelations of Science, Technology, and the Photographic Industry in the Nineteenth Century" (1966). Dr. Jenkins is currently a member of the Department of History of Science and Technology, Case Western Reserve University, Cleveland, Ohio.

Edward Daub, "Rudolf Clausius and the Nineteenth Century Theory of Heat" (1966 under Professor Hiebert). Dr. Daub is a member of the History Department of the University of Kansas, Lawrence.

David Dyck, "The Nature of Heat and its Relationship to Chemistry in the Eighteenth Century" (1967 under Professor Siegfried). Dr. Dyck is a faculty member at United College, Winnipeg, Canada.

Stanley L. Becker, "The Emergence of a Trace Nutrient Concept through Animal Feeding Experiments" (1968). Dr. Becker is Director of Interdisciplinary Studies, Bethany College.

In the fall of 1966 I was joined by my first post-doctoral student, Owen Hannaway, who is a participant in this symposium (Paper 17). Dr. Hannaway received his degree at the University of Glasgow under Andrew Kent, presenting a dissertation dealing with early university courses in chemistry. Dr. Hannaway is now a member of the History of Science Department at Johns Hopkins University, Baltimore.

It is also of interest to call attention to books which have resulted from activity of students in this area. Professor Hiebert's thesis was published by the Wisconsin Historical Society under the title "Historical Roots of the Principle of Conservation of Energy" in 1962. The same publisher brought out Dr. Costa's thesis in the same year under the title "Michel Eugène Chevreul, Pioneer of Organic Chemistry". Dr. White's thesis led to the publication, "American Industrial Research Laboratories", Public Affairs Press, Washington, D. C., 1961. Dr. Baker's thesis is forming the basis of a book, "Unsaturation in Organic Chemistry", published by Houghton Mifflin in 1968. The University of Wisconsin Press expects to publish a book which is being prepared by Dr. Becker from his thesis. In addition to the above, the master's dissertation of Edward Beardsley, who took his degree in the History Department, but with a minor in history of science, led to the publication of "The Rise of the American Chemistry Profession, 1850-1900" by the University of Florida Press in 1964.

The return of Dr. Siegfried in 1963 gives Wisconsin a particularly strong group in the history of chemistry with good balance between fields. Dr. Siegfried is interested in developments of the eighteenth and early nineteenth centuries, the formative period of the science when alchemical concepts were being discarded and a sound understanding of the weight relations in chemical combination was being developed. Dr. Hiebert's interest in the development of energy concepts concentrates his research in the physics and physical chemistry of the nineteenth and twentieth centuries. My own interest in the interplay between fundamental knowledge and its application leads me to stress nineteenth- and twentieth-century developments in analytical, organic, biological, and industrial chemistry.

Research in the history of chemistry at Wisconsin has been stimulated by an enlightened acquisitions policy of the University Libraries. More than a century as a leading American university (1) means that we have not only comprehensive holdings of current scientific books and periodicals but also long runs of leading publications, usually back to the first volume, e.g., *Journal of the American Chemical Society* (1879), *Chemical Abstracts* (1907), *Liebig's Annalen* (1832), *Annales de chimie* (1790), Berzelius' *Jahres-Berichte* (1822–1850), *Transactions of the Royal Society of London* (1665), *Berichte* (1865), *Zentralblatt* (1832). The library has also purchased several book collections of major significance to the history of chemistry. The Thordarson Collection, purchased in 1948, brought the university extensive early scientific works, particularly works of the early British scientists. The Duveen Collection (2) (1950) contained over 3000 items dealing with alchemy and early chemistry. Two Sinclair Collections (1953) contained virtually everything published by Robert Boyle and Joseph Priestley. Gaps in these collections have been filled by systematic purchase of out-of-print books as they become available on the market. A catalog of "Chemical, Medical, and Pharmaceutical Books Printed before 1800" in the UW collections was published in 1965 by the University of Wisconsin Press. It was edited by John Neu, the librarian in charge of science acquisitions.

It is evident from the above survey that the history of chemistry has grown from inauspicious beginnings in 1908 to vigorous activity six decades later. The discipline serves as a basis for integrating the various fields of chemistry and causes the student to view chemistry as a whole rather than as a collection of independent specialties. It also provides an opportunity to examine the interrelations between experimental and theoretical chemistry and the impact of this knowledge on the economic, political, and social realms.

Appendix

Subject matter of the history of chemistry courses at the University of Wisconsin.

Chemistry 107 was a one-semester course carrying two credit hours (2 lectures per week). The course was last given in 1963.

Chemistry 501 is a one-semester course carrying 3 credit hours.

Chemistry 502 is a one-semester course carrying 3 credit hours.

Chemistry 107, "History of Chemistry"

Week	Subject Matter
1	Prehistoric and ancient chemical technology. Material concepts of the Greek philosophers.
2	Alexandrian and Roman science.
3	Arabic alchemy. Latin alchemy.
4	Renaissance metallurgy and technology. Iatrochemistry.
5	The Seventeenth Century. The phlogiston period.
6	Experimental studies on gases.
7	Overthrow of the phlogiston theory.
8	Combining relations—atomic theory.
9	Electrochemistry.
10	The search for an organic system.
11	Later developments in organic chemistry.
12	Growth of chemical industry.
13	Discovery and classification of the elements.
14	Thermochemistry—solution theory.
15	Radioactivity and atomic structure.
16	The rise of biological chemistry.

Chemistry 501, "Foundations of Chemistry"

Week	Subject Matter
1	Primitive man and his use of matter.
2	Technological arts in antiquity.
3	Greek concepts regarding the nature of matter—The Pre-Socratics and Atomists.
4	Continued—Plato and Aristotle.
5	Alexandrian and Roman science.
6	Greek (Egyptian) alchemy.
7	Arabic alchemy.
8	Latin alchemy.
9	Science in the Late Middle Ages.
10	Renaissance technology and medicine.
11	Iatrochemistry.
12	Seventeenth-century chemistry—van Helmont.
13	Continued—Robert Boyle.
14	Phlogiston theory.
15	The pneumatic chemists.

Chemistry 502, "Development of Modern Chemistry"

Week	*Subject Matter*
1	Foundations of chemistry—Greek philosophy, alchemy, technology, medicine.
2	Phlogiston and pneumatic chemistry.
3	The Chemical Revolution.
4	Combining relations and atomic theory.
5	Origins of organic chemistry.
6	Mid-century problems re: atomic weights, formulas, *etc.*
7	Periodic law—chemical education and organization.
8	Development of chemical industry.
9	Growth of organic, agricultural, and physiological chemistry.
10	Physical chemistry, thermodynamics, solution theory, electrochemistry, colloids.
11	Analytical and organic chemistry.
12	Discovery and consequences of radioactivity.
13	Chemistry in the World Wars—Chemical industry.
14	Recent developments.
15	Recent developments.

Literature Cited

(1) Ihde, A. J., and Schuette, H. A., *J. Chem. Educ.*, **29,** 65–72 (1952).
(2) Ives, S. A., and Ihde, A. J., *J. Chem. Educ.*, **29,** 244–247 (1952).

19. A VIEW OF THE HISTORY OF CHEMISTRY FROM AUSTRALIA

LEONARD TRENGOVE

Department of History and Philosophy of Science, University of Melbourne,
Melbourne, Victoria, Australia

A brief description of the teaching of the history of chemistry in Australia is followed by the author's own views on the subject. Since its establishment as an academic discipline, the history of science has suffered from an over-close association with philosophy, partly because of untenable claims made for the educational value of the history of science and partly because philosophers have professed to have special insights essential to the historian of science. This has often resulted in students of the history of chemistry spending much time on the philosophy of science which could have been spent more profitably in other ways, and scholars concentrating on particular episodes that lend themselves to philosophical discussion rather than extending their labours to other fields of the subject not yet properly treated. Furthermore, this association with philosophy has sometimes led to faults in historiography. The teacher of the history of chemistry is frequently hampered by the products of research available to him. Badly needed are many more scholarly biographies of chemists as well as editions of the classics of chemistry copiously annotated for students.

In the History and Philosophy of Science Department at Melbourne University, a course in the history of chemistry is given to second-year arts students. This is a half-year course and deals mainly with eighteenth-century chemistry and the work of Dalton. A similar course is given at the University of New South Wales as an option in the second year. In the future, at New South Wales, this course, extended from Dalton to Cannizzaro, will be given to third-year honours students in the history and philosophy of science. At Melbourne, honours students in their fourth year may elect to make a detailed study of some topic of the history of chemistry such as organic chemistry in the nineteenth century, the development of the concept of valence, or the history of agricultural chemistry.

The degrees of M.A. and Ph.D. may be awarded for theses on the history of chemistry, both at Melbourne and at New South Wales.

At the University of New South Wales, Professor N. P. Mellor, Head of the Chemistry School, gives a course of ten lectures on the history of the subject to all B.Sc. students majoring in chemistry. They usually take this in their second year. The lectures deal with the history of atomism from the earliest times, but the emphasis is on the nineteenth century.

At Melbourne, where I have personal experience, we are surprisingly fortunate in our research collection in the history of chemistry. For some years now, all books and reprints on the subject have been bought, and we try to acquire everything in the second-hand booksellers' catalogues that we do not already have. Also, we aim to build up complete collections in certain fields by obtaining microfilms, xerox copies, and so on. A selectio of the more important chemical textbooks of the past has been obtained, for these are very useful for giving students an idea of the formalized knowledge at the period they are studying.

Philosophy and the History of Chemistry

I turn now to my own thoughts on the history of chemistry. In what follows, I do not make a rigid separation between teaching and research, for I believe that many of the difficulties of the teacher of the history of chemistry still stem from the inadequacies of some of the products of research available to him. Some of my ideas are probably typical of no one in Australia except myself, but I would point out that the positions that I shall be criticizing are not those of my colleagues at Melbourne.

"History and Philosophy of Science" (*nomen atque omen*) is often thought of and indeed treated as a single subject. Certainly the history of science has become more intimately connected with philosophy than has other history. This is no doubt partly due to some strange claims that have been made concerning the educational value of the history of science. I would be the last to deny that our subject has educational value. For instance, it would appear that the history of science, science as a human activity, has a special place in the program of that peculiarly American invention, the Liberal Arts College. But I refer now to the claim that the subject can be used to give arts students an insight into the nature of science, provided that the subject is presented philosophically, showing how concepts develop, their relation to theories, and so on. The trouble is that chemical concepts, for example, though theory-laden like other concepts, are understood only in the context of laboratory experience. The claim that such students can in this way be taught to assess scientific arguments is not worth discussing.

The fact is that if the historian of chemistry is to produce good work, and if the student of our subject is to profit from his labour, they must have a love of the history of chemistry for its own sake and for the pleasures that it can bring. My knowledge of the subject can transform many places for me. In London, along Albemarle Street I meet Davy coming from the Royal Institution. I can wander among the disused mines of my birthplace in Cornwall and see it as it was in happier days: the famous copper mine Wheal Clifford with its hot salt-water spring (*lithium* chloride, be it noted) . . . I fear that this will all seem very naïve to the philosopher, but I believe that there are all sorts of opportunities for what may be called "local history of science" that we have not begun to take advantage of yet. Thus in many places where the history of chemistry is taught, there will be some local history that could be followed up—a chemist who worked there, a chemical institution, a university chemistry department, some chemical industry, an old chemical art, and so on. This would be of the greatest interest and value for the students.

Also, my knowledge of the history of chemistry transforms chemistry for me. I love "our most excellent child of intellect and art", and I want to know how we came to our present position. To a large extent the writing of the history of chemistry arose from such a desire. Men became interested in the history of chemistry when they realized that it was making great progress and had an exciting future. Thus when Pringle became President of the Royal Society, "the spirit of experimental investigation into every part and property of Nature was high" (1), and when he presented the Copley Medal to Priestley, his discourse traced the development of pneumatic chemistry to the point to which Priestley had brought it. Every journey into the past which the chemist makes brings new meaning to his subject, for no field of endeavour has a history more full of interest and romance than has chemistry.

Nevertheless, though the close association of philosophy with our subject is to some extent bound up with mistaken views of the educational value of the history of science, that is not the whole of the matter. It has been claimed that the special character of the history of science makes the insights of the philosopher particularly relevant and indeed essential. The idea seems to be that the philosopher of science must tell the historian of science what to look for in the past so that the historian can tell the philosopher what has happened in the past so that the philosopher can tell the historian . . .

I wish to dissociate myself at once from those who hold that the historian of science should not learn all that he can from philosophy. However, I am surprised and disappointed that philosophy has been able to contribute so little to our study and shows so little promise of doing more. I have never known anyone working on the history of chemistry who has encountered a philosophical problem about which he had to consult a professional philosopher. Moreover, I have found my amateurish acquintance with certain ancient and modern languages and with general history and literature far more valuable than what I learnt about facts, concepts, hypotheses, theories, and the rest from my initial study of logic and scientific method. Learned books on these subjects are always appearing, but one never finds in them anything helpful in writing the history of chemistry. It seems that all the logic and methodology needed by the historian of chemistry could be written on the back of an envelope. In any case, the philosopher's attitude that the scientist is always seeking explanations will not describe the chemist's activity very well. True, like everyone else he wants to understand what he is doing, but there is so much more than that, and I do not see how the philosopher of science can be expected to throw light on these other areas of activity.

The issue is to some extent obscured by the fact that philosophers often make illuminating remarks on the history of science. On these occasions, however, it does not seem that they are using anything that may be called specifically philosophical expertise. Even Tertullian, who held philosophy to be "self-stultifying, since it is ever handling questions, but never settling anything" (2), never denied the *wit* of the philosophers. Being clever people, they often make valuable observations and criticisms, but the clever historian or the clever chemist, untrained in the technicalities of philosophy, could equally well have made them.

If this is so, we see at once the danger of requiring the student of the history of chemistry to do a great deal of philosophy. Besides demanding that we are chemists, our discipline requires many other accomplishments. The student may do philosophy if it does not crowd out more essential studies. *Tout est dans tout.* But he must not think that philosophy will necessarily help him more in the history of chemistry than will, say, archaeology, classics, Arabic, theology, Swedish, seventeenth-century English history, or eighteenth-century French literature.

The difference between general history and special histories like those of the sciences was pointed out by Carlyle as long ago as 1830. He said that the history of the sciences deals with separate special provinces of human action and so may be written without so exact a reference to the rest (3). It is not that the history of science is specially related to some philosophy—Marxism, logical empiricism, existentialism, or any other. Besides, the outlook of the historian is different from that of the philosopher. This is sometimes expressed by saying that the former is more interested in particular cases, and the latter in generalizations.

The historian is concerned with a multiplicity of events. True, there is such a thing as not being able to see the wood for the trees, but there is not much danger of this in the history of science at present. On the contrary, we take such panoramic views that we tend not to be able to see the trees for the wood. Often, with our ready-made ideas of what woods are like, we see all sorts of similarities between one wood and another, and we explain these similarities so easily, not because we know so much about the woods, but because we have not examined the trees in sufficient detail, and we are ignorant of the undergrowth with all its rich variety. If we were prepared to pay more attention to trees and undergrowth, we might well find that certain woods that we thought hardly worth a glance were in fact full of interest. We might even get a sense of proportion about that over-publicized wood phlogiston! The fact is that much more purely historical research would have been effected by this time if it were not for the endless philosophical discussions of a few episodes which lend themselves to this sort of discussion.

Historiography, Hindsight, and the Great Wall of China

There is a book by Joseph Agassi, "Towards a Historiography of Science" (4), which might have been called "a short and easy way with nearly all historians of chemistry". I may be wrong, but it seems to propound the curious views that there is only one right way of writing the history of science and that if a reader finds a book boring it must be the author's fault. Now any book on our subject must be based on a thorough knowledge of and respect for the facts, but granted that, we are quite likely to learn more from works not written in the way that we think they ought to have been written, than from those which are. Gibbon wrote (5):

I was soon disgusted with the modest practice of reading the manuscript to my friends. Of such friends some will praise from politeness, and some will criticize from vanity. The author himself is the best judge of his own performance; no one has so deeply meditated on the subject; no one is so sincerely interested in the event.

I used to think that Gibbon was just being conceited. Now I am inclined to agree with him as far as the writings of *scholarly* historians are concerned.

Agassi's book is valuable, however, for it puts very clearly most of the precepts of our philosophical advisers. It is for this reason only that I shall be referring to it.

It appears that among scientists there are no good guys and bad guys, but among historians of science there are very definitely good guys and bad guys. There are even very bad guys.

The very bad guys are the inductivists. Their error is to believe that theories emerge from facts. Agassi does not seem to state where theories do come from but only discusses what happens to them after they have been conceived. The historian feels that this may be all very well as far as it goes. Yet it seems to him inadequate. How theories are conceived evidently varies from chemist to chemist. What constitutes falsification may even vary with the same chemist, according to his age. But be this as it may, why must we always be playing down the importance of facts in science? Whatever else theories come from—and it is obvious that something else is involved—they do come from facts, real or imagined, and whatever else chemistry may be, it does contain an enormous number of facts. We may look back with amusement at the German professor who began his lecture, "Gentlemen, we will now deal with the nine hundred and forty-seven reactions of methyl alcohol". We hastily add that chemistry is being turned from a vast catalogue of facts to a highly systematized science. But meanwhile the reactions of methanol run into four figures. The presentation may improve, but the catalogue of facts gets bigger and bigger, and that is certainly an important part of what we mean by the progress of chemistry.

Also bad guys, but not so bad as the inductivists, are the conventionalists. We are told that they believe that scientific theories are neither true nor false but are mathematical pigeonholes for classifying facts. I was not surprised to learn that they are unsatisfactory, but it is no part of my present purpose to criticize scientific theories. In fact, as I continued to read on, I was delighted to find that I have been following Sir Karl Popper all my life without knowing it. Even so, I had certain misgivings from time to time. For example, Agassi says (6):

> Since the ashes of metals were considered as exceptional and the ashes of coal as typical, the idea of the levity of phlogiston could not even be proposed before Lavoisier had shown, at a much later stage, that Stahl was mistaken here.

However, this error is probably not the result of following Popper but of not heeding something well-known to the historian of chemistry—that it s very risky to say much about work on metals in the eighteenth century without being thoroughly acquainted with the Swedish writings. The fact is that historians are born not made, but they can improve by diligent

practice of their art. I say "diligent" advisedly, for one of Agassi's conditions for any interesting or stimulating story to count as history is that
"it does not *often* violate factual information *easily* accessible to the author" !
(7) (Italics and exclamation mark mine).

The attitude of philosophical writers like Agassi to "loyalty to the up-
to-date textbook" also calls for comment. Most historians of science, they
claim, paint past events (and sometimes people) white or black according
to whether or not they agree with the up-to-date textbook. This means
that whenever the textbook alters, the history of science changes accordingly ! Philosophical writers often give the impression that the scientist
in his lifetime lives through a series of *bouleversements*. Yet one of the most
remarkable features of chemistry textbooks since Lavoisier is the way in
which they have appeared rather like successive editions of "The Chemistry
Textbook". In any case, no one can write the history of science *sub specie
aeternitatis*. The historian's book, in due course, itself becomes an historical
document, a document that may be studied not only for what it intended
to record but also for what it reveals of the time in which it was written.

It is, of course, important for the historian of chemistry to follow the
paths which led to dead ends in the past as well as those which led to modern
views. At the same time, because hindsight is not an unmixed blessing to
the historian, let us not forget that it *is* a blessing. So much emphasis on
the error of assessing past chemists and their work on the basis of modern
chemistry tends to obscure an equally important point—the value of the
present in understanding the past. We can give a better account of the history of pneumatic chemistry in the eighteenth century than Thomas
Thomson could. This is not because we in the twentieth century are better
historians of chemistry than Thomson. Most of us are not. Neither is it
just because we have more records at our disposal. It is because we have
a better perspective of the work, and this in turn is connected with the
advance of chemistry up to the present time.

If there are in general no good guys or bad guys in the history of science,
this does not apply apparently to classical times. The Greek writers were
all good guys. If the philosophical historian of science has a greater horror
of prolepsis than most people, he sheds all his fears as he steps into the
golden mists of antiquity. In particular, "the tyranny of the Stagirite"
over twentieth-century historians of science is a most remarkable phenomenon. I believe that Sarton was disappointed that he could not induce
the classicists to take more interest in the work being done by historians
of science on the Greeks, but what could they learn from what has been
done so far ? (I am, of course, excluding the work of the historians of mathematics.) It is true that until recently classical scholars had badly neglected
what is usually called Greek science and technology. It is not only that
the interpretation of these texts has not been pursued so diligently as that
of others, but in some cases editions are inadequate or even non-existent.
At the same time, it is easier for someone versed in ancient Greek language
and literature to acquire sufficient knowledge of modern science to enter
this field, than it is for the scientists to become an expert classicist. As
Professor W. K. C. Guthrie has suggested, classicists could do valuable

service in producing a more balanced picture of Greek science than the great majority who approach the subject from the position of the scientist or historian (8).

Moreover, even if I were more convinced about the worth of what has been done so far by historians and philosophers of science on Greek philosophy, I would still doubt the wisdom of getting Greekless students to study intensively extracts from the Greek philosophers translated into English. I am no Greek scholar but when, for example, I read Aristotle in the original with one of the great commentaries, it becomes far more illuminating. One must as least be able to check passages in the original, for here, if anywhere, *traduttori traditori*. Professor Guthrie has said (9): "Divorce the study of Greek philosophy from a scholarly appreciation of the details of Greek grammar and semantics, and we are like men walking through an unchartered minefield".

The historian of chemistry filled with a desire to plunge back into antiquity might at least be expected to turn more to the study of ancient materials, for example—a study which in the past he has been too ready to leave to the classicists and archaeologists. But this urge to begin the history of any science with Thales is another curiosity of the subject. It is what I call "Great Wall of China history", because, of course, there is a sense in which even this American Chemical Society Symposium at San Francisco cannot be fully explained without reference to the building of the Great Wall of China, though we do not usually feel it necessary to go back that far. It is true that one may write a continuous history of astronomy and perhaps of mechanics from antiquity, but it is otherwise with chemistry. Before 1750 there was not even a well-defined field of chemistry. Nowadays, though we may not be able to define chemistry properly, we know chemistry when we see it, so to speak. Looking back, we can see that in a sense there has been chemistry from antiquity—in fact much more than the traditional path which traces the theory of matter through Greek philosophy, alchemy, iatrochemistry ... But we have been so intent on not dismissing as out-of-date speculation all that came before the rise of modern science that we have tended to obscure the great difference between modern science and what went before, a difference qualitative as well as quantitative.

Another part of the history of science which is often done badly may just be noted. I refer to those parts where a knowledge of theology is required; for example, in dealing with some aspects of the Middle Ages and of the seventeenth century. This is not a matter of impiety but of ignorance. If it takes five or six years to train a theologian, any untrained writer should tread warily when he ventures into the field. Moreover, students seem only too willing to follow the erring authors, and often have the temerity to add something even more misguided of their own.

Two Desiderata of the History of Chemistry

(1) Biographies

One of the most remarkable effects of the idea that the history of science is so different from history in general is that histories of science are frequently written without any mention of scientists or at least without mention of them as human beings. One would have imagined that there was no likelihood of anything analogous happening in the history of technology (as far as I know there is not at present a philosophy of technology), but a writer of a history of mechanical engineering (*10*) explains to his readers that he has found it impractical to leave out the names of engineers altogether!

We are well aware that in order to win his battles, General Grant, for example, needed thousands of men whose names do not appear in the history books. In Carlyle's well-known phrase, "history is the essence of innumerable biographies" (*11*). The history of chemistry, however, is the essence of *numerable* biographies, for it can be studied without such strict reference to the activities of men in general. In this history, moreover, it is extremely important if a great man of science happens to be living at a particular time. True, even Newton stood on the shoulders of giants. Nevertheless, though he lived in an age of genius and was reluctant to publish, only he could write the "Principia". Hooke plus Halley plus Wren plus the other members of the Royal Society did not equal Newton. Again, the discoveries of Newton would doubtless have been made at various times by diverse people in the course of the eighteenth century. But, as Whitehead pointed out, the same impact would not have been made. Pope would not have written those oft-quoted lines, and the history of science and indeed the history of Western thought would have been different. On the other hand, there have been times when the conditions seem to have been favourable for an advance, but the great man of science needed was not living, or his lot forbade and he joined that company in Gray's churchyard "born to blush unseen". (The historian is, of course, concerned with many other factors that are not relevant to the philosopher's enquiry as such. Thus the availability of funds for research is important, and is becoming increasingly so.)

Biography is, then, of particular importance in the history of chemistry. In fact, after a preliminary survey of the field, the best introduction to the subject is through biography. In this way the student can get the "feel of the period" (including the philosophical outlook of the time, of course), the relation of the particular chemist's work to what others were doing in the same or related fields, the difficulties encountered, and so on. Here I come to the first desideratum for teaching our subject, the need for many more full-scale, scholarly biographies of chemists. According to Boswell, who should have known, biography occasions a degree of trouble far beyond that of any other species of writing. Some authors of biographies of scientists, for example, have not troubled to get an adequate knowledge of the period, and sometimes have plainly not taken the trouble to visit the places they write about! We do have some good biographies, but we need a far greater number, including many on chemists who have not as yet attracted biographers.

Here I will interpolate a brief account of a course given to fourth-year honours students at Melbourne, though it is only partly concerned with chemistry. It is a year's course on Newton, a biography of Newton, so to speak. At the outset, the students are advised to read a number of books during the course to give them that "haze in the middle distance" so essential to the historian—books like Pepys' "Diary", Evelyn's "Memoirs", Sprat's "History of the Royal Society", Aubrey's "Lives", Burnet's "History", and various modern histories of the period. The course covers Newton's mathematics, mechanics, optics, chemistry, theology, chronology, and his work at the Mint, and it is all related to other work being done at the time. The examination paper at the end of the year gives quite a wide choice of questions, for the students cannot be expected to cover each part of the work in equal depth and detail. Nevertheless, they usually find the course a fresh experience in the history of science. Obviously, a similar course with a greater chemical content could be given, taking someone like Priestley as subject, for example.

The fact that great chemists themselves have not generally been disposed to write *autobiographies* is a matter for regret but one which cannot be rectified. It is all the more important that anecdotes about them should be preserved and incorporated into biographies. To the historian, anecdotes may not merely point a moral or adorn a tale, but they often give valuable insights into a chemist's work or his influence on other workers.

(2) *Editions of the Classics of Chemistry*

Badly needed for the student who has made some progress in the subject are more editions of the classics of chemistry with good introductions giving the historical background in detail and copious notes on the text. (By classics of chemistry I mean not only the great books, but also the great papers.) Though these editions are intended primarily for students, there should be no omissions. Apart from the sacrilege involved, any omission would make them useless for anyone engaged in research, for they would have to check what had been omitted in any case. No one can judge beforehand that something will be unimportant for *any* investigation. Further, if the text is in a foreign language, it may be translated, but the original should also be given, difficult points of translation clarified, and technical terms explained.

What is required in these editions is the same care and scholarship that has been bestowed upon the Latin and Greek classics. In fact, a book which comes very near to what I am envisaging might be regarded as one of these Greek classics rather than a work on early chemistry. I refer to Professor Eichholz's edition of "Theophrastus de Lapidibus" (*12*). The introduction and the commentary are very good, and the translation facing the Greek is ideal as an aid to the student reading the original. If it had been possible to publish the mineralogical chapters for which the geologist collaborator was to have been responsible, I do not think the book would have left much to be desired. But we need many such works dealing with the classics of our subject up to the present time. The precise form of each will, of course, depend upon the nature of the text itself. Also, collections of letters of the great chemists with appropriate commentaries and without omissions should be made available to the student. He will learn much about the chemists and the times in which they lived from these writings not intended for publication.

Apart from the actual history learned by studying such editions as I have suggested, the insights gained and the skills acquired (in particular, *attention to detail*) will greatly benefit the student if and when he begins his own research into the history of chemistry.

Conclusion

Better biographies and editions of the chemical classics would follow naturally from a changed attitude toward our subject. It was perhaps to be expected that a philosophy like logical empiricism, which regarded scientific knowledge as the norm, would have had great influence on the history of science. As a matter of fact, the history of chemistry has not been affected so much as the history of physics, for the good reason that our so-called philosophy of science is really a philosophy of theoretical physics, which, *pace* the positivists, is not typical of science in general. But be that as it may, it is time that the history of science came of age. The philosopher of science has never been able to persuade the chemist that his special insights are essential to chemical investigations, so it is difficult to see why he should have more success with the historian of chemistry. The historian of chemistry has no more and no less need of the philosophy of science than the historian of Christian doctrine has of the philosophy of religion.

This does not mean, however, that the historian of chemistry should now talk in isolation. On the contrary, he should see his subject more clearly as part of history in general, with chemistry playing an ever increasing part in that history. His investigations would enrich general history, and also a new and better history of chemistry would emerge. This would be the best contribution to the improvement of the teaching of our subject that could be made.

Literature Cited

(1) Kippis, A., "Six Discourses delivered by Sir John Pringle, Bart...", p. xxxv, London, 1783.
(2) Tertullian, "Liber de Praescriptione", vii.
(3) Carlyle, T., "Miscellaneous and Critical Essays", Vol. II, p. 356, London, 1839.
(4) Agassi, J., "Towards an Historiography of Science", Mouton, The Hague, 1963.
(5) Gibbon, E., "Autobiography", p. 308, Oxford University Press, Oxford, 1907.

(6) Agassi, J., *op. cit.*, p. 42.
(7) *Ibid.*, p. 74.
(8) Guthrie, W. K. C., "Greek Philosophy, the Hub and the Spokes", p. 18, Cambridge University Press, Cambridge, 1953.
(9) *Ibid.*, p. 28.
(10) Burstall, A. F., "A History of Mechanical Engineering", p. 10, Faber and Faber, London, 1963.
(11) Carlyle, T., *op. cit.*, p. 348.
(12) Eichholz, D. E., "Theophrastus de Lapidibus", Oxford University Press, Oxford, 1965.

20. TEACHING THE HISTORY OF CHEMISTRY IN JAPAN*

BUN-ICHI TAMAMUSHI**

Nezu Chemical Institute, Musashi University,
Nerimaku, Tokyo, Japan

After describing the place of the history of chemistry in the Japanese system of
secondary and higher education, the author cites his experiences in three types of
courses—(1) a chemistry course for nonscience students with liberal use of historical
background material intended to acquaint them with actual scientific procedures;
(2) an elective general education course in the history of science (Part I: Physics;
Part II: Chemistry) for both science and nonscience students, primarily utilizing
Conant's "case study" approach; and (3) a four-semester program for training
professional historians of science or of chemistry. Special problems are then discussed,
such as bridging the gap between the modern, scientific, technological culture rapidly
assimilated from the West in the century since the Meiji restoration and Japan's
traditional cultural values. Finally, the activities of Japanese scientific societies and
journals with respect to the history of chemistry are considered.

This paper is based chiefly on my personal experience in teaching, but
I hope that it may give more or less a general idea of the state of the
teaching of the history of chemistry in Japan.

In the early 1920's, when I was a student in the Chemistry Department
at the University of Tokyo, Professor Yuji Shibata, now President of the
Japan Academy, gave us a lecture on inorganic chemistry which was not
merely information on the systematic knowledge of this field but was
accompanied by an historical introduction for every main subject. I remember that his lecture was particularly inspiring because of his treatment
of subjects which otherwise might have been rather monotonous.

Soon afterwards, when I began to teach chemistry to students of a
preparatory school for universities of the prewar system in Japan, I could
hardly find time for weaving the historical background into my course
plan for introductory chemistry, though I endeavoured to give students
interest and stimulation in learning chemistry by relating to them occasionally the history of some remarkable chemical discoveries.

My own interest in the history of chemistry, however, gradually increased
through my teaching experience, and I later came to believe that some
training in the study of the history of chemistry should be a prerequisite
for every good chemistry teacher. I also remember that the *Journal of
Chemical Education* began publication by the American Chemical Society
in 1924, just as I started my career as a chemistry teacher and that, since

* Another version of this paper appeared in *Japanese Studies* in the *History of
Science*, 8, 9–16 (1969).
** Work done at Department of Chemistry, Tokyo Joshi Daigaku, Zempukuji,
Suginami-ku, Tokyo, Japan.

then, how much I have profited and been stimulated by articles on the history of chemistry which now and then appeared in this journal.

After World War II the educational system of Japan changed radically. We adopted the so-called six-three-three-four-year school system after the model of the United States in place of the prewar German-type system. At present, the teaching of chemistry as an independent subject begins in senior high school, and a certain number of credits in chemistry are required for all students who enter colleges and universities. There is a minimum standard for the course plan of the secondary school chemistry set up by the Ministry of Education, in which no special stress is given to teaching historical topics, although many high school textbooks are usually illustrated with portraits of great chemists and appended with chronological tables of Nobel prize laureates or of important chemical discoveries. Nevertheless, through the years I have found that interest and knowledge of college freshmen in historical matters are generally poor and immature. In a typical class, only some ten to twenty percent of the students can give satisfactory answers to such questions as: What are the chief works of Lavoisier, Dalton, and Mendeleev and what are the approximate dates of their publications? This seems to indicate that secondary school students are so crammed with actual chemical facts to be memorized that they have little time for the history of chemistry.

In Japanese colleges and universities the undergraduate course consists of two parts, namely, the general education course and the specialized education course. The former covers usually the first three semesters, while the latter covers the remaining five semesters, one academic year being divided into two semesters. Accordingly, chemistry is treated also as a subject of the general education program, which is commonly further classified into two course plans: one for science students and another for nonscience students. The former plan usually takes the form of general chemistry as exemplified by Linus Pauling's well known textbook, whereas the latter takes various forms and contents, according to the instructor's choice and inclination.

Teaching the history of chemistry is naturally a problem concerned with either the course for science students or that for nonscience students. From my point of view, every college or university chemistry department should provide some practical plans for teaching the history of chemistry to both types of students. In actuality, however, curricula set up by most chemistry departments in our institutions are too overcrowded to spare time or space for teaching the history of chemistry. For science-major students, even in the introductory chemistry course, most instructors feel the shortage of time for handling historical subjects because of the ever-increasing amount of technical material that must be mastered by today's students. In such a situation it is natural that our experiences in teaching the history of chemistry have been mainly relevant to the course for nonscience students in liberal education programs.

During these eighteen years I have been occasionally engaged in teaching chemistry to nonscience students at the University of Tokyo and the Tokyo Woman's Christian College, and based upon this teaching experience

I have written a textbook (*1*), in which I have tried to treat historically some important concepts in chemistry, such as atoms and molecules, ions, nuclear atoms, chemical bond, chemical affinity, reaction equilibrium and kinetics, structural isomerism, macromolecules, *etc.* For example, when I treat the concept of "ions", I first introduce students to the phenomenon of electrolysis through a demonstration experiment on a solution of zinc bromide as an example in order to give them a visual impression of the separation of elements at the positive and negative electrodes, and I tell them how Faraday arrived at the notion of "ions" as moving particles carrying electricity. Then I touch upon Hittorf's work on determining relative velocities of anions and cations in a given electric field. After showing demonstration experiments on electric conductance through gases, I explain how J. J. Thomson arrived at the discovery of electrons. Meanwhile, students carry out in the laboratory the determination of the Faraday constant and learn about Millikan's work on the determination of the elementary charge. By comparing these two quantities students can conceive of "ions" as particles carrying elementary charges in simple integral amounts. After relating the story of Rutherford's discovery of the atomic nucleus, I proceed to explain the Bohr models for atomic structure without going into detailed mathematical treatment of the theory. On the basis of such models, students can finally recognize the hydrogen ion or other ions as atomic nuclei or kernels deprived of some integral numbers of outer electrons.

This course is, however, not a course on the history of chemistry but rather a course on chemistry referred to the historical background of the subject. I presume that such a method of introducing chemical concepts as exemplified above should be effective in giving students an understanding of scientific method, which is to be considered one of the most important objects of teaching chemistry to nonscience students. Though I am still not certain if my attempt has been successful, I could at least find some progress in the student's grasp of scientific thinking and their appreciation of historical subjects by their responses to questions on final examinations.

It is often pointed out that in a liberal education it is important to give students an understanding of the relationship of science to general human culture. For this purpose, it might be better to design a course in the history of chemistry (or of science) as a single subject in a curriculum and to treat it according to the basic idea suggested by George Sarton (*2*). The traditional outline course on the history of chemistry would be rather tiresome to ordinary students, whereas the method of case histories proposed by J. B. Conant (*3*) is considered more effective.

At the Tokyo Woman's Christian College there is a course on the history of science open to both science and nonscience students in the general education program. This course is a one-year course, consisting of two parts: Part 1, which is taught by Dr. Watanabe, includes such topics as: astronomy from ancient times through Copernicus to Newton; studies on the nature of heat by Rumford, Joule, Carnot, and Helmholtz; science in relation to religion and literature during the seventeenth and eighteenth centuries; the development of science in modern Japan, *etc.* (*4*); and Part 2,

13 Teaching the History of Chemistry

which I teach, includes topics such as: the establishment of modern chemistry by Lavoisier; the development of atomic theory from Dalton to Rutherford; Pasteur and spontaneous generation of life; the development of synthetic chemistry and industrial applications; the twentieth century's scientific scene and its philosophical implications, *etc*. This course, as it appears, is not an outline course but consists of case histories. The number of students in the class often exceeds more than one hundred, and we instructors feel quite a heavy burden in assigning reading materials to students and in reading their reports on these topics.

There are several other examples of similar courses on the history of chemistry (or of science) which are offered at Japanese colleges and universities. I mention here the names of only a few of the chemists who are teaching such courses in their respective institutions: Drs. T. Dono (Nagoya Technical College), H. Kashiwagi (Nagoya University), M. Tanaka (Tokyo Institute of Technology), and Y. Tsuzuki (Tokyo College of Science). Dr. Tsuzuki has recently published a book on the history of chemistry (5), which is characterized by covering not only various aspects of the history of chemistry from ancient to modern times but also the history of chemistry in modern Japan. A chapter on this latter subject may be considered interesting case study material.

As is widely known, the development of science and technology in Japan has been amazingly rapid and extensive. It is indeed a remarkable fact in the history of science that Japan, after such a long period of national isolation, was able to import scientific and technological learning from western countries and rapidly to assimilate and develop science and technology during the last century. On this point, I should like to refer to a paper published by M. Tanaka (6), in which he critically reviews the development of chemistry in Japan during the period of 1837–1930. He further divides this period into the following four subperiods: the period of germination of scientific and technical learning (1837–1867), the period of transition from traditional to western modes of learning (1868–1876), the period of the founding of educational and research institutions (1877–1900), and the period of independent research in science and technology (1901–1930). In scientific and technological research, Japan is now recognized as one of the five or six most active countries in the world. Nevertheless, I cannot avoid noticing that there is still a wide gap between modern scientific, technological cultures and our own traditional culture. The general public, including the literary people and politicians in Japan, tend to evaluate science mainly from the practical point of view. Their understanding of science is rather superficial. I therefore think that it is especially important for our educational system to give both future scientists and nonscientists in Japan some sound understanding of the historical and philosophical background of modern science, which has been formulated in western countries since the time of Galilei and Kepler.

In Japan, we are faced with another problem, *viz*., how to train and educate the specialist in the history of science or of chemistry. There have been no educational facilities in our colleges or universities for this purpose, except for one at the University of Tokyo, which was established in 1951 as one of the senior courses in the College of General Education for the study of the history and philosophy of science. Students, not more than ten each year, who have completed the first three semesters of the college, are accepted into this course. The curriculum of this special course consists of: (1) basic subjects in the humanities and social sciences including history and philosophy, of which a certain number of credits are required; (2) basic subjects of mathematics, symbolic logic, physics, chemistry, biology, and cosmology, which are treated with special reference to methodology and history, of which the student elects two subjects as majors; (3) foreign languages: in addition to English, either German, French, or Russian is required; (4) seminars and research work in the chosen major field.

When I was in charge of this newly established course, I used for reading material in my seminar some classical works in chemistry such as Lavoisier's "Elements of Chemistry", Einstein's paper on Brownian motion, or Staudinger's work on macromolecules, and through such materials the historical and methodological aspects of chemistry were illustrated. In as much as a graduate course in the history and philosophy of science has not yet been established, the graduates from this course have to utilize other preexisting facilities of the same university if they wish to continue their study. Otherwise they accept positions, for instance, in journalism. Among the graduates are some excellent science journalists who are on active service.

Let me conclude by mentioning some activities of Japanese academic societies relating to the study of the history of chemistry. The Japan Academy has been publishing volumes on the history of science in Japan, one volume of which deals with the history of physical science and includes chapters on the history of chemistry in this country both before and after the Meiji restoration (1868). The Chemical Society of Japan, established in 1878, has at present several publications, among which two journals, *Kagaku to Kogyo* (Chemistry and Industry) and *Kagaku Kyoiku* (Chemical Education), occasionally include historical articles which may serve to arouse the interest of professional chemists and teachers in the history of chemistry. The publishing committee of this society has edited a monograph series on chemical topics for young students, in which a volume on the history of chemical discoveries is added.

The History of Science Society of Japan, established in 1941, now publishes two journals: *Kagakushi Kenkyu* (Studies in the History of Science, quarterly) and *Japanese Studies in the History of Science* (in foreign languages, annually since 1962). In these journals one can find original papers, short notes, resource papers, and book reviews concerning the history of science. In the last-mentioned journal, in addition to the paper by Tanaka referred to above, there is an article entitled "On the Studies of History of Chemistry in Japan" by Tsuzuki and Yamashita (7), which gives a brief but excellent survey of the papers on the history of chemistry that have appeared in this country during the past twenty-five years.

In Japan at present there are only a few scholars who actually specialize in the study of the history of chemistry, but there are many chemists and chemistry teachers who are more or less interested in this subject.

13*

Their recognition of the importance of the history of chemistry with respect to education is increasing. I therefore expect that this Symposium on Teaching the History of Chemistry organized on an international scale by the Division of the History of Chemistry and the Division of Chemical Education of the American Chemical Society will certainly be of great interest to Japanese chemists and chemistry teachers.

Finally, I would like to express my best thanks to Professor George B. Kauffman, Chairman of the Symposium, for his kind invitation to contribute a paper. I also thank Dr. Minoru Tanaka for his kind advice and information given to me in preparing this paper.

Literature Cited

(1) Tamamushi, B., "Kagaku" (Chemistry—the Process of Inquiry on the Nature of Matter), Baifukan Co., Tokyo, 1964.
(2) Sarton, G., "The History of Science and the New Humanism", Harvard Univ. Press, Cambridge, 1937.
(3) Conant, J. B., "Harvard Case Histories in Experimental Science", Harvard Univ. Press, Cambridge, 1950–54.
(4) Watanabe, M., and Tsukuba, T., "Kindaikagaku no Seiritsu to sono Haikei" (Foundation of Modern Science and its Background), Nisshin Shuppan Co., Tokyo, 1966.
(5) Tsuzuki, Y., "Kagakushi" (History of Chemistry), Asakura Shoten Co., Tokyo, 1966.
(6) Tanaka, M., "Hundert Jahren der Chemie in Japan, I. and II.", *Japanese Studies in the History of Science*, **3,** 89 (1964); **4,** 162 (1965).
(7) Tsuzuki, Y., and Yamashita, A., "On the Studies of History of Chemistry in Japan", *Japanese Studies in the History of Science*, **4,** 41 (1965).

21. A VIEW OF THE TEACHING OF THE HISTORY OF CHEMISTRY FROM THE UNIVERSITY OF LEEDS, ENGLAND

Maurice P. Crosland*

Department of Philosophy, The University of Leeds,
Leeds, England

Some general observations on bibliography and methodology in the history of chemistry are made. A number of histories of chemistry as a whole and of specialised aspects of chemistry are discussed, together with the advantages and disadvantages of specialisation and the value of primary sources as opposed to secondary sources. The teaching of the history of science and of chemistry at British universities is briefly considered, and the undergraduate as well as graduate programs at the University of Leeds are discussed in detail. Suggestions for future work in the field are given.

Just 200 years ago (1), Joseph Priestley accepted the post of Minister at the Unitarian chapel in Leeds and came to live there. Probably the most famous single experiment of Priestley, the "father" of pneumatic chemistry, was his preparation of a new type of "air" (later called "oxygen") from red mercury calx (HgO) on August 1, 1774. By then Priestley had left Leeds and had moved to the west of England, but it is generally agreed by historians (2) that his basic research on gases was done while he was at Leeds. It was the celebration of the centenary of the discovery of oxygen by a group of American chemists gathered around Priestley's grave at Northumberland, Pennsylvania in 1874 which led to the formation of the American Chemical Society. It may therefore seem appropriate in a way that at the time of another Priestley centenary, some remarks on the history of chemistry have been requested from Leeds. In one sense, it is hardly more than a coincidence that the university established in Priestley's city should be one of the few to offer a complete undergraduate course in the history of chemistry. Before considering the details of this course, however, I should like to make a few more general observations about the history of chemistry today.

General Observations on Bibliography and Methodology

Among those scientists who have taken an active interest in the history of their science, chemists have been particularly prominent. This interest has resulted in the publication of many general histories of chemistry so that today there are a number of books available on the subject. This is in marked contrast to the state of affairs in, say, physics or the life sciences. There are a few old histories of physics (mainly in German) to be found

* Visiting Professor (1967) at Cornell University and the University of California, Berkeley.

gathering dust in library stacks, but in the English language one of the standard works on the history of physics is a reissue of a book originally published in 1899 (3)! The situation is not much better in biology.

Part of the reason for this may be that it is easier to see chemistry as an entity. After all, chemistry was a recognised study before 1800, yet the term "biology" was only introduced after this date and the expression "life sciences" is much more recent. It would therefore be more just to compare the history of chemistry with the separate histories of botany, zoology, and physiology. It is less obvious why physics does not seem to have presented an integrated subject of study, unless it is that "physics" in one sense of the term did not come into being until the nineteenth century, being dependent, for example, on the elucidation of such general concepts as energy. Alternatively, it may simply be that the whole field is just too vast. It is therefore easier to deal separately with the histories of different branches of physics. There is a danger, however, in trying to consider the history of one particular branch of physics (*e.g.*, light) in complete isolation from a related branch (*e.g.*, sound). Thus for Newton at the end of the seventeenth century, there was a close analogy between light and sound, and indeed for a whole century afterwards any discussion of the possible wave propagation of light was based upon the assumption that these waves must be of the same kind as those of sound (*i.e.*, longitudinal rather than transverse).

The relevance of these remarks to the study of the history of chemistry is that the fact that "chemistry" has seemed to present a coherent whole has led many historians to attempt to study it in isolation from the development of related sciences. In the eighteenth century one can draw a useful distinction between natural history, on the one hand, and physics and mathematics, on the other. If, as I would suggest, the main achievement of Lavoisier was to draw chemistry away from the natural history tradition (4) and to establish it unambiguously as a physical science, then we cannot afford to ignore completely the traditions of collection and classification, on the one hand, and the discipline of the exact sciences, on the other. Lavoisier devoted considerable attention to the concept of a fluid that he called "caloric", which he regarded as "a real and material substance" (5). But how can we possibly understand Lavoisier's caloric unless we see it in the context of the "subtle fluids" of the eighteenth century? How could a rational man of affairs like Lavoisier, so insistent on the rejection of entities which went beyond immediate experience, accept an all-pervading imponderable fluid such as caloric?

It has been too much of a temptation for historians of chemistry—as witness, the great Partington (6)—to dismiss Lavoisier as having been "wrong" about caloric. Lavoisier, says Partington, was mistaken about two important things: caloric and the existence of oxygen in acids. On the other hand, he was correct about other things, such as the composition of water and of the oxyacids. But is it the task of the historian of science to segregate what is "right" from what is "wrong" in the past and to concentrate attention on the former at the expense of the latter? Some of us would say that one of the values of studying the history of science would be to see in some kind of perspective the transitory nature of many hypotheses. But, even assuming that in any particular year (say 1968) we were in a position to pass final judgment for all time on what was right (an enormous assumption), what would be the value of this exercise? Should not the historian of chemistry be concerned above all with *under-standing* the problems of the past? But how could he hope to understand the thought of a chemist who lived two hundred or three hundred years ago if he extracts only that small part, the validity of which is acceptable today, and completely ignores the remainder?

Despite what I have said about the dangers of narrow specialisation, there is an obvious place for detailed studies of particular topics in the history of chemistry. M. E. Weeks' "Discovery of the Elements" has gone through so many editions that there can be no doubt as to the popularity of this particular approach. Some would feel, however, that this subject lends itself too easily to a catalog type of history, and they would recommend this book and any like it to their students as complementary to their own course of lectures on the history of chemistry.

Of more value might be a study of the history of a particular concept or theory. One example might be the history of the phlogiston theory. In a way, it is a pity that J. H. White's pioneer "History of the Phlogiston Theory" was so soon superseded (7), as far as the later history of the theory is concerned, by the definitive series of papers by Partington and McKie. It was taken for granted by historians of chemistry in the 1930's (and even by some up to the present) that phlogiston was *the* theory of chemistry in the eighteenth century. I would suggest that not less important in this period was the theory (or theories) of chemical affinity. There are two valuable articles on this subject by A. M. Duncan (8), but we are still awaiting a book on the subject to recommend to our students.

An example of a valuable study of a particular field of the history of chemistry which has recently become available to a much wider circle of readers is the translation from the Hungarian of Ferenc Szabadváry's "History of Analytical Chemistry". No one can lecture on chemistry in the nineteenth century without considering the development of organic chemistry. If we wish to refer our readers to standard secondary works on organic chemistry, we find that the only two adequate books devoted to the subject (by C. Graebe and E. Hjelt) were published half a century ago and are in German.

This brings me to the question of the value of primary sources as opposed to secondary sources. It seems to me that even the beginning student of the history of science should be exposed directly to some of the writings (in translation where appropriate) of the men that he is studying. The "Source Book in Chemistry", edited by H. M. Leicester and H. S. Klickstein, is a handy collection of material. Probably, however, no two historians of chemistry would agree on what sources the student should read, and it seems to me that anyone teaching the history of chemistry must prepare at least a few sources in conjunction with his own teaching. Mimeographed sheets with source material can be taken away by the student and digested more fully after the lecture. The preparation of source material does, however, impose a responsibility on the teacher. The student cannot be expected to read many thousands of words written by each chemist studied, and it is usually not difficult to select a short passage to illustrate a particular point. Yet one of the objectives of the use of source material must be to place a given man's work in context. It is therefore important that one should not carry out a "scissors and paste" operation in which, for example, a chemist's "correct" ideas are always selected and any of his "wrong" ideas ruthlessly expunged.

In the literature of the history of chemistry the usual method of specialism (apart from biography) has been by period. Thus A. J. Ihde's "The Development of Modern Chemistry" (9) summarizes pre-Lavoisier chemistry in 50 pages, which is one seventeenth of the entire book. Nearly all the remainder is devoted to the nineteenth and twentieth centuries. The period approach has been emphasized by the publication of Partington's multivolume "A History of Chemistry" (10). Whatever criticism one might want to make of this book, it is indispensable to the historian of chemistry as a reference work. It is as well, however, to let one's students know that it is also possible to write history of chemistry in an interesting way.

One general conclusion that may be drawn about the bibliography of the history of chemistry is that students cannot be referred simply to books. They must also read papers on specialised aspects of the history of chemistry, scattered through a wide variety of journals. It is worth building up a library of photocopies of articles for purposes of reference.

The History of Science and the History of Chemistry in Britain

The history of science is taught in many British universities, usually by faculty whose sole concern is this study. Traditionally, the subject in Britain is "history and philosophy of science", and often it is taught in a department of philosophy (e.g., at Durham or Leeds). Sometimes the subject constitutes a whole department, as in the case of University College, London (11). In a few cases, the subject is taught by a member of the history department (e.g., at Edinburgh or Lancaster). Finally, the history of science may be associated with the history of technology as it is at London (Imperial College of Science and Technology) and Manchester (University of Manchester Institute of Science and Technology).

Actually, the formal structure of teaching in any university is not the main criterion for deciding whether the history of chemistry is taught. As any such course has its obvious audience among students in the chemistry department, at least some of the chemistry faculty must believe that the study is not a waste of time. Then there must be someone somewhere in the university with a special knowledge who is willing to teach. If the structure of the university is flexible enough and departmental chairmen approachable, a course may be arranged.

A critical factor may be the number of faculty appointed to teach the history of science and their individual specialities. It is sometimes assumed by university administrators that one person can teach adequately "the history and philosophy of science"—as if any one man could speak authoritatively on science from the Babylonians to World War II, from astrophysics to neurophysiology, from the problem of induction to evolution. Of course, if such a man appointed does not break under the strain of these responsibilities, and he has some special interest in chemistry and its history, he might conceivably give a special course on the history of chemistry. It is more likely, however, that a specialist course will be given in a university sub-department, in which a variety of different disciplines are represented. This is the case at Leeds, where there is a young faculty group of five as well as a research fellow.

One of the reasons why Leeds is one of the very few universities in Britain to provide a special course of lectures in the history of chemistry is, therefore, that Leeds is not in the impossible position of being a "one man band" and that one of the faculty (the present writer) has a particular interest in the history of chemistry. A prior reason, however, is the pioneering work of one of the former members of the chemistry department, E. F. Caldin, now Professor at the University of Kent. Caldin (12) was teaching the history of chemistry to first-year undergraduates when I arrived in Leeds in 1963. First-year chemists at Leeds are required to do one or more subjects, in addition to their principal study, and sometimes the choice may be between, say, agricultural chemistry, physics, and the history and philosophy of science. On the basis of Caldin's work and enthusiasm all "freshers" in the chemistry department who opted for the history of science were required to take an *additional* course and examination in the history of chemistry. Since then, the numbers have shown an encouraging increase, and indeed no other department of the university provides a greater number of students for the first-year course in the history of science than does the chemistry department.

The history of chemistry course as now given consists of one one-hour lecture a week for two and a half of our three terms, giving a total of about 24 in a year. Students are required to attend a small tutorial group once a term in the history of chemistry, in addition to their more frequent general history of science tutorial. They write one essay a term on a topic in the history of chemistry.

The subjects discussed in the lectures range in time from Aristotle's theory of matter to the establishment of organic chemistry in the midnineteenth century. Special attention is given to the work of Lavoisier and his immediate successors, since this is a decisive period in the establishment of the science of chemistry. It seems to me that around 1860 there is a definite turning point in the history of chemistry, and I choose this to conclude my detailed treatment. There will be some who consider that this date should mark, if anything, the beginning of the course (13). This I feel is not a question that can be decided either one way or the other—it is essentially a matter of taste and interest. I think that the chemistry of the last hundred years provides less *historical* difficulties in its understanding than the earlier period (I am not saying it is easier, because obviously there are more technical complexities). I do not feel that I have betrayed a student when I leave him with Butlerov, Guldberg and Waage, and Mendeleev and refer him to van't Hoff, Nernst, and Moseley. If he is a student who insists that he is not interested in past history, a young man who is impatient with outmoded theories propounded by men whose facilities for research and communication were so different from our own, I recommend him to supplement my course by studying the parts of Ihde's very readable book which deal with the twentieth century. Apart from the reading required specifically for the writing of the term paper, each student is required to read Partington's "A Short History of Chemistry" (14). This is not exactly an exciting book to read, but it is generally reliable. It gives a survey of the whole history of chemistry with dates and summaries, and in some ways it serves as a complement to my own treatment, which, I would like to think, tends to deal rather more with problems than with facts, with theories and concepts rather than with "discoveries". Students are also told to read certain chapters of H. M. Leicester's "The Historical Background of Chemistry" (15).

History of chemistry also features in the Leeds graduate program. We have only just begun to benefit from the British Science Research Council's decision that the history and philosophy of science constitutes an approved subject for the award of scholarships given to a small proportion of the best students who graduate each year in a scientific subject. These students are supported by state funds for two or possibly three years. We accordingly have one student writing a dissertation for a Master's degree on the *Annales de chimie* (1789–1815), and a second enrolled for a Ph. D. is studying chemical industry under the Napoleonic régime. For graduate work, library resources are of fundamental importance, and we are fortunate to have in Leeds not only complete runs of the main scientific periodicals of the late eighteenth century and the nineteenth century but also a special collection (the "Chaston Chapman collection") of printed books on early chemistry and alchemy.

The Future

I should like to conclude with a few remarks looking to the future of the subject. British universities have begun to accept the principle that each of them cannot hope to teach the whole variety of studies conceivable in the modern world. If serious teaching and research is to extend to other universities in Britain, this will depend on teachers and on libraries. The University of Glasgow, which has in its library the magnificent Ferguson collection on the early history of chemistry, might well justify an additional staff member, specifically concerned with the history of chemistry, in its new History of Science Department. It is also to be hoped that the University of Cambridge may eventually be able to add to its faculty, which already has specialists in the history of astronomy, mathematics, and geology, a further member whose research interests include chemistry.

In conclusion, I should like to ask the question "whither the history of chemistry?" I began by suggesting that the history of chemistry had attracted more attention than the history of other sciences, and, by implication, that its history had been more thoroughly investigated. To some, it might even seem that with Partington's monumental "A History of Chemistry" the history had been finally written and that all that was left was to squabble about footnotes. It seems to me rather that Partington's "History" brings to a head an important problem. I suggested earlier that the historian of chemistry must not turn a blind eye to the world of physics. Even more important, he must not turn a blind eye to the world. Science has never developed in a vacuum. It is true that in the discussion of some detailed technical problems it may not be necessary to go beyond the staightforward internal approach to the history of science. But in general, we cannot be content with the narrative that X was born in 1850, say, that he synthesised a new compound in 1875..., *etc.* Why should this man have become a chemist in the first place? Who were his teachers? How did he come to be doing the particular experiment that resulted in the production of a new compound?... To answer these questions demands some knowledge of the general, educational, and social history of the period, in addition to the history of science.

Let me take one particular example. The chemical revolution associated with the name of Lavoisier was at the time often referred to as "the French chemistry" because of the close association of Lavoisier with his colleagues, particularly with Guyton de Morveau, Fourcroy, and Berthollet (*16*). Studies of the first three have already appeared (*17*), so that, of the four great French chemists, there remains to be written a full study of Berthollet. Berthollet is probably best remembered for his discovery of the bleaching action of chlorine ("oxymuriatic acid") and his studies on combining proportions. The attitude that he adopted on the latter question ("wrong" for the nineteenth century) arose out of his view of chemical reactions. Berthollet argued that the product depended not only on the reactants but on their quantities and other conditions. This is the theme of his great book, the "Essai de statique chimique" (*18*).

If one asks how Berthollet obtained his ideas—and surely this is an important question for the historian of chemistry and his students—the answer is complex. Briefly, however, Berthollet found himself dissatisfied with the current view of affinity when he was called upon after the French Revolution to give lectures on chemistry at the École Normale. This, therefore, presents a situation with many parallels when the necessity of presenting work to an audience stimulates new thinking or at least brings about the crystallisation of thought. It also links Berthollet with the important institutions for higher education established in Paris after the Revolution. He found a natural example of his idea of the influence of mass when, as a member of Bonaparte's expedition to Egypt in 1798–99, he saw the great soda lakes and correctly inferred their origin. It was at a meeting of the Institut d'Égypte that he first spoke of his ideas, which were to be revived in the mid-nineteenth century and developed into the Law of Mass Action. Berthollet's interest in bleaching is understandable for a man who was director of the government dye works. His influence was exerted through his lectures at the École Polytechnique and particularly in the private Society of Arcueil (*19*). It is therefore impossible to understand

Berthollet's work without knowing something of his life and of the political and institutional history of the time.

I hope, therefore, that the next few years will see a greater integration of the history of chemistry with the history of other sciences and with history in general. By all means, let us continue to teach history of chemistry to chemists. This will be even more worthwhile if it is an open history alive to developments outside its own specialist concern.

Literature Cited

(1) In September, 1767. This paper was written in August–September, 1967.
(2) For example, see Gibbs, F. W., "Joseph Priestley, Adventurer in Science and Champion of Truth", pp. 36, 67, T. Nelson, London, 1965. Priestley himself wrote: "Nothing... engaged my attention while I was at Leeds so much as the prosecution of my experiments relating to ...the doctrine of air", Boyer, J. T., ed., "Memoirs of Dr. Joseph Priestley", p. 54, Barcroft Press, Washington, 1964.
(3) Cajori, F., "History of Physics", Macmillan, New York, 1899, rev. ed., 1929, reprinted by Dover Publications, New York.
(4) Crosland, M. P., "The Development of Chemistry in the 18th Century", *Studies on Voltaire and the 18th Century*, **24**, 369–441 (1963). This paper also outlines the influence of Newton on eighteenth-century chemistry.
(5) Lavoisier, A. L., "Elements of Chemistry", p. 4, transl. by R. Kerr in 1790, Dover Publications, New York, 1965.
(6) Partington, J. R., "A History of Chemistry", Vol. 3, p. 377, Macmillan, London, 1962.
(7) White, J. H., "History of the Phlogiston Theory", Arnold, London, 1932. Partington, J. R., and McKie, D., four papers on phlogiston theories published in *Annals of Science*, **2**, 361 (1937); **3**, 1, 337 (1938); **4**, 113 (1939).
(8) Duncan, A. M., "Some Theoretical Aspects of 18th-Century Tables of Affinity", Part I, *Annals of Science*, **18**, 177–194; Part II, 217–232 (1962).
(9) Ihde, A. J., "The Development of Modern Chemistry", Harper & Row, New York and London, 1964.
(10) Partington, J. R., "A History of Chemistry", Macmillan, London, vol. 2, 1961; vol. 3, 1962; vol. 4, 1964. Vol. 1 was in the course of preparation at the time of the author's death in 1965.
(11) This department has recently been recognized.
(12) The present examinable course in history of chemistry was begun by Dr. E. F. Caldin in the session 1962–63, but in previous years he had already given some lectures in the history of chemistry. History and philosophy of science has been taught in some form at Leeds since 1948. The later work of Professor S. Toulmin and Dr. J. Ravetz was responsible for the building up within the Philosophy Department of a sub-department of History and Philosophy of Science in the late 1950's and early 1960's.
(13) This feeling would be all the more natural in many parts of the U.S.A., where science has been a subject of serious study only in the last 100 years.
(14) Conveniently available in a paperback (3rd) edition (Harper Torchbooks, New York, 1960).
(15) Leicester, H. M., "The Historical Background of Chemistry", John Wiley, New York, 1956.
(16) The most famous occasion of the association of these four chemists was in the publication of the "Méthode de nomenclature chimique", Paris, 1787. This collaboration is described in: Crosland, M. P., "Historical Studies in the Language of Chemistry", pp. 168–192, Harvard University Press, Cambridge, Mass., 1962.
(17) Lavoisier has had numerous biographers. A very readable account of his life and work is given by McKie, D., "Antoine Lavoisier, Scientist, Economist,

Social Reformer'', Henry Schuman, New York, 1952. A definitive study of Lavoisier is in preparation by H. Guerlac. There are two recent biographies of Fourcroy by W. A. Smeaton (W. Heffer, London, 1962) and G. Kersaint (Editions du Museum, Paris, 1966). The only biography of Guyton de Morveau (Bouchard, G., "Guyton de Morveau, Chimiste et Conventionnel", Perrin, Paris, 1938) does not discuss his scientific work in any detail. Guyton's contributions to chemistry have been discussed in a number of papers by W. A. Smeaton (*e.g.*, in *Annals of Science* and *Ambix*).

(18) Berthollet, C. L., "Essai de statique chimique", Paris, 1803, English translation, London, 1804. A facsimile reprint of this book is planned by Johnson Reprint Corporation.

(19) The role of chemists and chemistry was particularly important in the hitherto neglected Society of Arcueil. This society published its own series of memoirs, where may be found, for example, the original memoir by Gay-Lussac describing his law of combining volumes of gases (Crosland, M. P., "The Society of Arcueil: A View of French Science at the Time of Napoleon I", Heinemann Educational Books, London, 1967).

22. HISTORY OF CHEMISTRY IN ISRAEL

I. KALUGAI

41 Rav Harlap Street, Jerusalem, Israel

The teaching of the history of chemistry in Israel has not as yet evolved into its final shape. Some of the leading figures in this field are briefly considered, together with their courses at the Israeli universities and technical schools. An opinion is crystallizing that teaching the history of chemistry on the undergraduate level should be divided into two parts: (a) information given in general chemistry courses on the basic concepts, and (b) a special course in the cultural and historical background of chemistry in the third or fourth year of studies. It is believed that in postgraduate studies a closer contact should be established with history and philosophy of science, archaeology, and mediaeval history.

The teaching of the history of chemistry in Israel is still in the process of trial and pioneering, in spite of the interest in history that is characteristic of this country. The Jewish people returned to the homeland to which religious and cultural traditions had bound them through the centuries. Furthermore, Israel is a country with extensive archaeological excavations. Some of the chemists who, during the early period of resettlement of the country, were working in the experimental agricultural station of the Jewish Agency for Palestine and in the institutions of the Mandatory Government were approached by archaeologists and museum custodians for advice on questions connected with the primitive chemical industries and on problems related to the cleaning and preservation of excavated findings. In addition, Christian missions and monasteries had always included scholars interested in and acquainted with the technologies of the past. One example is the permanent exhibition of the history of the oil industry in this country, kept by the Franciscans at Kfar Nahum (Capernaum) (1).

Teaching chemistry in Hebrew and translating the literature of science into this language required the creation of a new terminology. This promoted the search for chemical, mineralogical, and botanical terms in Scriptures and in the Talmudic literature and, *ipso facto*, brought scholars into contact with the history of chemistry. From the beginning, specialists in scientific terminology were active on the "Language Board", which regulated the creation of new terminology.

Establishment in 1925 of the Hebrew University of Jerusalem and the Technion, the Hebrew Institute of Technology, at Haifa, increased the interest in historical roots. The Biochemical Department of the Hebrew University was started in 1923 under the guidance of Professor Andor Fodor, previously a collaborator of Emil Abderhalden and a prominent chemist with a very broad outlook on education. Professor Fodor was interested in history and included historical remarks in his lectures. In the Technion, which started with emphasis on civil engineering and architecture, chemistry was only a subsidiary subject. The small teaching staff in chemistry was also active in the local "Society for the Propagation of Scientific Studies", which conducted free evening classes on scientific topics—mathematics, physics, chemistry, and biology. The present author, for example, lectured on the history of chemistry. These lectures resulted in two books, "A Short History of Chemistry", the first book of this nature published in Hebrew (1935) and "The Seven Metals" (1937). The latter was enlarged and published in 1959 under the title, "The Book of Metals". Back in 1927 some of the same Technion teachers had made a study of the historical traditions of glass blowing in the primitive glass industry in Hebron, which dated from the Middle Ages.

By the early 1950's the Technion at Haifa included a Faculty of Chemical Engineering and a Department of Chemistry in the Faculty of Sciences. Some beginnings were made in teaching the history of chemistry. We introduced historical surveys into the courses in general, inorganic, organic, and physical chemistry. A noncompulsory course in the history of industrial chemistry (something along the lines suggested by G. Fester (2)) was offered to seniors in chemical engineering. For students of chemistry there was a course that included selected chapters in the history of chemistry as related to the cultural development of mankind (3). Since the retirement of this author, the courses have not been available.

Some historians of chemistry emigrated to this country in the 1930's. Two of them should be mentioned. The first, Professor Walter Roth, an historian of chemistry, was formerly the editor of *Chemiker-Zeitung* in Germany. He sought to induce chemists with whom he came into contact to take an interest in the history of chemistry. The second, Dr. Noah Shapiro, had been a Privat-Docent at the University of Kaunas (Lithuania), and when he settled in Tel-Aviv, he sought to arouse an interest in the history of chemistry. A scholar of Judaica, he dedicated much energy in searching for references to chemical processes in ancient and mediaeval Hebrew literary sources. Teaching chemistry in secondary schools and in evening courses, he always included historical interpretation in his lectures. From 1961 until his sudden death in 1964 he gave a course in the history of chemistry at Bar-Ilan University at Ramat Gan. He had been very active in the Israel Society of the History of Medicine and Natural Sciences, which was founded in 1953, and he wrote for their quarterly publication, *Koroth*. In his teaching and writing, he supported the bio-bibliographical position.

There is considerable emphasis on the history of science at the Hebrew University of Jerusalem. Prof. M. Plessner, a prominent scholar of Islamic Studies, deals with Arab Science in the mediaeval period. The Eleanor Roosevelt Chair of the History of Sciences was established in 1959. The present incumbent, Prof. S. Samburski, gives a two-year course in the history of physics. Shorter courses in the history of biology and the history of chemistry are rotated with courses in the history of mathematics or astronomy. Three series of lectures on the history of chemistry have been given in recent years. In 1964, Prof. A. Kachalski of the Weizmann Institute of Science at Rehoboth offered a course on the History of Chemistry in the 19th Century up to the Karslruhe Congress (1860). In 1965, this writer lectured on the history of chemistry in Europe between the two Revolutions (1640–1789). In the current academic year (1967–68), Prof. E. Bergman of the University Chemistry Department is lecturing on "The History of Organic Chemistry in the 19th Century". Some postgraduate students with B. S. degrees in chemistry are working for the Ph. D. degree in the history of science, and it is hoped that within a few years there will be a generation of chemists with suitable historical preparation.

At a recent ceremony celebrating the 50th Anniversary of the Balfour Declaration (1917), recognising the historical ties of Jews to Palestine as a national homeland, it was announced that an "Arthur Balfour Chair in the History of Science" would be established at the Weizmann Institute of Science in Rehoboth. It may be expected that the history of chemistry will be given considerable emphasis in an institute founded by a famous chemist.

On the basis of past developments in teaching the history of chemistry at different institutions of higher learning in Israel, one may make certain assumptions. The history of chemistry will be included in the study of the history of science. Students in general courses should learn of the development of chemistry since the 17th century in relation to: (a) pure substances, (b) elements and compounds, and (c) molecules, atoms, and subatomic particles (4).

More advanced undergraduates should hear a course on the history of chemistry which considers the cultural and historical background of chemistry. Attention should be paid to two aspects of chemical knowledge: chemistry as a natural science using physical experimental methods and the application of chemistry to medicine and industry. For the graduate students, courses must integrate the history and philosophy of science as well as archaeology and mediaeval history.

Literature Cited

(1) Maisler, Benjamin, and Yeivin, S., "Palestine Guide", Tel Aviv, 1940.
(2) Fester, G., "Die Entwicklung der chemischen Technik bis zu den Anfängen der Grossindustrie", Julius Springer, Berlin, 1923.
(3) Leicester, Henry M., "The Historical Background of Chemistry", John Wiley & Sons, New York, 1956. See Preface.
(4) Caldin, E. F., "The Structure of Chemistry in Relation to the Philosophy of Science", p. 5, Newman History and Philosophy Series No. 8, Sheed & Ward, London and New York, 1961.

23. PROBLEMS IN THE INSTRUCTION OF HISTORY OF SCIENCE AND THE TEACHING OF HISTORY OF CHEMISTRY IN HUNGARY

Ferenc Szabadváry

Institute of General Chemistry, Technical University of Budapest,
Budapest, Hungary

The classical and scientific-technical systems of education are contrasted. Whereas classical subjects are taught historically, scientific ones usually are not, and the reasons for and consequences of this neglect are given. The advantages and importance of education in the history of science are discussed. Two opinions exist as to the best time in the student's higher education to teach the subject—(1) at the beginning as an introductory course, and (2) at the end as a synthetic course designed to demonstrate relationships. The second viewpoint prevails in Hungary. Instruction in the history of chemistry in Hungary is discussed with emphasis on the program at Budapest.

Two Ways of Education

It is a commonplace to speak of two different ways of education, *viz.*, classical and scientific-technical. But human culture is homogeneous. The aforesaid two branches, which exist even today, are the result of historical development. But progress in the future tends toward the unification of education, and this process is an imperative concomitant toward a limited specialization within the restricted area, which is not satisfactory for the individual. For the technician it is a mere mental pressure to become acquainted with human culture and to enjoy the arts that should save him from intellectual indifference, while for the man of classical erudition it is a physical stress to acquire the very little technical and scientific knowledge required in order to survive even in Europe during the age of motor cars and labor-saving devices, when tradesmen are gradually disappearing.

Our current educational system in Hungary is now tending to contain the proper distinctive features of a homogeneous system after a long period of struggle against exaggerations toward both extremes, *i.e.*, the centuries-old predomination of the so-called classical subjects and the other tendency, the reaction against the former, according to which only scientific instruction was considered necessary.

Why Is the History of Science Neglected?

At present, there is one more fundamental difference between the instruction in classical and exact sciences: while classical subjects are taught historically, *i.e.*, according to their temporal continuity, natural sciences are instructed not in chronological order, but in a closed system that

14*

corresponds to the momentary experience. This situation is easily understood, for the subject of the classical sciences is the totality of what has
been produced by mankind in the given field. In literature or the arts,
the products of not only the present but the past as well are continuously
with us; we read, see, or listen to them either on the stage or in the concert
hall, and we are impressed by them. But as far as natural or technical
science is concerned, only the present lives; many previous discoveries
are now but outworn concepts of no importance for the man of today.
A wonderful novel, a masterpiece of music, a legal system, or a philosophical
theory remains valid and impressive throughout centuries, but even the
most brilliant scientific theory becomes obsolete in a comparatively short
time, and the most ingenious machine becomes obsolete within an even
shorter period. Consequently, the instruction in natural sciences does not
proceed in an historical or chronological order. The knowledge of the
development of these subjects is not necessary for their effective understanding. There is no legal expert without a knowledge of legal history,
nor is there a literary or art historian, as indicated by the expressions
themselves, who is not acquainted with the evolution of these subjects.
On the contrary, one can become an excellent analyst or electrical engineer
without knowing the history of chemistry or the history of physics, respectively. Therefore, one of the reasons why the history of science is neglected lies in the very character of the sciences themselves.

Moreover, at the time when the modern natural sciences first came into
being some two or three hundred years ago, they generally had to fight
for their existence and for the right of proclaiming their principles. The
foremost opponent to be fought against was the scholastic "science", the
chief support for which was the mere citation of the ancients. Even during
the later development of the natural sciences, a new theory was often
accepted only at the cost of a struggle with and destruction of an old one.
The old theory often was a source of irritation to the proponent of the
new idea. The old concept often must have been competitive with the
new one, and the earlier it was forgotten, the better. In this manner, a
spontaneous dislike for scholasticism and dogmatism of any kind as well
as for earlier concepts arose in the field of natural science, and this dislike
was extended even to its own history.

Disadvantages of the Neglect of the History of Science

It is obvious that the foregoing form of education cannot distinctly
convey the historical character of the development and evolution of natural
sciences, although for these the historical development and the influence
of earlier workers upon later workers are of much greater importance
than those in the domain of other sciences or arts. There is no scientific
discovery without antecedents. In the arts a genius often appears to create
something that has absolutely no connection with its precedents, but in
the sciences every new generation must proceed from the latest research
of the previous ones.

Development in science is not a straight-line progressive function. It is replete with false starts, *culs de sac*, and even retrogressions. Along with great discoveries, great errors were sometimes made. Occasionally, what were regarded as great discoveries proved later to be great errors and vice versa.

The university student is given minimal instruction regarding this problem. Not only does he fail to master an absolute fact, but he regards as eternally valid concepts that merely reflect the momentary state of human knowledge and that will be either changed in due time or become absolutely invalid. Thus the student will be unable to think without bias. And the more rapidly science develops, the shorter the period of validity becomes. Aristotle's theory of the four elements had been satisfactory for two thousand years, whereas Dalton's atomic theory lasted only a hundred years, and today's theories of chemical bonding will probably be superseded within our own lifetimes.

Why Is the History of Science Useful?

On the other hand, the history of science enables us to think critically without dogma. One discovers that scientific problems are not orderly or solved once and for all. This points to a moral: if a scientist's experiments contradict existing theories, he should not consider his research as incorrect and terminate it at once; rather, he should continue it critically and without fear.

Furthermore, a knowledge of the history of science prevents the researcher from pursuing the other extreme. Anyone who has carried out scientific research knows how easy it is to read his own ideas into the experiments and this type of spontaneous prejudice is more dangerous, the more celebrated the scientist is, for the acceptance of the theory may be furthered by his own scientific authority. The history of science demonstrates with examples of the past how dangerous this prejudice is, and at the same time it admonishes us to make an even more detailed analysis of the phenomenon.

But aside from this, everyone is aware of the evolving unity of education. Does not the mere knowledge of the recent scientific achievements belong to our general culture? It is proper that a cultivated person be acquainted with the creative minds of humanity. As for writers and artists, we generally know them well. But did not the great scientists contribute at least as much to the progress of mankind? However, they are generally unknown to the man in the street. Often even the chemist is better acquainted with Shakespeare or Mozart than with Berzelius or van Helmont. It is proper to be familiar with the history of the world and especially that of one's own country. Likewise, one should master the history of the different sciences and especially that of one's own specialty.

Aside from cultural considerations, historico-scientific attainments are very often of the greatest practical importance; frequently, new ideas can arise from them. Throughout history, scientists have had many ingenious thoughts. Many of these could not be realized in practice at the time because of technical limitations which were later overcome. These potentially valuable ideas have been preserved only by the history of science, and occasionally it has been amazingly fruitful to encounter them.

At the commencement of any research task, every scientist should survey the literature and examine all that has been written on the problem in question. Moreover, how can he be creative in the field that he has chosen to be engaged in throughout his lifetime, while ignoring all that has been produced in it up until his time? What a contradiction!

To Whom Is the History of Science Indispensable?

As mentioned above, one can deal with the natural sciences without being acquainted with their history. Examples were then given to demonstrate that a knowledge of the history of science is useful for the researcher in the natural sciences as well. But there is a special field where this is not only useful but indispensable, *viz.*, in teaching. In my opinion, one cannot teach natural sciences without being acquainted with their history. How can the grammar school teacher make his pupils approach his abstract subject other than through the researchers by whom it was elaborated, to say nothing of the numerous opportunities thus given to make the lectures more vivid and to arouse the faltering attention of the students? He who teaches also educates. How could he educate the student best for a love of one's profession if not by presenting its luminaries, who can be set up as examples? It is indispensable for the teacher of the future to be acquainted with the history of science.

When to Teach the History of Chemistry

If we agree that instruction in the history of science, in our case that of the history of chemistry, is necessary and useful, the question arises: when is the most advantageous time to teach it? In Hungary, there are two opinions concerning this problem.

According to the first opinion, history should be taught immediately at the beginning of the student's higher education, almost simultaneously with the commencement of his professional studies. First, the student must become acquainted with the antecedents, then with the present, so that he will become acquainted with chemistry from a really phylogenetic point of view. In applying this method, one naturally has to teach chemistry itself to some extent too, particularly the more so as the present period is approached. In this way, the history of chemistry greatly disburdens the special subjects because their elements are considered in the course of the historical lectures, and the special subjects can then begin with the most up-to-date results. For example, Dalton's atomic theory, the determination of molecular weight, Avogadro's formula, Kekulé's benzene model, structural theory, electrolysis, the periodic system, the laws of thermodynamics, the ionic theory, *etc.*, in short, everything that has been created in nineteenth-century chemistry, but which is still effective, or to say the least indispensable, is transferred to the introductory historico-chemical lectures.

This, however, comprises a considerable part of contemporary chemistry, the delivery of which requires a sufficient number of lectures, for it is not enough merely to refer in passing to the material; it must be explained thoroughly. According to this viewpoint, the history of chemistry becomes a real basis for a knowledge of the special branch of chemistry.

According to the second opinion, the history of chemistry is to be taught during the last term. After the students have already passed the special subjects, the history of chemistry should serve as a great synthesis which points out the connections between the various branches of chemistry. It should thus demonstrate the unity of chemistry, its human aspects, the way in which scientists made their discoveries, and the psychology of research.

Instruction in the History of Chemistry in Hungary

Attendance at lectures on the subjects required for the diploma is prescribed with an obligatory force by the Hungarian university education system. The sequence and number of lectures are prescribed as well. The maximum number of lectures that can be prescribed per week to the students is also fixed. In addition, there are elective lectures that might be attended by the students, but they are not compulsory ones. Therefore the importance of the obligatory subjects is very great, and the initiation of any new subject is possible only at the cost of other ones, so that its introduction into the curriculum is rather complicated.

Admittedly, instruction in the history of the sciences including that of chemistry generally has no past in Hungary. There is no institute or department for this purpose at any of the country's universities, a most regrettable situation.

In the Chemical Engineering Faculty of Budapest Technical University, an elective subject entitled "The History of Chemistry and Chemical Industry" has been instituted with one term (14 weeks), consisting of two lectures per week. It corresponds to the first opinion, *i.e.*, the lectures are of introductory character. But the elective character of the course prevents it from fulfilling its main goal; lectures of releasing character cannot be delivered in this manner, as they are attended by only a mere fraction of all the students.

In the latest reform of training chemistry teachers, which is being carried out at the faculties of natural sciences of all three universities, the students were required to attend a course of two lectures per week called "The History of Chemistry" during the last semester. This gratifying occurrence shows that even in Hungary, at least in the field of teacher training, the importance of the history of science is being admitted. One can also applaud the fact that in this case the second opinion prevails, *i.e.*, the lecture is not of introductory but of synthetic character.

Both lectures on this subject are delivered by the present writer at the Budapest Technical University and the Budapest University of Arts and Sciences. At the latter institution, the course has been given for only one semester. The writer cannot give an account of his experiences, for he has had to struggle himself with the difficulties inherent in beginning any new course.

At any rate, lectures of synthetic character are more thrilling and fascinating than introductory lectures. One can assume a knowledge of the subject on the part of the students. Hence, it is sufficient merely to refer to it and then to deal in detail with connections, reasons, and scientists, whereas the introductory lecture requires much more time, and two lectures per week could scarcely be considered sufficient.

The first textbook in Hungarian on the history of chemistry for the Universities of Arts and Sciences is currently being written by the lecturers on the subject. This book will consist of twenty sheets more than is required for the lectures. But our intention is to produce a work that can be used by the students as a companion even without teachers. Therefore we intend to present in it the most important discoveries and concepts with quotations from the original texts, which will constitute one third of the text.

I hope that I have demonstrated that the history of chemistry is beginning to awake in Hungary.

24. TEACHING THE HISTORY OF CHEMISTRY IN RUSSIA*

Yurii Ivanovich Solovyev

Institute of the History of Science and Technology,
Moscow, U.S.S.R.

There are three basic approaches to teaching historico-chemical material: (1) giving special courses on the history of chemistry, (2) using data from the history of chemistry in courses on general, inorganic, and organic chemistry, and (3) investigations on the history of the origin and development of specific problems in chemistry in master's and doctor's dissertations. Although no provision existed for courses in the history of chemistry at Russian universities or polytechnic and technological institutes, many eminent pre-revolutionary Russian chemists introduced historical material into their courses, e.g., D. I. Mendeleev, N. A. Menshutkin, A. M. Butlerov, D. P. Konovalov, and L. A. Chugaev, University of St. Petersburg; M. I. Konovalov, A. N. Reformatskiy, A. G. Doroshevskiĭ, A. E. Chichibabin, M. N. Popov, and I. A. Kablukov, University of Moscow; K. Schmidt, University of Dorpat; P. I. Walden and M. G. Tsentnershver, Riga Polytechnic Institute and Cultural University, respectively; and I. P. Osipov, University of Kharkov. This tradition has been preserved and developed by many Soviet chemists and historians of science. Current workers in the field together with their institutions are cited.

Even in the second half of the nineteenth century, many scholars who combine scientific investigation with teaching have encountered complex problems in explaining to students the rapidly growing theoretical and experimental material of chemistry, either by means of the historical approach or by presenting to the student only the most recent science without examining particularly *how* it was obtained or *who* made this or that discovery. The second approach nourishes the young only with the pure filtrate of existing science and discards the precipitate which remained on the filter of previous epochs.

This was not an idle question, for there was discussion about how best to lead the hearers to the boundaries of science without burdening their memories with the structures of science like loading a furnace with damp wood. The concern was always the fire on the hearth and not the smoke. Scientists gradually came to the conviction that it was helpful to resort to the historical method of teaching chemistry, for such a method permitted the student to remember not a mass of facts, but science in the process of movement. This allowed the beginning scientist to understand and interpret best the increasing and complicated "scientific economy", its internal and external relationships, and the path of its further evolution.

We can see three basic approaches to teaching historico-chemical material in pedagogical and scientific circles:

* Translated by Henry M. Leicester, School of Dentistry, University of the Pacific, San Francisco, California.

1. Giving special courses on the history of chemistry.
2. Using data from the history of chemistry in courses on general, inorganic, and organic chemistry.
3. Investigations on the history of the origin and development of specific problems in chemistry in master's and doctor's dissertations.*

We will now discuss these questions in the light of the activities of Russian chemists.

No provision existed for teaching courses in the history of chemistry in the program of instruction of students in the universities or polytechnic and technological institutes of Russia, yet this did not prevent students taking the general chemistry courses from being introduced to facts from the history of chemistry as part of their chemical knowledge. Thus from the very beginning of his pedagogical activity in the University of St. Petersburg (from 1857 to 1890), D. I. Mendeleev discussed the history of chemistry, a knowledge of which in his opinion was necessary for an understanding of the processes which occurred in the origin and development of various scientific theories. In the eighth edition of his famous "Principles of Chemistry" he used historico-scientific material extensively, bringing in various items of historical information in order to explain why certain questions or problems had currently received such a notable development.

"Comparing the past of science with its present", wrote Mendeleev, "I try to develop in the reader a spirit of searching without being satisfied with simple description or content, but being excited and accustomed to persistent work, everywhere seeking a place where an opinion can be tested by experiment" (1).

Emphasizing the value of the history of science, Mendeleev said, "You may say that this is history, but it is not torn out separately from history; history is the unavoidable track along which all scientific or social progress moves. This is the past, but it is very important for an understanding of the present" (1, p. xxiv). Further, "Acquaintance with the history of contemporary chemistry is an unavoidable necessity, not only for specialists in this field, but also for those who desire to understand the evolution of scientific thought of our time" (2).

Lectures on the history of chemistry, while benefiting students with historico-chemical information, at the same time served to train them in a spirit of patriotism and internationalism. Sharply criticizing nationalism and chauvinism in science, Russian chemists (N. N. Zinin, A. M. Butlerov, D. I. Mendeleev, and A. N. Engelhardt) in 1870 published a statement against the German chemists Volhard and Kolbe (3), who in their papers

---

* The defense of master's and doctoral dissertations has always been an important event in Russian scientific life. Many of these dissertations contain deep historico-scientific analysis of one or another problem in chemistry. As examples we mention the dissertations of A. I. Khodnev, "The Union of Inorganic and Organic Chemistry into One Whole", Kharkov, 1848; V. V. Markovnikov, "The Isomerism of Organic Compounds", Kazan, 1865; A. L. Potylitsyn, "Methods of Measuring Chemical Affinity", St. Petersburg, 1880; L. A. Chugaev, "The Chemical Structure of Complex Compounds", St. Petersburg, 1910; and many others.

distorted the history of science and tried to disparage and belittle the scientific services of Lavoisier. "Kolbe wrote wickedly and falsely, and therefore we answered him", wrote D. I. Mendeleev (4).

In 1878–1886 N. A. Menshutkin taught individual chapters from the history of chemistry at the University of St. Petersburg. He raised the problem of acquainting students with the development of chemical views from the end of the eighteenth century to the 1880's. On the basis of these lectures, Menshutkin published in 1888 a book entitled "Sketches on the Development of Chemical Ideas", the first original general work on the history of chemistry to be published by a Russian scholar. "...For an understanding of contemporary chemical ideas", wrote the author, "it is useful to be acquainted with the theories which preceded them. Considering both the purposes of teaching and the small number of works on historical chemistry in our literature, the selection of a subject for this work is sufficiently motivated. Therefore it has seemed to us most expedient to explain each view, each theory, at the moment of its full development."

The titles of the lectures from Menshutkin's course on the history of chemistry are: "Theory of phlogiston; Lavoisier's system; law of constant and multiple proportions; atomic theory; Bergman's and Berthollet's theory of chemical affinity; electrochemical theory; dualistic theory of acids, bases, and salts; application of atomic and electrochemical theories to organic compounds; metalepsy and theories based on it; unitary system; fall of the electrochemical theory; new type theory; Kolbe's new theory and the fusion of it with Dumas' and Williamson's type theory; theory of chemical structure; theory of atomicity of elements; periodic law; application of physical methods to the solution of some questions of chemical statics; solutions; chemical kinetics; studies on chemical affinity."

From this program we can see that Menshutkin's course on the history of chemistry touched upon almost all the basic problems of chemistry, the discussion of which led to its contemporary state.

Menshutkin's lectures on the history of chemistry were given in the very years (end of the 1870's and beginning of the 1880's) when there was sharp conflict in the field of theoretical chemistry between the supporters of the theory of chemical structure of organic compounds and its opponents. It is noteworthy that the history of chemistry was involved in this struggle as a unique "unifier". For example, Menshutkin, as an opponent of the theory of chemical structure, expressed the opinion that this theory did not emerge as a result of regular development of previous theoretical views, that is, so to speak, that it was an historical accident. To a certain extent, in order to counteract this erroneous thesis, A. M. Butlerov in 1879–1880 gave students of the third and fourth courses of the physico-mathematical faculty of the University of St. Petersburg a course of lectures on the development of chemistry from 1840 to 1880.

The following outline of the program of this course has been preserved: "Sequence according to ideas: origin, development; table of important facts by years; connection of ideas and facts in columns; graphical development of ideas over the generations; regular comprehension of changes" (5).

Thus the chief purpose of the lectures was to explain the theoretical views of the precursors of the theory of chemical structure in order to show that this theory was not an historical accident. "Historical necessity leads to the idea of chemical structure", noted Butlerov. He hoped "that by a glance into the past the young chemist will derive for himself the direction in which to work with great benefit in the future" (*5*, p. 280).

Continuing the tradition of Mendeleev and Butlerov, D. P. Konovalov, and then L. A. Chugaev, as professors in the University of St. Petersburg, in their lectures on general and inorganic chemistry devoted much attention to questions about the history of chemistry. Noting the value of the history of science in teaching, L.A. Chugaev said, "The possibility of observing each question of science in historical perspective has the advantage that this makes easier the objective evaluation of those views and theories which arise before us and are the last word of science" (*6*).

At the University of Moscow during various years a course in the history of chemistry has been given. Thus in 1892–1894 a course of lectures devoted to the development of chemistry was given by M. I. Konovalov; this course was continued by A. N. Reformatskiĭ in the 1894–1895 school year. In 1898–1901 a course in "History of Chemistry" was given by A. G. Doroshevskiĭ, and then by A. E. Chichibabin (in 1903–1904). From 1913 M. N. Popov began to give a course "History of Russian Chemistry". A number of courses on general and inorganic chemistry actually had a historico-chemical character.

Thus Professor I. A. Kablukov in his lectures on physical and inorganic chemistry which he gave for a long time after 1885 to the students of the University of Moscow always began with historical information from the history of chemistry and biographies of famous scientists.

At the University of Dorpat in the 1870's lectures on the history of chemistry were given systematically by Professor K. Schmidt. The text of these lectures has not been preserved, and so it is difficult to say what they contained. However, from the testimony of W. Ostwald (*7*), then a student at the University of Dorpat, Schmidt's lectures were interesting and impressive. In contrast to the other lectures, which he barely attended, Ostwald heard Schmidt's course on the history of chemistry to the end. It is very significant that young Ostwald began from these lectures to see living people in great scientists, people who "were not found on in-accessible heights above the intelligence and understanding of poor mortals". It should be noted that the characteristics which Schmidt gave the individual scientists were distinguished by striking animation and three-dimensional depiction, which helped Ostwald to grasp the "technique of plastic renewal of great men", which is clearly shown in his book "Velikie lyudi" (Great Men) (Russian translation, St. Petersburg, 1910). Writing in Riga in 1884–1886 the two fundamental volumes of his "Lehrbuch der allgemeinen Chemie", Ostwald set forth the general chemical material with wide consideration of historico-chemical data. His historical analysis presents an introduction to the consideration of the contemporary state of existing problems. Thus, for example, in explaining the basis of chemical kinetics, he illustrated the history of this problem and incidently introduced a series of historical scientific analogies. In the chapters devoted to affinity, thermochemistry, and electrochemistry, Ostwald also considered in detail the development of these problems from the moment of their origin.

At the Riga Polytechnic Institute in the first decades of the twentieth century, P. I. Walden devoted the first five to seven lectures of the general course in inorganic chemistry to the history of chemistry. The basic purpose of these lectures was to introduce the students to contemporary chemistry through the definite stages of its development. Walden deserves the credit for creating the first history of chemistry book in Russia, published in 1917. At the same time as Walden, in Riga at the Cultural University M. G. Tsentnershver gave a course of popular lectures on the history of chemistry, which were later published by him under the title of "Sketch of the History of Chemistry" (2nd edition, 1927).

At intervals in various years, lectures on the history of chemistry were given in the Universities of Kazan and Kharkov. Thus Professor I. P. Osipov at Kharkov in the 1890's gave a course on the history of chemistry in the nineteenth century. Some materials from these lectures were published in the book "Sketches on the Development of Chemistry in the Nineteenth Century" (Kharkov, 1898).

The tradition of the distinguished Russian chemists was carefully preserved and developed by many eminent Soviet scholars. N. S. Kurnakov, I. A. Kablukov, B. N. Menshutkin, and many others followed this tradition.

The founder of physico-chemical analysis, Academician N. S. Kurnakov, in his scientifically generalizing work and in lectures, particularly emphasized the succession of scientific ideas, noting the role of such scientists as Berthollet and Mendeleev in the development of ideas concerning definite and indefinite compounds. "The famous conflict in the history of chemistry between Berthollet and Proust", Kurnakov told his students, "should be continued at the present time. A hundred years after its conclusion, a great amount of information has accumulated in the scientific stock, especially from the new and more perfect methods of experimental investigation. The state of our knowledge already permits us to think that the victory of Proust over his brilliant opponent was only temporary" (8).

Courses in the history of chemistry were given in the 1930's by M. A. Blokh (Leningrad Pedagogical Institute), B. N. Menshutkin (Leningrad Polytechnic Institute), and S. A. Shukarev (Leningrad University). This was reflected in corresponding textbooks. A lithographed summary of Blokh's lectures was published, and much information on the history of chemistry was included in Menshutkin's textbook of general and inorganic chemistry.

In the following period, the history of chemistry was taught at all the leading institutions of higher learning of Leningrad. At the University the history of chemistry was given by Corresponding Member of the Academy of Sciences I. I. Zhukov and Professors S. A. Shukarev, V. F. Martynov, and V. M. Levchenko; at the Chemico-Technological Institute by Academician A. E. Poraĭ-Koshits and Professors Yu. S. Zal'kind and V. Ya. Kurbatov; and at the A. I. Herzen Pedagogical Institute by Professors V. M. Levchenko and V. P. Shishokin.

During the last five years, courses in the history of chemistry have again been revived at the University and Pedagogical Institute; the subject is given by Chief Scientific Worker A. A. Makarenya, who has introduced teaching the history of science in a number of specialties of the philosophical faculty. The portion of the course devoted to the history of chemistry is given by Docent R. B. Dobrotin and Chief Scientific Worker A. A. Makarenya. Lectures on the history of chemistry for teachers and scientific workers are regularly given at the D. I. Mendeleev Museum in Leningrad University.

At the Riga Polytechnic Institute a course in the history of chemistry has been given for many years. Initially, these lectures were due to Chief Scientific Worker of the Institute of Organic Syntheses Ya. P. Stradyn.

At the Yaroslav Pedagogical Institute the course in the history of chemistry is given by Professor I. N. Lepeshkov.

In 1946, for the first time in the U.S.S.R., at Moscow University a chair in the history of chemistry was organized, and a course of lectures on the history of chemistry was introduced into the compulsory program for training students. The chair was occupied by Professor N. A. Figurovskiĭ, under whose direction specialists in the history of chemistry were prepared; students of the chemical faculty heard and now hear a course in the history of chemistry, the basic purpose of which is to acquaint the students with the chief moments in the history of chemistry and the names of famous chemists of past generations whose discoveries helped the development of chemistry in important ways.

There have been some difficulties in extensively introducing the history of chemistry into institutions of higher learning. These are chiefly connected with the overloading of the programs in the basic disciplines, the fact that there are not good textbooks in the history of chemistry, and the fact that not everyone yet understands that without the history of science we cannot succeed if we wish to understand the evolution of knowledge and the direction in which science is going.

Literature Cited

(1) Mendeleev, D. I., "Osnovy khimii" (Fundamentals of Chemistry), 9th ed., Vol. 1, p. xlix, Leningrad–Moscow, 1927.

(2) From the preface to Meyer, E., "Istoriya khimii" (History of Chemistry), Russian trans., St. Petersburg, 1899, "Collected Works", Vol. 15, p. 633, Leningrad–Moscow, 1949.

(3) S.-Peterburgskie Vedomosti, 1870, 12/X, No. 281; St. Petersburger Zeitung, October 9, 1870.

(4) "D. I. Mendeleev Archives", Vol. I, p. 93, Leningrad, 1951.

(5) Butlerov, A. M., "Collected Works", Vol. III, p. 345, Moscow, 1958.

(6) Chugaev, L. A., "Evolyutsiya ucheniya o katalize" (Evolution of Studies on Catalysis), in "Novye idei v khimii" (New Ideas in Chemistry), No. 8, p. 5, Petrograd, 1924.

(7) Ostwald, W., "Lebenslinien, eine Selbstbiographie", Vol. I, p. 96, Klasing & Co., Berlin, 1926.

(8) Kurnakov, N. S., "Sobranie izbrannykh rabot", (Collected Works), Vol. 2, p. 197, Leningrad–Moscow, 1939.